PHOTOGRAPHIC TECHNIQUES
in
SCIENTIFIC RESEARCH

PHOTOGRAPHIC TECHNIQUES
in
SCIENTIFIC RESEARCH

Edited by

A. A. NEWMAN

VOLUME II

1976

ACADEMIC PRESS · LONDON · NEW YORK
SAN FRANCISCO

A Subsidiary of Harcourt Brace Jovanovich, Publishers

ACADEMIC PRESS INC. (LONDON) LTD.
24/28 Oval Road
London NW1

United States Edition published by
ACADEMIC PRESS INC.
111 Fifth Avenue
New York, New York 10003

Library of Congress Catalog Card Number: 72-84353
ISBN: 0-12-517960-X

PRINTED IN GREAT BRITAIN BY
T. and A. CONSTABLE LTD.
Hopetoun Street, Edinburgh

Contributors

Dr GILLIAN BULLOCK, CIBA Laboratories, Horsham, Sussex.

Mr D. J. DRURY, Head of Department of Medical Illustrations, The Children's Hospital, Ladywood Middleway, Birmingham B16 8ET.

Mr H. LOU GIBSON, Kodak Research Laboratories, Rochester, New York, USA.

Mr E. E. LARNER, Atomic Weapons Research Establishment, Aldermaston, Reading RG7 4PR.

Dr RODNEY PARSONS, CIBA Laboratories, Horsham, Sussex.

Mr GEORGE W. ROGERS, Department of Medical Illustration, University Hospital of Wales, Heath Park, Cardiff CF4 4WX.

Mr J. C. RUCKMAN, Atomic Weapons Research Establishment, Aldermaston, Reading RG7 4PR.

Mr C. J. E. SMITH, Atomic Weapons Research Establishment, Aldermaston, Reading RG7 4PR.

Mr THOMAS E. WARD, Hoole, Chester.

Preface

After the gratifying reception accorded to the first issue in this series, it is a pleasure to release a further volume.

The principles which guided us in the past were again adhered to on this occasion. Volume II contains six relatively short, but comprehensive, surveys by eminent contributors describing the applications of advanced photographic techniques in half a dozen important fields of scientific research.

It is my sincere belief that the study of the large amount of information contained in the present volume cannot fail to benefit all inquisitive practitioners of research photography.

April, 1975   A. A. NEWMAN

Contents

1

Photography in pharmacological research

GILLIAN R. BULLOCK and RODNEY R. PARSONS

2

Some aspects of the reproduction of diffraction patterns

D. J. DRURY

A*   ix

3
Infrared photography, a versatile tool
H. LOU GIBSON

4
Photography in pædiatrics
GEORGE W. ROGERS

5
Photography in materials science
J. C. RUCKMAN, E. E. LARNER and C. J. E. SMITH

6

Photographic aspects of archæology

THOMAS E. WARD

I

Photography in pharmacological research

GILLIAN R. BULLOCK and RODNEY R. PARSONS

I. INTRODUCTION

In the field of pharmacological research, the use of photography is an integral part of the many disciplines involved. In order to understand how any particular drug or group of drugs can modify a disease process, information is required as to the detailed development of the disease process itself, the biochemical parameters involved, the effect of different classes of drugs on both normal and diseased tissues and the relationship between results obtained from test animals to possible effects on man.

Many of those results are in fact obtained from visual information, either reflected by changes in the external appearance of the test animal's body as with skin injected dyes or skin grafting tests or in the actual tissues themselves where light microscopy and electron microscopy play a vital interpretative role. Similarly, the use of radioactive tracers in tissue metabolic or drug location studies is useful where the photographic emulsion in contact with the specimen is activated by the emission of soft β-particles resulting in the formation of a latent image. By this technique, concentrations of labelled drugs throughout the whole body can be determined by whole body autoradiography, together with autoradiography of specific organs and then of specific cells or even organelles within the cells. With the development of techniques to overcome the problems inherent in the use of soluble drugs, i.e., frozen sections or freeze drying, this type of study is beginning to have more relevance in the pharmacological field.

Where data has been recorded photographically, it is absolutely essential to ensure that bias in recording has been eliminated as far as possible so that experiments repeated in another laboratory are likely to produce the same results. To this end, the use of stereology, often in its simplest terms to allow detailed analysis of negatives founded on mathematical principles, has proved essential. This technique can be applied to both light and electron microscopy and will be described in detail later on in this chapter.

In order to maintain a high standard of reproducibility in recorded data, the atmospheric conditions and equipment have to be maintained to the same standard and methods used which allow for processing large quantities of photographic material rapidly without loss of quality. We have found that introduction of air conditioning is of very considerable benefit in maintaining consistency of results. Frequently the results have to be presented either by prints or slides and information can be totally lost if the presentation is poor.

II. GENERAL—RECORDING AND PROCESSING TECHNIQUES

A. The importance of the methodological approach

When attempting to evaluate the effect of a drug on any one tissue, it is safe to assume that, owing to the heterologous collection of cells within that tissue, the response will not be uniform. The mode of injection of the compound will influence the rate at which the drug will arrive at the test tissue, the area in which it first exerts its influence and the degree to which metabolism and breakdown of the drug has occurred before it reaches the target tissue. An excellent example is that of carbon tetrachloride which, when given subcutaneously, is less effective in producing liver damage than when given orally and exerts its effect normally in the centrilobular area of the liver tissue only.

This inbuilt variability in response inevitably makes sampling and analysis of the tissue extremely difficult, in particular for the electron microscopist, where only very small samples, usually up to 3 mm in diameter, can be handled at any one time, the size of the sample depending on the method of fixation and embedding. The investigator has, therefore, to ensure that sufficient numbers of random samples are taken to give closely matching results in a test series. The use of perfusion fixation techniques where uniformly good fixation can be obtained has helped considerably with this problem, but, obviously, this technique cannot be applied to isolated tissues which are incubated *in vitro*, in the presence of the drug.

An important basic principle in any sampling technique is to orientate the tissue as far as possible within the resin block so that sections can be removed at a predetermined angle. For example, with skeletal muscle, it is far easier to relate micrographs to the basic known structure if the sections are taken either along the long axis or strictly transversely. An oblique section, unless taken for a deliberate reason, merely complicates interpretation. Again, stretch-fixed skin is far easier to orientate than small rolled-up pieces dropped into fixative. With liver the identification of the different lobes so that samples are taken from the same part of the same lobe each time is important as each lobe may respond differently to the test drug. This is, obviously, difficult with a diffusely structured tissue but most tissues do have some identifiable organization. Sections can also be removed at predetermined intervals so that a complete survey of the tissue is carried out.

1. Use of specific stains or histochemical reactions for enumeration of changes. In order to obtain the maximum amount of information from a section, it is often useful to develop a staining technique, or use a histochemical reaction with a clearly definable end product which will enhance one particular aspect of the tissue more than another. Mitochondrial enlargement and possibly fusion is a morphologically recognizable parameter resulting from the effect of a glucocorticoid on skeletal muscle (Bullock *et al.*, 1971). However, the use of the Altmann stain on those mitochondria demonstrated clearly that the drug had increased the ability of the tissue to bind the stain and so a different differentiating time in the histological processing had to be used. Successful use of this particular

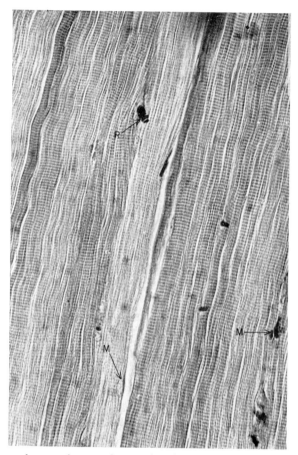

Fig. 1. M = elongated control mitochondrion; R = red blood corpuscles.

stain resulted in a clear picture of red staining mitochondria and red blood cells against a clear yellow background. Although this could be recorded most clearly as a colour micrograph, in fact, black and white pictures gave a perfectly adequate result for recognition and measurement (Fig. 1).

Having clearly defined the target organelle, in this case the mitochondrion, it was then relatively easy to use a Polaroid camera on top of the microscope and record each field with a scale included in the eyepiece so that it appeared superimposed on the picture. To do this we used the

Polaroid MP3 camera in conjunction with a Zeiss microscope. (See section II.B (2).)

Four photographs were made of each section (magnification × 200) taking one in each outer quarter and the sectioning was repeated through

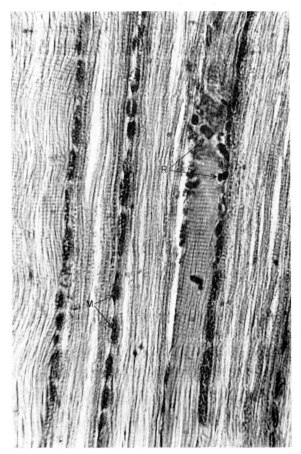

FIG. 2. M = mitochondria; R = red blood corpuscles.

the sample at a constant depth. Mitochondria or groups of mitochondria of greater length than the upper range of control values were then counted and a close correlation between the increase in number of enlarged organelles with time and dose was obtained (Fig. 2). Comparative checks with electron micrographs were sufficient to ensure that the right organelles were being evaluated. Photographic records of this kind are invaluable in that the original photography and the evaluation of the photographs can be done independently. Comparison of several different glucocorticoids also demonstrated that they modified the appearance of the stained tissue to different degrees.

2. Direct counting techniques. The difficulties involved in expressing changes in tissue structure seen under the electron microscope as well as the light microscope, have given rise to a whole new range of interpretative procedures called stereology. The technique has been developed by Ewald Weibel, among others, and an elaborate system of point and line intersection techniques allied to computer analysis has been evolved. The basic methodology has been well described in "Quantitative Methods in Morphology" edited by Weibel and Elias (1967) and is based on the fact that infinitely thin sections of a three-dimensional structure such as a tissue can be analysed from a photomicrograph. This technique has been applied by many authors very successfully to a number of tissues, particularly the liver. Loud (1968) applied it to the analysis of normal parenchymal rat liver cells obtained from the peripheral, midzonal and central regions of the lobules and then this author and some colleagues, Wiener *et al.* (1968) applied it to an analysis of the effects of cortisone on rat liver.

Even more involved measurements and analyses were made in the papers by Weibel *et al.* (1969) and Stäubli *et al.* (1969) where the effects of phenobarbitol on the rat liver were being measured. Lattices of differing densities were applied to light and electron photomicrographs so that the volume of each organelle or structure under consideration could be accurately determined. The authors were then able to correlate these changes with changes in enzymes and cell constituents which had already been determined biochemically.

However, these complicated analyses involve both time and considerable expense in setting up an analytical system allied to a computer, and as stated by Loud (1968) '. . . in general, it is not necessary to carry out such detailed work to establish most comparisons in cytoplasmic morphology'. In fact he considered one major advantage was to be able to correct interpretations obtained from non-quantitative studies.

We have found in our laboratories that a considerable amount of information can be obtained from micrographs by performing very simple counts to determine the incidence of a certain structure or material. If a preliminary scan of the material has suggested a change in the number of certain organelles in a cell or the particle distribution in a cell or between cells, then a large number of photographs can be taken at constant magnification, always at the same position on a grid, or using the same structure as a reference point. This method of enumeration has been applied with advantage in two studies we have undertaken.

The first such study was of the early changes in rabbit epidermis following internal injury, i.e., 60°C for 1 min. Preliminary scanning of the tissue indicated that in particular three possibly related events had occurred which had not been previously described in detail. First, there had been a considerable build-up in intercellular particles which were shown by a range of histochemical tests to be ribonuclear protein (RNP) particles (Fig. 3). Second, there were in many cells, peripheral aggregations of

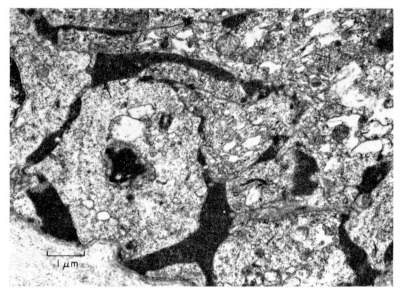

FIG. 3. Arrow indicates intercellular RNP particles.

what appeared to be the same type of particles (Fig. 4). Finally, in many of the cells, there were granule coated vesicles, looking similar to swollen rough endoplasmic reticulum (Fig. 5) and yet those structures are very rare in control epidermis. To analyse these findings on a numerical basis, samples were taken from control animals and then at set intervals after burning. At least 14 photographs were taken from each animal, each photograph taken at the same magnification and covering the same area of the basal epidermal cells and surrounding tissue. It was then possible, using a positive or negative score for each photograph to obtain an interesting picture of the events occurring within the tissue (Fig. 6). Thus the granular change could be associated with time and loss of cytoplasmic density and could possibly represent a recycling of material from damaged cells for utilization elsewhere.

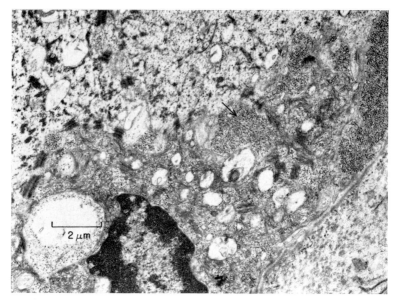

FIG. 4. Arrow indicates peripheral aggregation of particles.

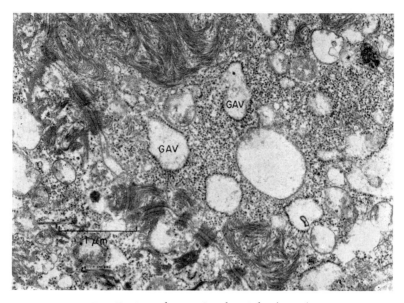

FIG. 5. Granule associated vesicles (GAV).

Another tissue where this technique has been applied very successfully is the liver. In conjunction with Professor T. F. Slaters' group at Brunel University, we have studied the morphological changes induced in the isolated perfused liver where drugs affecting bile flow have been used. Close examination of the photographs made of the tissues suggested that

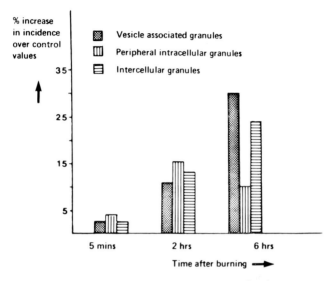

FIG. 6. Type and quantity of granule formation after burning at 60°C.

the numbers of mono- and multi-vesicular bodies increased or decreased with bile flow compared with control values.

In order to enumerate these findings, we decided to take a large number of photographs from each test sample. As with the skin, each photograph was taken at 7·5 thousand diameters to avoid inclusion of extracellular space and the number of vesicles per μ^2 tissue was counted. Bile canaliculi were chosen as the central reference point for each photograph because of their relevance in any bile flow study (Fig. 7).

A close correlation between numbers and bile flow was observed, the ratio between mono- and multi-vesicular bodies was remarkably constant and where an anomalous result was obtained, it was found that the bile flow before treatment had been abnormally high.

Another simple system used in our laboratory is the grid system where a frame containing a carefully tensioned, evenly spaced grid of wires is placed on top of the photographic paper and the negative then exposed. Where the lines cross, the incidence of each organelle or subcellular structure found at this intersection can be recorded and hence the changes seen over a wide range of subcellular structures measured. The production of a photograph with and without the grid overlay enables accurate identification of the underlying object (Figs 7 and 8).

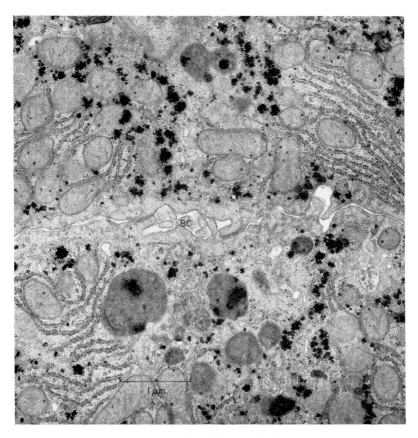

FIG. 7. B.C. = bile canaliculus.

Use of any one of these systems is vital where accurate comparisons are being made between control and treated tissue. They can be used on light microscopic sections prepared by usual histological techniques and also on thick resin sections stained with toluidine blue or some other dye, a useful technique when areas occupied by a particular cell type are being measured. By using photographic images, the bias associated with direct visual observation can be removed.

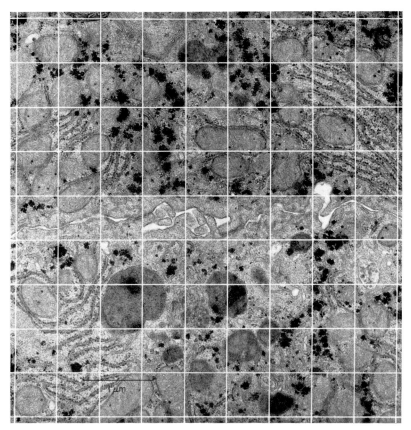

FIG. 8. Production of photograph with grid overlay.

B. Rapid access systems

In common with all the sciences, the research worker in the pharmacological field requires results, where they are presented in a photographic form, as rapidly as possible.

1. *Stabilisation processing.* Until the recent introduction of resin coated papers, which are discussed later, the most significant development in increasing the rate of small-scale production of routine black-and-white prints has been the advent of stabilization processing. Instead of the conventional processing stages of development, stop, fix, followed by a long wash and then drying, the paper is processed more or less instantly in a compact bench-top machine. This consists of a series of rubber rollers rotating at a fixed speed, which transport the exposed material through

two chemical baths, situated under them. The print emerges in a damp/dry state, fully developed and light fast, within approximately 10 s.

Prints produced in this way are semi-permanent and under normal filing conditions will last at least three to four years, before discolouration or fading becomes a problem. Dimensional stability is better than that of normal bromide papers as the paper base does not become fully saturated

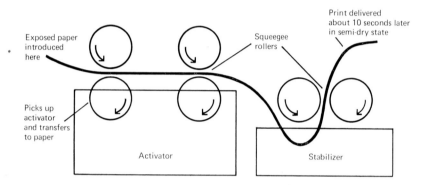

FIG. 9. Schematic diagram of a stabilization processor.

during processing and so stretching is minimal (less than 0·1%). If required they may also, at a later date, be rendered more stable by fixing, washing and drying/glazing in the normal manner. This leaves a print virtually identical in every way to a conventional bromide print. There are certain disadvantages.

Firstly, print size is limited by the size of the machine in use. The most popular, costing between £100-150, permit a maximum print width of about 14 in—this makes 12× 15 in the maximum standard size. However, in practice this is of little consequence as the exhibition prints sometimes required are best suited to conventional processing, where more control can be exercised. Slight variations in exposure cannot be compensated for in the "development" and so exposure times in the enlarger are very critical. Mains voltage fluctuations can also cause a problem where a number of prints are made from the same negative. Very short exposures are particularly vulnerable, so keeping exposures to a minimum of approximately 10 s will help overcome this. In extreme cases a voltage stabilization unit as already fitted to enlargers used for colour printing will cure the trouble. The main constituent of the stabilizer, ammonium thiocyanate, tends to leave prints rather sticky after they have emerged from the machine, and it is inadvisable to stack them until they are fully dry. Moreover, for this reason it is inadvisable to stack prints face to face, as is the usual practice with normal bromide prints. If a batch of prints are required really urgently they can be dried safely in a negative-drying cabinet.

This form of processing provides a very fast and convenient method for producing good quality prints quite suited to the majority of routine work passing through a research department. An important consideration is that a one print-off-one negative job becomes a practical proposition as the processor is ready for instant use. Final print finishing, should it be required, may be done later at the user's convenience.

An area where this has been found to be almost a necessity is in electron microscopy, where there is usually a very high proportion of one print off each negative printing. This form of printing, particularly with variable types of negative, can be very time consuming, and stabilization processing enables a much higher throughput to be maintained.

However, with the launching by Ilford Ltd of their Ilfospeed system in the autumn of 1974 the merits of stabilization processing over this new system are now in question.

Ilfospeed and Veribrom (the Kodak equivalent) are a new generation of bromide papers which have a polyethylene coating laminated on each side of the paper base. This not only makes them flatter and easier to handle than conventional papers but by preventing the chemicals soaking into the base during processing much shorter times may be achieved. This is particularly apparent at the wash stage, where unlike conventional papers, prints of archival permanence may be produced in only 2 min. Drying is ideally carried out on one of the special dryers now available for this type of paper, usually incorporating a roller transport system with fan blowers and radiant heater bars. These are considerably smaller than the widely used rotary dryer/glazers and consume less power. The surface of the paper is "built in", so a high-gloss finish is achieved without the need for glazing. Alternatively they can be blotted off and placed in a negative drying cabinet, but this is obviously slower and more tedious and only suitable where small numbers are involved.

At the time of writing this system is in its early days, but with the very definite advantages it shows over conventional methods, without any sacrifice in quality, it is not difficult to forecast that polyethylene coated papers will completely supersede conventional bromide papers in the years to come.

The precise role of stabilization processed papers is now less clear-cut. Although it is still a faster process there is a slight loss of quality and if prints are required for prolonged storage the extra processing involved completely negates the speed advantage. Dimensional stability is also no longer an advantage because polyethylene coated papers are equally as good.

TABLE I

Typical time-savings over conventional systems (Ilford data)

	Polyethylene coated	Conventional
Developer	60 s	2 min
Fix	30 s	5 min
Wash	2 min	30 min
Dry	30 s	3 min
Total	4 min	40 min

Nevertheless it would still seem to be very useful where numbers of prints are required quickly for evaluation and long-term permanency of the record is unimportant. Electron microscopy again is a good example, and, of course, the negative is still available should further permanent prints be required for publication, exhibition or long-term storage.

Finally on a cost for cost basis, unless the section has a fairly high through-put, the initial cost of equipping for stabilization processing is probably not worthwhile as these new papers provide a system which is still much more rapid than those using conventional bromide paper.

2. *The "instant" picture.* Polaroid (using this name in its generic sense) materials are another way of achieving very quick results from the photographic process. The Polaroid Corporation market their own camera, the MP3 technical camera (now updated to the MP4 model), which has a very wide range of uses in the laboratory, and would be particularly useful in a small research unit where budget difficulties limit the amount of expenditure on photographic equipment. As can be seen from Fig. 10, it is basically a vertical copy camera, sliding on an alloy V-shaped column fixed to a wooden baseboard with its own flood lighting attached. Reflex viewing is provided through an adjustable viewer and hood. The lens/shutter assemblies are interchangeable and the range available allows for macrophotography of small objects or pieces of tissue, slide making and copying diagrams or photographs. A useful

accessory is the lenseless shutter assembly and tube, which allows the camera to be lowered straight over the ocular of a microscope. This enables it to be used for photomicrographic work without the need for extra, often expensive, camera attachments for the microscope.

Polaroid film backs, either roll or pack type, and a standard international 4×5 back are mounted on a sliding carriage which facilitates

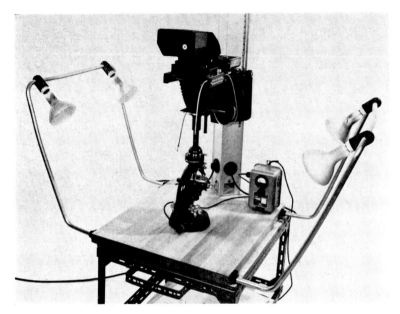

FIG. 10. MP3 technical camera (now updated to MP4 model).

changing from one film type to another. Thus, apart from the full range of Polaroid materials, black and white or colour, any conventional 4×5 material may be used. Including line or "lith" materials for the copying of diagrams and tables. A 35-mm back is also available, but with the lenses currently available, which are not designed for the 35-mm format, higher quality results will be better obtained with a standard 35-mm camera. A bracket is now obtainable to take such a camera and this then provides an ideal set-up for producing 35-mm slides. (See section II.C.)

Polaroid materials are used frequently in light microscopy work where a routine record is required, and it is felt unlikely that further copies will be needed. Quality is quite adequate for routine use and the cost is very reasonable when time savings are taken into account. Perhaps the biggest advantage is that untrained staff can use the system successfully and can be sure of their results immediately without having to return at some future date and re-take unsatisfactory shots.

Colour Polaroid as applied to biological work has in the authors' experience proved less satisfactory than conventional systems. Colours of histological stains are more difficult to reproduce with sufficient saturation and colour fidelity.

C. Making and presentation of slides

Any shortcomings in the standard or presentation of data and results are nowhere more apparent than in the preparation and making of projection slides. Sufficient time and care should always be devoted to this aspect, which is frequently one of the more widely seen end-products of a research programme.

1. Preparation of artwork. Not many departments, except possibly large hospitals, have trained artists and illustrators on their staff. In the absence of these, the task of preparing artwork for slides has to be carried out by laboratory technicians or the authors themselves. Nevertheless, there is no reason why quite adequate work cannot be produced, particularly as there are now many materials on the market specially designed to assist the "amateur".

The type of lettering chosen is a significant factor in deciding whether a slide is successful or not. Here an electric typewriter of the IBM Executive type can be very useful: the type it produces is very legible, evenly spaced and looks neat and tidy on the final slide. Tables and summary slides can be produced very rapidly and with the minimum of specialized effort. The IBM Compositor or varityper is even more useful and has a range of interchangeable typefaces, serif and sans serif, up to 11 pt in size. Unfortunately, to justify their cost (approx. £2000) a high throughput would be necessary (Fig. 11).

Rubdown or transfer lettering is also very useful but is time consuming and it is difficult to space and align the letters correctly. However, the wide range of type-faces and sizes, symbols, arrows, tints, hatchings and coloured films available in this form make very professional and easily reproducible artwork within the reach of most people. Uno stencils were at one time very popular, but the lettering produced by them is unattractive, and unless one is used to them, results can be unpredictable and messy.

Probably the most frequently seen fault on slides is that of attempting to include too much information on one slide. In all probability the audience will not be as familiar with the subject-matter as the author, and consequently complicated, cluttered slides will be detrimental to the overall effectiveness of the presentation. A similar effect will be achieved if the lettering is not of sufficient size to be read easily by all members of the audience. In practice, it has been found that, provided that the minimum height of the lettering is kept to 1/50 of the length of the longest side, this important requirement will be satisfied, assuming that the

Incubation with an antibiotic — 11 point Univers Bold

Incubation with an antibiotic — 11 point Univers Medium

Incubation with an antibiotic — 11 point Press Roman Bold

Incubation with an antibiotic — 10 point Univers Bold

Incubation with an antibiotic — 10 point Univers Medium Italic

Incubation with an antibiotic — 8 point Univers Bold

FIG. 11. Some of the IBM Compositor type faces available.

recommended screen/room size ratio is adhered to. This is usually based on a formula (Ollerenshaw, 1962), that the minimum screen width should be approximately 1/6 of the distance measured from the screen to the back row of the audience. If this recommendation is adopted, it will cater for people with below average vision, which, based on surveys carried out among undergraduates, is more common than one would immediately realize. There is some controversy over how near to the screen the front row may be situated but the most often quoted figure is a distance of the order of two screen widths. This provides the eyes with a comfortable scan width of 60°. Some observers have quoted figures as small as 1·4 screen widths but we consider this to be too close, unless space available is very limited (Fig. 12).

The principal factors limiting the amount of material that can be displayed on any one slide can be summarized as follows:

1. Degree of audience familiarity;
2. Size and type of lettering;
3. Types of symbols and/or colours;
4. Time allowed for viewing;
5. Slides intended for use in self-instruction programmes can contain much more detail, as they are studied at close quarters and for a length of time decided by the student.

Graphical representation of data is one of the most common forms of illustrating results of investigations in any scientific research. However, they can provide misleading information if unsuitable scales are chosen. By expanding or compressing one scale or the other dramatic distortions

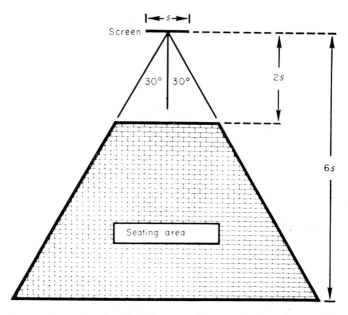

FIG. 12. Proportions for the ideal lecture theatre. (Taken from Ollerenshaw (1962).)

in "apparent" results may be shown. Figure 13 (a) and (b) shows the effect of various drugs on the level of β-glucuronidase in lymph after injury. In (a) these levels are expressed in units/100 ml and it is clear that there was little or no effect. However, if these same values are expressed as a percentage of control (injured) an apparent effect is seen and this is due to a misleading interpretation of the true results. Figure 14 (a) and (b) shows the importance of including standard errors.

Artwork for photography of graphs is quite satisfactory in the form of tracings. In this way it is easy to retain the accuracy of the original graph plots by tracing directly from them and this also has another advantage that the grid lines on the graph paper may be used for aligning axis and lettering.

2. Slide processes. In recent years the growth in popularity of diazo slides (i.e., usually white lettering/blue background but other colours available) for diagrams and tables has been very marked. They provide sufficient contrast to make them easily legible, yet in comparison with purely black and white slides are very restful to view for long periods. Another important point in their favour is that the mechanics of producing

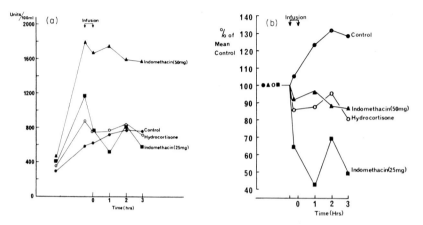

FIG. 13. Effects of various drugs on the level of β-glucuronidase in lymph after injury.

them are very simple and straightforward. Firstly, a 35-mm "lith" negative is produced from the original artwork and then this is contact-printed on to a diazo material, and exposed under an ultraviolet light

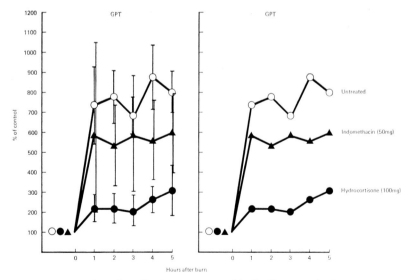

FIG. 14. Showing the importance of including standard errors.

source. The final slide is produced by "developing" this diazo material in ammonia vapour. The master negative can then be filed and thus be available for producing further copy slides or black-and-white prints, should they be required. We use a very convenient and compact machine marketed by Ozalid which enables up to approximately 30 slides to be exposed and subsequently developed at any one time. It requires no setting up and is available for almost instant use.

An alternative process may also be used to produce a similar looking result. The original camera negative is first bleached and then toned. Suitable formulae may be found in the Kodak Data Sheets FY5 and FY6. For our purposes, however, we have found this to be unsuitable for two reasons. Firstly, there is no master negative retained so the artwork must be rephotographed if further copies are wanted, and secondly, as the processing is relatively long and complicated it is really only of use when there are large numbers to be dealt with.

Simple coloured overlays may be prepared if any particular point on a slide requires emphasis. Diazo material is available in a range of colours of which yellow and red respectively provide the best contrast. First, two "lith" negatives of the original are produced in the normal manner. One of these is then used to make a conventional diazo; the other is blocked out so that only the artwork required in a different colour is left showing. This is then contact printed on to "lith" film so that it yields a positive, which in turn is printed on to yellow or red diazo film producing the appropriate coloured image on a clear background. By sandwiching the two diazos in register, a two-colour slide is produced.

Slides are frequently required from electron micrographs. Theoretically one would expect to produce them directly from the negatives with no intermediate stages in which to lose quality. However, in practice this method has been found to be unsuitable for a variety of reasons.

The method we now use is to produce standard size glossy prints from the negatives in the aspect ratio of a 35-mm slide (i.e., 3 : 2—150×100 mm has been found to be a convenient size), and then to photograph this directly on to a medium speed 35-mm film which is then reversal processed to yield transparencies. Very slow fine-grain films are not usually suitable as they produce strongly sepia-toned images on reversal which we consider aesthetically unacceptable in this type of work. A principal advantage of this system is that variations in contrast and uneven illumination can be compensated for comparatively easily in printing. One can appreciate that it would be virtually impossible to shade or "dodge" an image only 36×24 mm. This then provides a standardized original to work from, on which the scale of magnification or any other annotation needed can be included by drawing or lettering directly on to the prints. Insets or multiple images present no problems, although care must be taken that individual images are of sufficient size for detail to be seen.

Large numbers of transparencies can be produced quickly and economically with the minimum of specialized equipment. Any conventional 35-mm single-lens reflex camera is ideal with, if necessary, a close-up lens or extension bellows/ring to extend its focusing range. The only other equipment required is some form of rigid copying stand with means for providing even illumination (see section II.B (2) concerning the MP3 camera).

3. Final presentation. There can be no hard and fast rule whether it is better to mount transparencies between glass or in glassless mounts. If they are to be handled to any extent glass mounting is definitely preferable, otherwise they will be very susceptible to finger marks and abrasions which are usually impossible to remove. Card mounts of the Kodachrome variety tend to become distorted in use, when they inevitably jam in automatic projectors.

On the other hand, mounting between glass takes longer and dust sealed between the glass and transparency is always a problem. The thicker sort of glass mounts should be avoided, as projectors of the popular "Carousel" variety have a tendency to jam with these. Plastic mounts, whether glass or glassless, are rapidly superseding the older card mounts which require the use of a special heat press to seal them. If slides are to be sent by post the fragility of glass and its added weight should be taken into account.

Finally, it is essential that all slides should be "spotted" in the accepted manner if they are to be projected correctly. The spot should be on the bottom left-hand corner with the slide correctly orientated for viewing. When placed in a projector the spot will then be in the top right-hand corner and facing towards the projectionist.

D. Autoradiography

While the direct effect of a test compound or drug may be recorded by a change in the structure of a tissue, and is often also associated with biochemical and physiological changes, frequently there is no change in the tissue that can be recorded visually. This occurs frequently when very low doses of a test compound are used, when metabolism of the compound reduces its potency and when the compound is only bound for a short time. In many instances autoradiography—whether macro- or micro- or

B

at the ultrastructural level has a very useful role to play. The test compound can be labelled in a number of ways, ^{14}C and ^{3}H being the most commonly used but many others such as ^{125}I and ^{35}S have been studied.

At the macro-autoradiographic level, the method developed by Ullberg (1954, 1958) has not been superseded although small variations from his method are often made. The concise practical description by Gahan (1972) is excellent so that only a very brief outline is needed here. The test animal, usually a mouse, has the labelled drug administered intravenously and after a defined interval of time is anaesthetized and killed by immersion in a mixture of carbon dioxide snow and acetone ($-78°C$). The animal is then processed further in a freeze room ($-10°C$) where it is frozen on to a stage using a carboxymethylcellulose-water mixture instead of the original frozen layers of wet cotton wool. The freezing mixture used is hexane saturated with solid CO_2. When sufficient tissue has been removed from the block by rough trimming on a microtome, then "Scotch tape" is applied to the surface and a section of the desired thickness removed. The section is then freeze-dried and brought to room temperature before being placed in contact with a suitable x-ray film such as the Kodak No-screen x-ray film (Kodirex), Kodak "Blue Brand" Medical x-ray film, or Structurix D10 (Agfa-Gevaert). Slight pressure is applied to keep the section in close contact with the emulsion and after a 3-4 week exposure, (depending on the type of material) the section and the emulsion are separated and stained or developed separately. By comparing the stained section with the developed emulsion, the location of the tracer can be identified.

The method is used routinely in the Pharma Department of CIBA-GEIGY, Basle, with some modifications. The artefacts seen previously and the effect of those modifications on the method are described below.

As mentioned by Gahan, one of the major artefacts encountered is pressure effects. Sections of freeze-dried material from whole animals can be problematical in this respect as very hard structures like bone tend to project and give a false positive. Also, with freeze-dried sections shrinkage will often occur making comparison with unfrozen stained sections more difficult. Dr Schmidt and his colleagues have avoided this fault by embedding their animals in Sephadex C50 (Pharmacia Uppsala) and after sectioning to the required depth they expose the still frozen block face to the chosen film using a plastic-covered lead block to ensure maximum contact between the tissue and the film. The sealed box containing the film, tissue and lead block is then stored at $-20°C$ for the period of the exposure. For good results, they recommend trying 4 μCi/animal for

[14]C-labelled material and 400 μCi/animal for ^{3}H labelling, using compounds with the highest specific activity possible.

Another artefact mentioned by Gahan and which can prove misleading, where drugs metabolized by the liver are concerned is positive or negative chemography. Some bile ingredients, for instance, can react with the film thus producing chemical development and a darkened image. To act as a control on this and in other cases of chemical development, a separate organ analysis must be carried out to demonstrate a true correlation between isotopic content and a positive autoradiographic result. For negative chemographic effects, it is normal practice to check whether desensitisation of the bromide crystals has occurred by deliberately exposing the film to light causing it to fog. Areas of desensitized grains then show up as white patches.

The length of exposure of the specimen containing the isotope to the film is very important as under-exposure will result in too faint an image, particularly where a compound is rapidly metabolized. It is essential for fair comparison that the exposure is kept constant for all the sampling times, which would normally be 1-5 and 30 min, 2, 6 and 24 h. If the first exposure at 1 min is inadequate, then further exposure must be given. In general, 10 days exposure is usually sufficient, but it is essential that the times are re-evaluated for every experimenter and situation.

The distribution of the isotope within the body can yield valuable information such as where a test drug is bound, how long it remains in any one organ, and whether it is able to penetrate the blood brain barrier. The compounds we have used to illustrate the technique, have also been chosen to illustrate the organ specificity which may be found. With ^{14}C hydralazine for example, Fig. 15 shows the general localization of the drug in the body particularly in the salivary glands and in the major blood vessel walls, 1 min after injection of the isotope. Four minutes later, the kidney is very obviously involved and also the liver (Fig. 16). Two hours later, the drug is disappearing rapidly from the body, some is left in the gut and the vessel walls are still heavily involved. Finally, at 6 h, only the stomach and the vessel walls retain any considerable amount of the isotope (Fig. 17). Figure 18 illustrates selective absorption by the liver with no trace of penetration through the blood/brain barrier by the drug. Figure 19 shows a different drug which is absorbed by the brain to a marked extent.

The type of film used in these experiments is that used by Ullberg in his original work, that is Agfa-Gevaert Structurix D10. It is important to stress the necessity of using fresh film and so a reliable supplier is required.

Structurix D10 film has one disadvantage and that is a tendency to fog with long development times. Where the Structurix D10 film is not available, then any sensitive x-ray film should be adequate and, in fact, Gahan (1972) mentions two other Kodak films as possible choices.

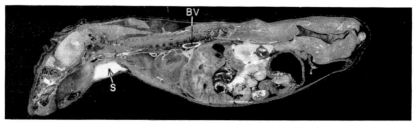

FIG. 15. Whole body autoradiograph. S = salivary glands; BV = major blood vessels.

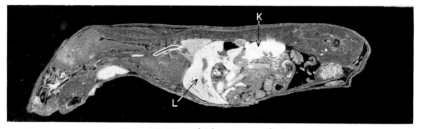

FIG. 16. K = kidney; L = liver.

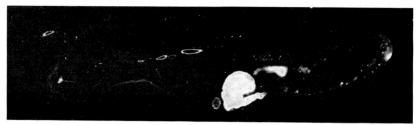

FIG. 17. Isotope retained after 6h.

Whereas macro-autoradiography will give the general localization of any labelled drug, it is not sufficiently sensitive to demonstrate in which region of any particular organ the drug or its labelled metabolites might be located. Here, the techniques developed for diffusible and non-diffusible substances at the light microscopic level play an important role and reference can again be made to "Autoradiography for Biologists", edited by Gahan (1972). Here, the stripping film technique developed by Appleton is described in detail and also the dipping technique described by Bogoroch. Similarly, alternative techniques can be found in "Auto-radiography of Diffusible Substances", edited by Roth and Stumpf (1969).

With strongly bound compounds it is quite feasible to use paraffin-embedded or resin-embedded material, but there is always some un-

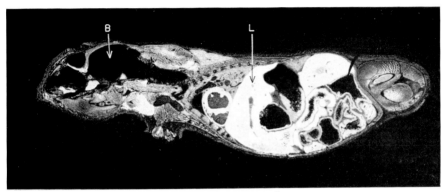

FIG. 18. L = liver; B = brain.

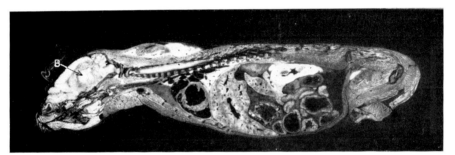

FIG. 19. B = brain.

certainty as to whether the binding of the drug to its receptor is sufficiently strong as to prevent extraction during the processing. Monitoring of solutions for radioactivity during processing will show whether the tracer has been extracted by the solvents but will not give any information on the shifting of the compound within the tissue itself.

The frozen-tissue technique originally described by Appleton (1964) has much to recommend its use in pharmacological research. By keeping the tissue frozen from the time of its removal from the animal until the end of the exposure period, movement of the isotope within the tissue is minimized. The AR10 stripping film used in this technique is easy to use under conditions of controlled humidity, and when the emulsion is in contact with the radioactively labelled tissue and kept at $-25°C$, latent image fading is avoided (an important factor with long exposures). The background is half that of the same film exposed at $+4°C$ which more than off-sets the 24% reduction in sensitivity found at $-25°C$. These advantages of low temperature exposure become more apparent when very low doses of isotope are used, which is often the case.

Where problems are encountered in keeping the frozen sections and the emulsion in close contact during the final development and staining, at the end of the exposure period, the slides can be dipped in a solution of 1% celloidin for 5 min, drained for a few seconds and hardened in 80% ethanol for 2 min. This effectively prevents any movement and allows free penetration of the stains. The celloidin itself, however, has a certain grain, which although not interfering with the usual interpretation of the autoradiograph, could be detected by an automated grain-counter.

Electron microscopic autoradiography of soluble compounds would be a natural corollary to this technique, and based on fresh dry-cut ultrathin frozen sections is being developed (Baker and Appleton, 1974). Embedded tissue will yield much information but there are still the same artefacts to consider as for the light microscope methods.

III. LIGHT MICROSCOPY

A. Introduction

End results of photography through the light microscope depend for quality on rigorous observation of the correct conditions. A clean, well aligned microscope, adjusted for Köhler illumination and with the right combination of lens and objective is the first requisite. The correct thickness of cover slip which is engraved on the body of the objective (most commonly 0·17 mm) must also be used and finally, most important, the general quality of the section or smear to be photographed must be good.

It is not proposed to discuss at length the general techniques of taking photographs through the light microscope, as this has been extensively covered in various other textbooks. Lawson's "Photomicrography" (1972) is a recent and particularly useful example. However, we should like to discuss some practical aspects of our own work.

In black-and-white photomicrography the image colour of a stained area can be enhanced or subdued with the use of appropriate coloured filters. Filters of the same colour as the stain lighten, and those of the complimentary colour darken. Thus, the densities produced by different colours on an emulsion can be altered at will to provide the best contrast possible from a stained specimen. Blue light has roughly twice the resolving power of red, so that the resolution of the image will be improved by shortening the wavelength of the light used. Lawson discusses the use of filters in some depth (pp. 138-145) and advocates the use of a filter/s whenever the subject matter allows. An extremely useful table is included which lists the most commonly used stains along with those filters which will produce the maximum contrast from the specimen.

B. Phase contrast

Use of phase contrast to improve the visibility of the specimen has some advantages in that black and white photomicrographs can be used to

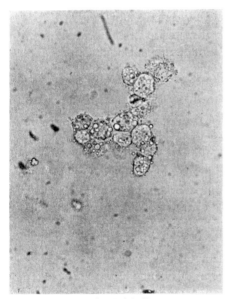 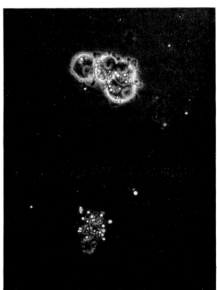

FIG. 20. Bright field illumination.   FIG. 21. Phase contrast.

illustrate differences in refractive index and thickness of a transparent specimen. The human eye is relatively insensitive in this area.

Figures 20 and 21 illustrate the enhanced contrast obtained over directly transmitted light using isolated adrenal cells. Introduction of a green interference filter appears to give even greater cellular detail and the lipid droplets present in the steroid producing cells show up very distinctly allowing easy and rapid identification.

Where thick resin sections are used for orientation of tissues or locating areas of interest prior to ultramicrotomy, these can be viewed and photographed under phase contrast conditions either unstained or stained with a dye such as toluidine blue or azure II/methylene blue.

C. Colour

1. Application and techniques. It is unwise to assume that colour photomicrographs will necessarily provide more information than a corresponding black-and-white shot. In some cases colour can actually detract from the final result by drawing the eye to the wrong part of the subject and adding emphasis in the wrong quarter. Where photographs are required for publication it is still comparatively unusual for them to be accepted in colour, owing to the greatly increased production costs. Colour plates are normally only included where there is no other adequate way of illustrating a point.

We feel that the practical use of colour materials in photomicrography has not been adequately covered in the literature and hope that a clearer understanding of the various factors involved will enable better and more consistent results to be attained.

Unfortunately for the photomicrographer, commercially produced colour films are made with the colour balance aimed at optimum reproduction of the flesh tones. This is inevitably at the expense of the neutral tones on a grey scale, good reproduction of which has been shown to be best for work in this field. Also nearly all mass-market films are designed for daylight quality illumination at comparatively short exposure times, conditions which are rarely met in the field of photomicrography.

Although some microscopes have the facility for using xenon arcs as their light source, with the attendant advantages of near daylight quality light permitting short exposure times, by far the most common form of illumination is the low-voltage tungsten filament lamp with a colour temperature of approximately 2900°K. Also gaining popularity is the tungsten halogen lamp with the slightly whiter light of 3200°K. Photometric filters are used for raising the effective colour temperature of these light sources, but these are relatively inefficient and can require up to a 5× increase in exposure. This makes exposures much longer than the film was designed for and differential reciprocity failure of the three emulsion layers may occur producing noticeable colour casts. For example with Kodachrome II: the daylight balanced version at exposures in excess of 2 or 3 s tends to have a slight magenta cast, while the Professional Type A version tends towards cyan, both casts increasing in intensity as the length of the exposure increases. Providing the cause of this is understood it can be avoided by adding correction filters of the complimentary colour to the cast. The most widely available in this country are the Kodak 'C.C.' series which are supplied in six different strengths or densities in yellow, blue, magenta, green, cyan and red. In the above examples green and red filters respectively would be needed, i.e., Kodachrome II Daylight: 1 s—no filter; 10 s—CC10G; 100 s—CC20G. Kodachrome IIA Professional: 1 s—CC10R; 10 s—CC20R; 100 s—CC25R. (Loveland, 1970.)

Another problem is that the spectral quality of the light emitted from the microscope lamp will be altered to a certain extent by passing through the optics of the microscope. This varies with the types of optics involved, but is usually a yellowish green in colour and becomes more pronounced at higher magnifications.

Colour transparency films in general register ultraviolet light as blue and so if an excess of ultraviolet light is present a blue colour cast will result. Variable ultraviolet absorption of the optics, microscope slide and cover-glass and mounting medium makes the amount of ultraviolet present unpredictable. A wise precaution therefore, is to include a Wratten 2B filter in the light path as a matter of routine. This will eliminate nearly all the ultraviolet present and enable more consistent results to be obtained.

Accurate reproduction of histological dyes poses specific problems for present-day tri-pack colour films. Their construction and the principle on which they work is such that they have known deficiencies in certain areas. For those unfamiliar with these working principles, Spencer's "Colour Photography in Practice" (1969) and Fisher's "Photography for the Scientist" (1968) are recommended.

These dyes, such as eosin, often have narrow absorption bands which occur just where the sensitivity bands of two layers of the emulsion overlap. If this is the case, the original highly saturated colour will, in the reproduction, appear degraded and in some cases a noticeably different colour. Unfortunately, there is little one can do to overcome this problem completely, except to experiment with different filters and/or films until an acceptable result is achieved.

Often, of course, the true colour of the result is unimportant so long as the detail required can be seen clearly and with sufficient colour contrast. However, it is disconcerting if a well-known stain is rendered a different colour, and therefore there are good reasons for aiming at accurate reproduction in the final print or transparency.

If colour prints are required it is usual to use the negative/positive

B*

system, and if, as is more often the case, these have to be sent to a professional colour laboratory for developing and printing, it is very likely that the colours in the print will be inaccurate, if not completely different from the original. Automatic printers, which provide the cheap en-prints suitable for inclusion in reports and notebooks, work on the principle that the light transmitted from average colour negatives will, when integrated, add up to a neutral grey. The exposures required are calculated from this integrated reading and made in turn through the three colour filters. For normal subjects this provides a very satisfactory method, but with any subjects where one or possibly two colours predominate, a good example being biological stained material, the system breaks down and dramatic distortions in colour balance usually result. It is extremely unlikely that the average printer will recognize such a fault in a micrograph, as he will have no point of reference to indicate what the original colours of the specimen were. Loveland suggests an ingenious technique for overcoming this.

An alternative is to have direct reversal prints from transparencies made. Here the colour balance is not such a problem, as it has already been worked out at the transparency stage, but quality is slightly inferior to the negative/positive system.

The contrast of "most" colour films available is generally too low for the majority of biological material and this is particularly noticeable with the negative/positive system. Some experiments were conducted with a special high contrast, high resolution colour film marketed by Agfa-Gevaert as Scientia-Color. This has a practical speed rating of approximately 2 ASA and a very high gamma of 3·0, compared with approximately 0·5 γ for a conventional colour material. It is balanced for 3200°K illumination and is available in both 35-mm bulk lengths and in sheets. The negatives produced are unmasked and appear sharper and more contrasty than with conventional materials. Prints made from these negatives were of higher contrast, appeared sharper and fine detail was better resolved.

Reversal processing was tried, but results were disappointing. Strong colour casts occurred and exposure latitude was minimal. It is suggested that a better way of producing transparencies with this system would be by contact printing with the negative. Colour balance would then be easily controlled by using suitable filtration. One disadvantage with this film is that it has to be processed in Agfacolor paper chemicals at non-standard times, and consequently none of the commercial laboratories, in the authors' experience, offer a service for processing it. Nevertheless, user processing is quite straightforward if the facilities are available.

Kodak now market a slow speed, high contrast and resolution film—Photomicrographic Film Type SO-456. This is balanced for daylight at 16ASA and, with the Wratten filter 80A, 4 ASA at 3200°K. Processing is via the standard E4 chemistry, as used for the Ektachrome range of films, and is therefore easily user or commercially processed. We have found the results to be very acceptable with improved colour saturation, contrast and sharpness in comparison with Ektachrome-X or High Speed Ektachrome. Conversely exposure latitude is very limited, fluctuations in mains voltage being sufficient to alter the result appreciably, but this is an inherent characteristic (see Fig. 26) of any high contrast film. Another disadvantage is its very slow speed to artificial light which would become inconvenient at high magnifications or at the low lighting levels associated with phase contrast or fluorescence work. As most photomicrographic work is carried out under tungsten illumination, a tungsten balanced film would, in the author's opinion, have been a more suitable choice. However, on balance this material does offer significant advantages in improved quality, and this action by Kodak in introducing a film especially catering for the photomicrographers' specialized requirements is a very welcome one.

2. *Processing.* Whether to process one's own colour work or send it out to a commercial laboratory is very much dependent on individual circumstances. On purely economic grounds, user processing cannot be justified unless a large throughput is envisaged. However, it is undeniably convenient to be able to view results within a couple of hours of taking the pictures, and in this respect the commercial laboratory cannot compete. It is also advantageous to have complete control over each stage of the processing and this is particularly important in printing where so much is dependent on the printer's own interpretation of the subject. Unless communications with a laboratory are unusually good, this stage can be the most troublesome.

Unfortunately, colour processing is time consuming and requires specialized knowledge and equipment at the printing stage. Processing of transparencies and negatives is comparatively straightforward, accurate timing and temperature control are the most important parameters. Most laboratories will already have suitable thermostatically controlled waterbaths, and so investment in new equipment is also minimal.

The speed of Ektachrome-X and High Speed Ektachrome can be increased considerably by modifying the processing, a fact not generally known, although most commercial laboratories do offer this service at extra cost. This can be very useful in fluorescence work where very low illumination may be encountered. It entails simply increasing the time of the first development viz.:

$$33\% \text{ increase} = 2\times \text{ the normal speed}$$
$$50\% \text{ increase} = 2\tfrac{1}{2}\times \text{ the normal speed}$$
$$75\% \text{ increase} = 4\times \text{ the normal speed}$$

This will increase the contrast which is an advantage in our work and also affect maximum density and graininess, but very acceptable results can be obtained.

Finally, it must be emphasized that all aspects of colour processing require the utmost care and attention to detail if results of consistent quality are to be achieved. There is very little of the latitude that exists in black-and-white processing.

IV. ELECTRON MICROSCOPY—THE EFFECT OF DIFFERENT PROCESSING METHODS AND MATERIALS ON THE FINAL IMAGE

The perfectly balanced, well contrasted negative, as will be discussed elsewhere, depends not only on the type of recording material, plate or film, or on the accurate alignment of the machine itself, but to a very large extent on the quality of the material being studied. It is possible to modify the image seen on the fluorescent screen quite extensively by the choice of fixative, method of fixation and also the resin in which the material is embedded.

A. Choice of fixatives

A cardinal rule always followed in our laboratory when dealing with a tissue for the first time is to try a wide range of fixatives in order to reach the optimum results. In some cases, this requires the continuous use of two fixation methods because, within one tissue, different types of cell may respond differently. In general, osmium tetroxide fixation will give excellent membrane definition (Fig. 22) and hence a well contrasted picture, whilst glutaraldehyde and the other aldehydes retain more matrix material which together with a less well-defined membrane system, gives a much flatter negative (Fig. 23). Frequently a very clear picture is obtained when fixation is poor, as can be seen from the picture of isolated dogfish adrenal cells (Fig. 24). In addition, graininess seen in the final photomicrograph may not be due to any photographic grain but contributed solely by the fixative. Poor quality batches of glutaraldehyde, for example, can leave a fine graininess throughout a tissue which is not removed by subsequent processing. Similarly, potassium permanganate can partially extract material and this will again appear as fine graininess throughout the specimen (Fig. 25).

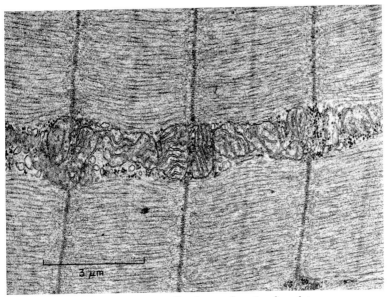

FIG. 22. Osmium fixed muscle mitochondria.

FIG. 23. Glutaraldehyde fixed muscle mitochondria.

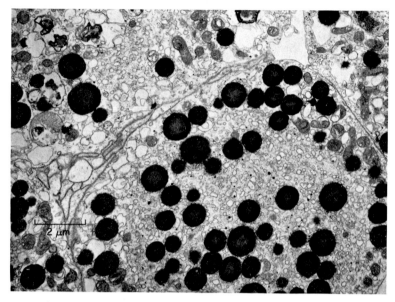

FIG. 24. Clear picture of isolated dogfish adrenal cells although fixation was poor.

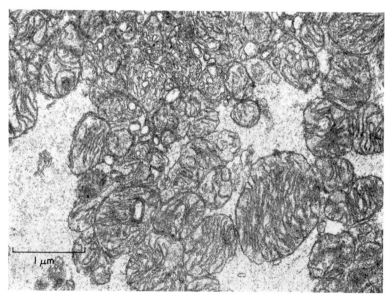

FIG. 25. Isolated mitochondria fixed in $KMnO_4$.

B. Emulsion grain

Granularity in the emulsion itself severely restricts the potential enlargement of the image and is dependent on a number of factors. The number of incident particles in an electron beam required to produce an image of a given density is very much less than that required on exposure to light waves. For this reason, it is essential that fluctuations in the beam are kept to a minimum as their effects will be much greater and hence affect the degree of granularity seen in the image more than the individual silver grains in the emulsion itself. In addition, a definite relationship exists between the sensitivity and the granularity of an emulsion so the detective quantum efficiency of an ideal material will have a value near one where every incident electron is recorded by the production of one or more developable grains. Thus all the information contained in the electron beam is shown without excessive degradation.

C. Plates and films

1. Density and exposure. The effective maximum density of the negative is determined by the practical range of exposures and is a function of the accelerating voltage. The maximum contrast achieved also increases with increased accelerating voltage but there are again practical limitations. The characteristics of photographic plates exposed to an electron beam have been studied by Digby *et al.* (1953) and they showed that there is a nearly linear relationship between the integrated electron charge falling on a plate and the resultant density. It is therefore necessary to ensure that as many electrons as possible are collected on the plate in the recording of the image so as to minimize the random contrast due to electron noise. The technical problems involved are clearly explained by Valentine (1964) and the results obtainable with the emulsions that were available at the time are tabulated. In practical terms the Ilford EM5 and EM6 plates have virtually the same characteristics as the N50 and N60 plates used by Valentine. In addition to these factors, the effect of the specimen thickness and of heavy metal stains on the inherent specimen contrast are obviously relevant (Burge, 1964).

Exposure latitude, with high contrast emulsions is much less than with more general purpose emulsions (Fig. 26). Slight under-exposure will bring the exposure range on to the toe of the characteristic curve and the image contrast will drop appreciably. However, emulsions exposed to electrons react in a different way to those exposed to light. While the contrast of a light exposed emulsion is constant for levels of exposure within the straight line portion of the curve (i.e., where a linear relationship exists between exposure and density) it is strongly affected by the degree of development. With electron-induced exposures the contrast is much more dependent on the level of exposure—increasing exposure and therefore density—producing higher contrast. Although contrast and maximum density may be raised a certain degree by increasing the development time or using a more active developer, this will not satisfactorily compensate for under-exposure and excessive development will lead to an undesirable rise in the fog level. Conversely, over-exposure will result in dense negatives with increased graininess and irradiation, which are difficult to print satisfactorily and will require inordinately long exposure times in the enlarger.

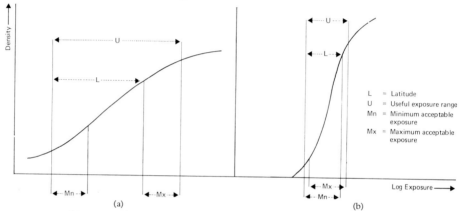

FIG. 26. (a) Medium speed and contrast general purpose emulsion. (b) Typical slow speed high contrast emulsion for electron microscopy.

The levels of the exposure and development should be carefully controlled to produce negatives of a standard density and contrast consistent with the different types of specimens normally encountered.

Exposure control on the latest electron microscopes is effected by a built-in photocell which measures the intensity of the electron beam incident on the central area of the fluorescent screen. On some instruments the exposure is made automatically via an electronic shutter and the film or plate also advanced automatically, ready for the next exposure. These methods work very satisfactorily in practice. The form of photometer fitted to some of the earlier instruments gave a spot reading of the screen brightness, and in our experience were generally unreliable. Readings were subjective and varied from one operator to another. Higher readings, leading to under-exposure, were obtained as the operator's eyes became accustomed to the dark. To overcome this we have used an external photocell with a remote sensor which can be placed on the viewing screen and a reading obtained on a micro-ammeter. After initial calibration this system has worked very well.

2. *Choice of material.* Up till now plates have been the most commonly used form of material for electron microscopy, although 35-mm and 70-mm film backs have been available for some time. Seventy-mm film is usually only available to special order in large quantities and 35-mm is often considered too small a format for high quality results. Both Kodak and Ilford now market electron microscope sheet film coated on a 0·007 in polyester base and our preliminary tests have shown no significant disadvantages compared with plates. Speeds are comparable with Ilford EM5 plates and dimensional stability is very high. They are not as susceptible to edge frilling or breakage as plates and they are also cheaper and easier to store. The only problem we have found is that they require degassing for a considerably longer period than plates, owing to the moisture content of the film base. In this respect, polyester based film is an improvement on the older tri-acetate film which required the use of various plasticizers and stabilizers in its construction. This disadvantage is offset by the greater quantity that may be degassed at any one time. Koster and Spiro (1963) substituted film for glass plates over 10 years ago, yet it is only now that a film has been developed specifically for use in this field.

Polaroid film backs are available for the electron microscope, but we have found that the image produced, which in some models is circular, is too small to allow sufficient detail to be resolved from most biological material, and hence the advantage of an instant recording method is restricted. This lack of resolution is mainly due to the external siting of the camera, which requires the image to be formed via a phosphorescent screen and a normal lens system. The development of a similar system, giving higher resolution, however, would be extremely useful and one could see how this could be applied, with advantage, to the scanning electron microscope.

3. *Printing.* In comparison with the production of a good quality negative it is as important that the same care and attention is devoted to the printing stage and a solidly constructed enlarger with good optics is essential. A conventional condenser enlarger with an opal lamp has been found in our experience to produce excellent prints with good sharpness and contrast. Some workers (Frey and Carter, 1963; Staugaard, 1969) suggest using a lamphouse fitted with a compact filament clear lamp,

erroneously known as a "point-source". Because light reaching the negative is specular, a brighter image is formed and more contrasty and better
defined prints may be produced. However, there are disadvantages:
exposure times are very short, often fractions of a second, the lens must
be used at open aperture to avoid forming an image of the filament, and
exposure control must be affected by altering the voltage applied to the
lamp. Any slight physical blemishes on the negative become more
noticeable, and changes in magnification of successive prints require
adjustment of the lamp-to-condenser distance. Any gain in quality is more
apparent when relatively high magnification prints are required, as with
35-mm negatives.

Despite these disadvantages this system can be recommended for
negatives from which the highest resolution is needed.

D. Reproducibility of results

Having standardized the technical requirements of exposure, contrast,
density and correct development the pharmacologist is left with a considerable and difficult problem, that of reproducibility of results obtained
from control and drug-treated tissues. It is a requisite that a random series
of pictures taken before treatment will always show similar structures,
otherwise any results obtained from drug-treated material become
meaningless. We found that when working with the short-term effects
of glucocorticoid treatment of rat hind limb skeletal muscle, the quality
of the control muscle stretch-fixed by immersion in glutaraldehyde left a
great deal to be desired. We, therefore, developed a technique for
perfusion-fixation of the muscle at 34° and used a peristaltic pump (Bowes
et al., 1970). This technique gave us high quality fixed material of very
even appearance suggesting minimum extraction of material. Producing
good photographs from this material proved to be less of a problem than
we had anticipated because the fine detail was so well preserved that a
good medium contrast picture was readily obtained (Figs 27 and 28). The
same system, slightly modified, was then applied to the rabbit hind limb
skeletal muscle with similar results.

We then applied the same technique to the rat adrenal gland, a notoriously difficult tissue to fix other than by perfusion. As we were working
on isolated cells, it was essential for identification purposes to know in
detail the full structure. The perfusion technique was not infallible, but
when it succeeded, beautifully preserved tissue was obtained giving well
contrasted negatives. The adrenal was halved and the exposed face divided
into four parts (Fig. 29). It was possible to cut large sections covering the

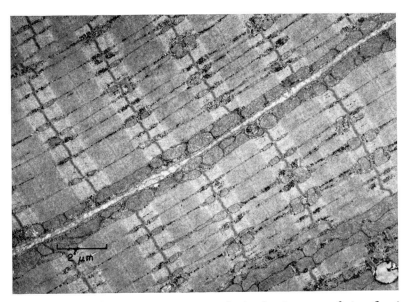

FIG. 27. Good medium-contrast picture obtained using a perfusion-fixation technique for the muscle.

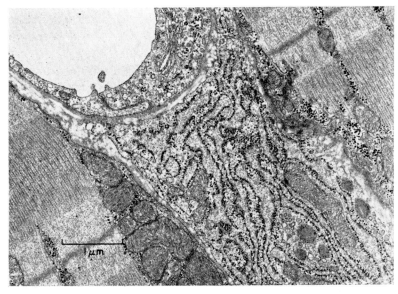

FIG. 28. See Fig. 27.

whole of each portion and stain with toluidine blue. The comparison between photographs of these sections, with electron micrographs of alternating thin sections, made identification much easier as far as the

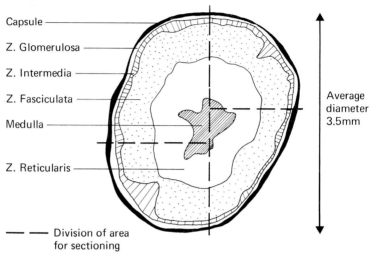

Fig. 29. Diagram of the minimally stressed rat adrenal (mid-section).

whole tissue was concerned (Figs 30 and 31). Careful study of the micrographs obtained from the intact gland revealed beautifully preserved microtubules in the mitochondria of the zona reticularis in particular, as described by Kjarheim (1967), but comparable photographs of the apparently identical isolated cells did not contain these structures. It was much easier to study the photographic image rather than the screen image owing to the increased resolution of the emulsion.

One way in which to preserve the isolated cells so that their general morphology was very similar to the intact gland was to fix them in 10% bovine serum albumin with glutaraldehyde. This technique has been used very successfully in our laboratory for lymphocytes and macrophages from lymph as the cells do not round up as with other methods and retain an undulating plasma membrane as seen with cine micrography or scanning microscopy. The cell–albumen mixture put on to a siliconized slide to reduce spreading of the droplets, gels within 2 to 3 min and the albumen-containing cells can then be fixed further as a free-floating gel. Only one centrifugation is required and the distribution of organelles within the cytoplasm does not become polarized.

Finally, the liver perfusion technique described by Fahimi (1967) was found to produce the same quality micrographs with minimal variation

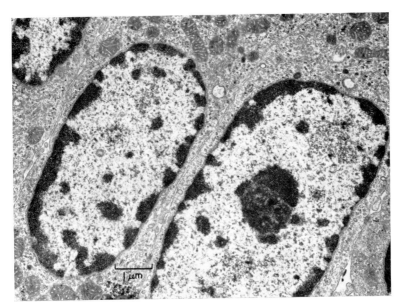

FIG. 30. Zona glomerulosa—rat adrenal.

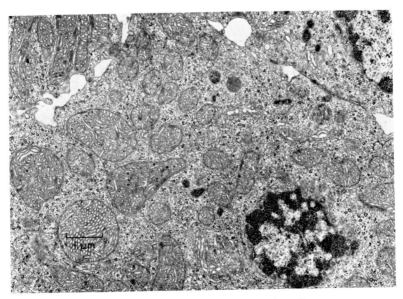

FIG. 31. Zona intermedia—rat adrenal.

between animals even when the photographs were taken of the isolated perfused liver.

E. Resins

The choice of embedding material has been found to have considerable bearing on the clarity of the picture obtained. Our own experience does not extend beyond the conventional epoxy resins where the material is dehydrated and infiltrated with the resin after using acetone or propylene oxide as an intermediate solvent. The use of Epikote 812, in our hands, has produced blocks of variable hardness and this has been supported by many other workers. With muscle, in particular, this was found to be a problem as a slight dragging of the sections past the diamond knife produced a far from crisp fibre image when recorded photographically. We experimented with a number of other epoxy resins and mixes and found that for animal tissue work in general, and isolated organelles in particular, the Epikote/Araldite mixture developed by Mollenhauer (1964) eliminated most of these problems and that, where only resin occupied part of a section, a very clear non-grainy background was obtained in contrast to the tendency to graininess and greyness seen after Epikote embedding. Similarly, with skin, the use of the resin mix developed by Spurr (1969) was found by Dr Baker in our laboratories to give excellent sectioning qualities and well contrasted pictures. Having found a successful fixing and embedding schedule, we have used it continuously, but there may well be many other equally successful combinations which we have not experienced.

ACKNOWLEDGEMENTS

We wish to thank Drs Karl Schmidt and Heine Keberle of CIBA-GEIGY, Basle, for their kindness in providing us with information and illustrations for the section on Autoradiography. We are indebted to Dr John Baker of these laboratories for his constructive criticism, to Miss Deborah Swandale for typing the many drafts of the manuscript, to Mrs Cilla French for printing the photographs and last, but not least, to all those people whose work we have quoted, notably Mrs Denise Bowes, Mr Robin Christian and Mrs Elaine Gillam.

REFERENCES

APPLETON, T. C. (1964). Jl R. microsc. Soc. **82**, 277.
BAKER, J. R. J. and APPLETON, T. C. (1974). The use of fresh-frozen sections in E.M. autoradiography of diffusible compounds. Proc. R. microsc. Soc. **9** (4), 20.

BOWES, D., BULLOCK, G. R. and WINSEY, N. P. J. (1970). Septième Congrès International de Microscopie Electronique, Grenoble, P. 397.

BULLOCK, G. R., CHRISTIAN, R. A., PETERS, R. F. and WHITE, A. M. (1971). *Biochem. Pharmac.* **20**, 943.

BURGE, R. E. (1964). Electron microscopy. Proceedings of the Third European Regional Conference. Prague, p. 19.

DIGBY, N., FIRTH, K. and HERCOOK, R. J. (1953). *J. photogr. Sci.* **1**, 194.

FAHIMI, H. D. (1967). *Lab. Invest.* **16**, 736.

FISHER, M. G. (1968). *In* ENGEL, C. E. (ed.), "Photography for the Scientist". Academic Press, London and New York.

FREY, S. and CARTER, Y. (1963). *Expl Cell Res.* **45**, 236.

GAHAN, P. B. (1972). *In* GAHAN, P. B. (ed.), "Autoradiography for Biologists". Academic Press, London and New York.

KJARHEIM, A. (1967). *Expl Cell Res.* **45**, 236.

KOSTER, L. W. and SPIRO, D. (1963). *J. biol. photogr. Ass.* **31**, 49.

LAWSON, D. (1972). "Photomicrography." Academic Press, London and New York.

LOUD, A. V. (1968). *J. Cell. Biol.* **37**, 27.

LOVELAND, R. P. (1970). "Photomicrography". **2**, p. 845. John Wiley & Sons, New York.

MOLLENHAUER, H. H. (1964). *Stain Technol.* **39**, 11.

OLLERENSHAW, R. (1962). *Photogr. J.* **102**, 41.

ROTH, L. J. and STUMPF, W. E. (1969). "Autoradiography of Diffusible Substances". Academic Press, London and New York.

SPENCER, D. A. (1969). "Colour Photography in Practice". Focal Press, London.

SPURR, A. R. (1969). *J. Ultrastruct. Res.* **26**, 31.

STÄUBLI, W., HESS, R. and WEIBEL, E. R. (1969). *J. Cell Biol.* **42**, 92.

STAUGAARD, B. C. (1969). *J. biol. photogr. Ass.* **37**, 25.

ULLBERG, S. (1954). *Acta Radiol.* Suppl. 118.

ULLBERG, S. (1958). Proceedings of the International Conference on Peaceful Uses of Atomic Energy **24**, 248.

VALENTINE, R. C. (1964). *In* "Electron Microscopy". Proceedings of the Third European Regional Conference, Prague, p. 23.

WEIBEL, E. R. (1967). *In* WEIBEL, E. R. and ELIAS, H. (eds), "Quantitative Methods in Morphology". Springer-Verlag, Berlin-Heidelberg, New York.

WEIBEL, E. R., STAUBLI, W., GNÄGI, H. R. and HESS, F. A. (1969). *J. Cell Biol.* **42**, 68.

WEINER, J., LOUD, A., KIMBERG, D. and SPIRO, D. (1968). *J. Cell Biol.* **37**, 47.

2

Some aspects of the reproduction of diffraction patterns

D. J. DRURY

I. PHOTOGRAPHIC REPRODUCTION*

The response of a photographic material to light is not exactly proportional. This was first described graphically by Hurter and Driffield in the 1890s. It will be seen from Fig. 1 that the increase in density of a silver image is proportional only over a limited portion of the curve. At the lower exposures and the higher exposures the response ceases to be proportional, rather regular increases in exposure show a progressive increase in density at the low end and decreasing density at high end.

The curve demonstrated might be modified by changing the development conditions. By increasing the time of development, or temperature, or, to a lesser degree, the amount of agitation, the gradient of the curve will increase together with the level of lowest density. The maximum density of the material depends on the amount of developed silver present. When all the silver halide is exposed and developed, no increase in density can be achieved by conventional processing.

From the variations of degree of development and gradient of the curve,

* Throughout this paper the materials considered are hypothetical.

two types of closely related curves can be calculated, the time/gamma curve and the Contrast Index/time curve. However, it is necessary first to consider how the gradients of the curves are measured. Hurter and Driffield, and many later workers, were concerned to derive some indica-

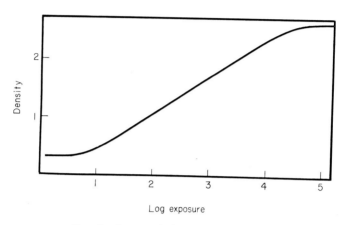

Fig. 1. A typical characteristic curve.

tor of sensitivity to light of photographic negative materials by reference to the characteristic curve, as it is now known. (It is also known as D Log E curve and the H and D curve.) Their work led them to consider the straight line portion of the curve to be important. In order to give a value to this gradient they used the tangent of the angle formed with the Log E axis and called it gamma (Fig. 2 (a)).

With more recent materials the straight line portion of the curve has diminished, and in some cases does not exist. Nowadays it is necessary to consider the lowest point on the curve which shows a useful increase in density over the base density (fog), and a straight line connecting it to the point of greatest useful density. The tangent of the angle of this line is called the Contrast Index (Fig. 2 (b)). Gamma and Contrast Index are closely related and in normal photographic practice may be considered interchangeable. This is not the case, however, when reproduction characteristics are considered. The time of development at a given temperature may be plotted against either gamma or C.I. whichever is applicable.

Having calculated the curves for different development times, it is possible to produce curves which indicate the degree of development in a given developer and which will produce a curve with a gamma or contrast index of the required magnitude (Fig. 3 (a), (b)).

An evenly illuminated, flat original which reflects and absorbs evenly all over has no brightness range. The one value that can be given to the reflectivity, that is, its brightness, may be placed on the characteristic

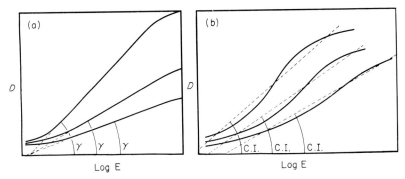

FIG. 2. Families of curves (a) having straight line portions which may be extended to the base line to give gammas. (b) In the case of a characteristic curve which does not have a straight line portion the Contrast Index is given by the tangent of the angle formed with the base line, by a line passing through the points of highest and lowest useful density.

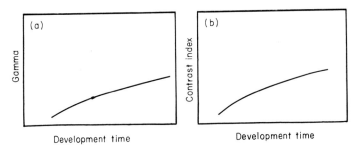

FIG. 3. (a) Time/gamma curve for Fig. 2 (a). (b) Time/Contrast Index curve for Fig. 2 (b).

curve of a photographic material at any position, above base fog, and not suffer any loss of tone quality (Fig. 4 (a)).

That surface, having no brightness range may, therefore, be placed on the characteristic curve in any position from A to J. However, if a shadow is cast over part of the surface then a brightness range exists. Similarly, if a face of a solid object, as illustrated in Fig. 4 (b) is illuminated, then a brightness range exists between it and the other faces. It may, for example, have a brightness value of 1 in the shadow area and 10 in the non-shadow area. This ratio represents a range of brightness from the lightest to the darkest portion of the surface. Since characteristic curves have logarithmic axes, a brightness range of 10 : 1 will represent an exposure variation of one unit on the Log E axis. However, if the brightest portion

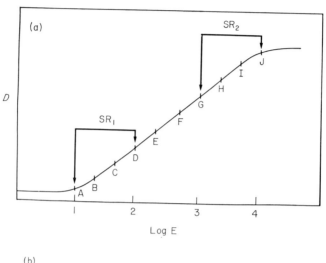

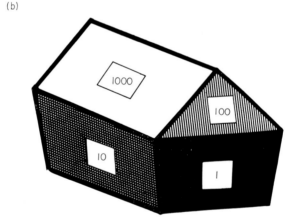

FIG. 4. (a) A subject having a brightness range of 1 : 10 represented by SR, may be placed at position A to D or position G to J without loss of tonal quality. A brightness range of 1 : 1000 may be placed only from A to J. (b) A solid object with four surfaces illuminated ranging in brightness from 1000 units to 1 unit.

of the range falls at 3 then the darkest will be 2. The brightness will, therefore, have a limited range within which to be placed if a linear response is desired, i.e., anywhere between A and J, (SR_1 representing the lowest position possible and SR_2 the highest). It follows from this that if an original subject to be recorded has a brightness range of 1000 : 1 this will fall over an exposure range of three units on the Log E axis, e.g., from 1 to 4, then only one position is correct.

From the practical point of view this means that when a photographic record is made of any subject, the brightness range of which is low, then considerable latitude of exposure is possible. If the brightness range is high the exposure becomes more critical. Should the brightness range exceed 1000 : 1, say 10,000 : 1, then it is no longer possible to record all the brightness values on the single emulsion used in the example.

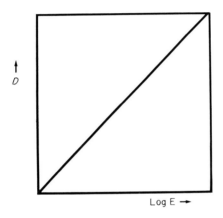

Fig. 5. Theoretical perfect negative reproduction.

The foregoing consideration has been of photographic transmission (excluding direct reversal) materials, usually negative materials. In the case of prints further restrictions apply. The maximum reflection density normally found in a photographic print material is about 1·8, this means that a maximum brightness range of only about 1 : 60 can be recorded.

Tonal reproduction does not, usually, depend only on one type of light-sensitive material. (Electron diffraction negatives are sometimes an exception here, if these negatives are considered to represent the original scenes.) Usually, a negative is made from an original and that negative is then printed. The tonal reproduction characteristics are, therefore, normally dependent on two responses to light, and may be affected by other phenomena. The ideal negative reproduction curve is illustrated in Fig. 5.

To obtain a reproduction curve of this sort, the characteristic curve of the print material would have to be a mirror image characteristic curve

(Fig. 6). However, this is not the case. Print paper characteristic curves vary with contrast grade, development, degree of fogging, etc. If a typical curve for bromide paper is taken and plotted together with a typical negative material used for monochrome photography the result will be similar to that shown in Fig. 7.

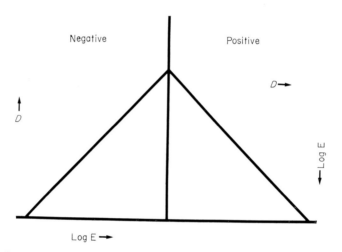

FIG. 6. Idealized negative/positive reproduction characteristics.

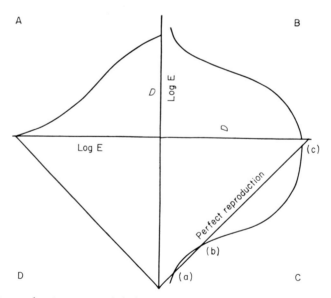

FIG. 7. Reproduction curves (C) derived from combining the characteristics of the negative (A) and positive (B) material (D = transfer curve).

If, as in the case with electron diffraction patterns, no negative is used but a print is made directly from the original pattern, then the conditions are somewhat changed. That is, the original electron diffraction negative can be considered the original scene and the reproduction of this as a print will be a one-step process providing a reversed reproduction curve (Fig. 8).

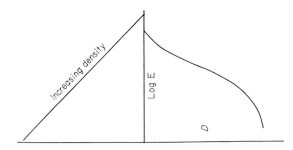

FIG. 8. Direct negative reproduction of electron diffraction pattern.

Given that a strictly proportional response is not possible in photographic reproduction it is now necessary to consider the effect of maximum density restrictions. As noted earlier, the maximum reflection density possible of photographic paper is of the order of 1·8. If photomechanical reproduction is considered, and this is the usual case for making prints of electron and x-ray diffraction negatives, a maximum ink density of somewhere between 1·3 and 1·7 is found (the latter density will only be found in "quality" printing). Halftone, photomechanical reproduction is very close to a directly proportional response if the technique is photolithographic or photogravure.

From the reproduction curve in Fig. 7 it will be seen that there is some decrease in the contrast at the bright end of the scale (a), an increase in the contrast at (b) and a further decrease in the portion (c). From this it is seen that reproduction is not directly proportional. Regular increases in brightness of the original scene are reproduced irregularly over the three major portions of the reproduction curve, i.e., the toe reproducing "flattened" increases in brightnesses, the straight line portion brightness increases at an increased rate: the shoulder brightnesses "flattening off" again.

An addition to these difficulties is that where a brightness range is in excess of the density range of either photographic print paper, or printing ink, then further distortion of the reproduction brightness range must be achieved if all the range is to be reproduced. In Fig. 9 an original scene is recorded on three negatives of the same material developed to different gammas. Each records information from the brightest to the darkest parts of the scene but the maximum density of the printing paper together with its particular gamma is the limiting factor. Negative (i) has too long a

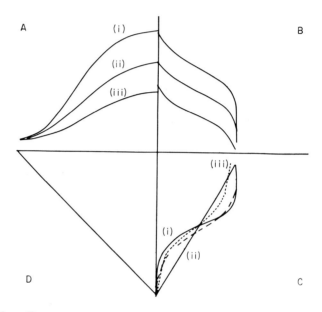

FIG. 9. The effect on reproduction characteristics (C) of varying the gamma of the negative material (A), and thereby its density range.

density range to be recorded on the printing paper and in the example the densest portion of the negative is printed placing the shoulder of the negative curve at the toe of the printing paper curve. By doing this, only about half the slope of negative curve (i) is reproduced by an inversely changing image. Information in the lower part of the negative curve (i) is reproduced as the maximum black of the paper print. The reproduction curve (ii) shows a slightly flattened, high brightness portion and a very considerable flattening of the dark end of the curve. In negative curve (iii) the highest density has been arranged in order to keep the total density range within the exposure range of the printing paper. This has produced a reproduction curve with considerably less distortion at each end of the brightness range, reproduction curve (iii).

II. X–RAY DIFFRACTION PRINTS

X-ray diffraction negatives can normally be reproduced by conventional photographic means. An intermediate negative can be made and a print produced from this. This is the conventional method used for x-ray diffraction reproduction, i.e., a reproduction which appears similar in light to dark orientation as the original diffraction pattern. The stages are illustrated in Fig. 10.

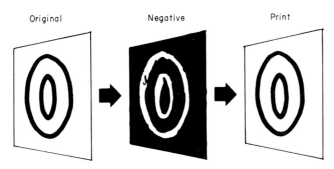

FIG. 10. Conventional x-ray diffraction reproduction method.

This straightforward approach may be used for many, if not most, x-ray diffraction patterns. However, when optimum quality of reproduction is required the inclusion of an unsharp mask can be of value (Fig. 11). The steps necessary to produce such a mask are simple but attention must be paid to processing which must be accurately controlled.

The intermediate negative is made on a low contrast, blue sensitive negative film. The unsharp mask is made from this negative by placing a piece of transparent spacing material, e.g. a thin piece of glass, between the negative and another sheet of the continuous tone film and exposing it to diffuse illumination. The exposure and development of this mask are adjusted to produce a gradient and maximum density which, when the mask is bound to the negative, will reduce the density range to be printed to that required to produce a reproduction with less flattening in the darkest areas. Figure 12 is a graphical representation of this masking technique. In quadrant C straight line (a) represents perfect tonal reproduction. Reproduction curve (i) approaches this for a considerable portion of its length. A near proportional response line (b) is achieved. This reproduction should be compared with reproduction curve (ii)'s relationship with perfect and proportional reproduction curves (c) and

C

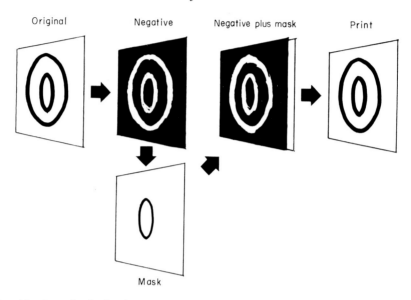

FIG. 11. A method of reducing the density range of x-ray diffraction patterns by means of an unsharp mask.

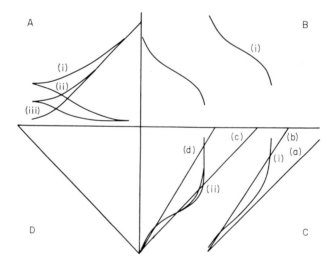

FIG. 12. Reproduction characteristics using masks of different densities. Print paper curve (Bi) has been moved to cover the whole range of densities shown by negative/mask combination (i).

(d). It will be seen that considerable flattening of the reproduction curve (ii) occurs in the darker portions of the print whereas although flattening does occur in curve (i) it is much less marked.

Sharp masks could be used for this technique but unsharp masks have been recommended for two reasons: (1) registration of the mask with the intermediate negative is facilitated by using an unsharp image; (2) use is made of a photographic effect to slightly exaggerate fine detail information in the original. Figure 13 illustrates this effect.

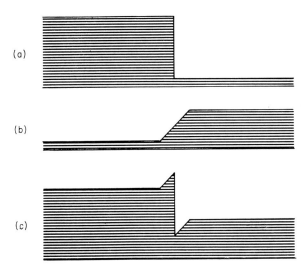

FIG. 13. The density difference between two adjacent parts of a negative are represented by (a). An unsharp positive of the difference is represented by (b) but having only half the density difference. When combined (c) the mask increases the apparent density of the less dense portion of (a) but not that of the denser portion, thus reducing the density range to half. At the border between the higher and lower density however the mask shows a gradual change in density. In the combination the less dense portion shows a decrease in density at the border while the denser portion shows an increase in density relative to the combined density range.

Although this effect produces reproductions which are not strictly representations of the original pattern negative, it is usual for reproductions to be used for illustrative purposes only: measurements will not be made from them, while a point may be better made or more easily taken where there is slight exaggeration.

III. ELECTRON DIFFRACTION PRINTS

In the case of electron diffraction patterns the difficulties of reproduction are greatly increased. Very high densities are usually found at the centre of the plate or film that fall away rapidly towards the edges. Figure 14 illustrates a fairly typical "profile" of such a plate.

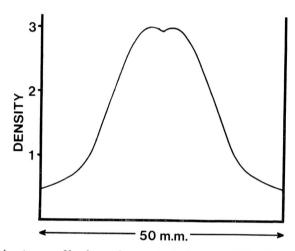

FIG. 14. A density profile through a typical electron diffraction pattern. The diffraction lines are not seen at this scale.

Maximum densities of 3 or 4 are not uncommon. While it is quite possible to reduce the overall density for reproduction in a way similar to that shown in Fig. 9, i.e., by arranging for an intermediate negative to be processed to a low gamma (or C.I.) in order to "fit" the range to the printing paper (negative curve iii to print curve iii), an already difficult problem is emphasized.

While the density range of electron diffraction negatives is considerable, the diffraction maxima show very little increase in density over the immediately surrounding density. The problem is further complicated by the convention that electron diffraction negatives are printed directly on to photographic paper—thus producing the reverse effect of x-ray diffraction patterns. However, as was noted above, if an internegative stage is used, a general reduction of the contrast takes place which reduces the already small differences in density of the diffraction lines (or dots).

The only way of a conventional type of printing, which may be used to reproduce this information is to successively print from the lightest part of the negatives to the densest on several pieces of printing paper, increasing the exposures each time in order to reproduce the next denser portion of the negative on the useful part of the paper curve. A set of prints which approximate the conditions existing in Fig. 15 (a) are illustrated in Fig. 15 (b). This method has its disadvantages if reproduction in a journal is being considered.

It is perhaps appropriate to consider here the value of reproduction of any photograph. Perfect tonal reproduction is not possible. A close approximation is, however, possible over a limited range—see Fig. 12 (where a considerable portion of reproduction curve (i) is fairly straight). It follows, therefore, that the value of knowing the relative density of particular density areas is limited unless the type of reproduction characteristics are known, and even then, for only a limited range. The spatial distribution, however, of diffraction maxima can be better reproduced if density factors are relegated to a subordinate position in reproduction techniques. That is, if the compression of the density gradient of a photographic image is not considered a great disadvantage, while the detail characteristics are to be retained, then reproduction can now be made simple.

One method of reproducing the detail information of electron diffraction negatives has been described by Murray (1966), in which he made use of a special print exposing machine. As the density of the electron diffraction patterns is substantially greater at the centre than at the edge, often from a density of 3 or 4 reducing to a density of around 0·5 (range of 2·5 or 3·5 densities) the exposure at the edge required to produce a middle grey in the print, will be approximately 300 to 3000 times less than at the centre. In order to achieve an increase in exposure at the centre which considerably increases the amount of light reaching that portion of the diffraction negative, a rotating sector wheel (Fig. 16 (a)) is positioned directly between the negative and the exposing light (Fig. 16 (b)).

This method allows a considerable degree of variation of exposure from the edge to the centre. Originally the equipment was designed so that the sector wheel rotated while the diffraction negative in contact with the printing paper remained stationary. Rotating the negative and print paper while the sector wheel remains stationary, however, is equally effective in producing good results. Figure 17 is an example of (left) normal print in a soft grade of printing paper and (right) the same negative exposed under a sector wheel.

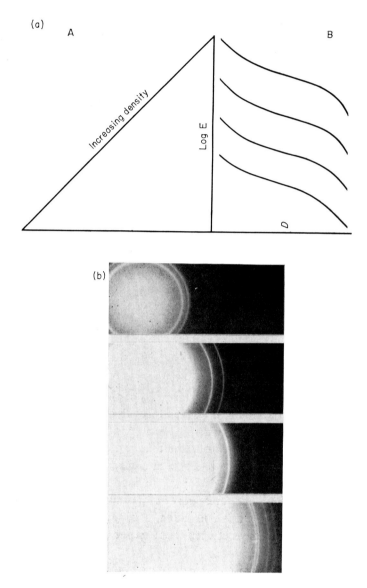

Fig. 15. (a) A method of reproducing the diffraction maxima by successively increasing printing exposure. (b) A series of prints corresponding to curves shown in B.

(a)

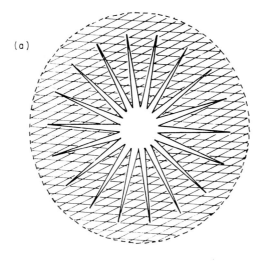

(b)

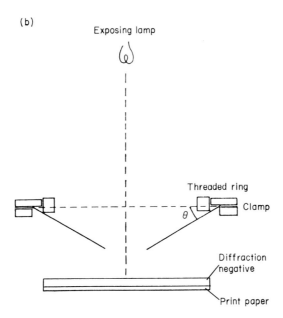

FIG. 16. Rotating sector wheel dodging device (after Murray). (a) Plan view of sector wheel. (b) Method used to expose electron diffraction negatives. Reproduced with permission from Murray (1966).

Another method that has been described (Drury, 1972) involves the photographic masking of the background density, to reduce the overall density range to a figure close to the maximum density range of printing paper. To do this the density range of electron diffraction negative is measured and an unsharp mask is made with a maximum density of sufficient magnitude to effectively reduce the diffraction negative density

FIG. 17. Prints made by use of sector wheel technique (left) and by direct conventional method (right). The same diffraction pattern was used.

range to that of printing paper. Figure 18 shows a print produced from such a masked electron diffraction negative. Figure 19 shows the reproduction curve and its derivation.

By taking this technique a step further most of the background density can be removed. That is, a further unsharp mask is made, this time of the combined, original electron diffraction negative and the first mask. This produces a very nearly horizontal curve for the combined diffraction negative and two unsharp masks (Fig. 20).

As this curve now effectively represents an evenly illuminated original which has no brightness range (see II) it can be reproduced on printing paper in any position on the characteristic curve it is desired. As an unsharp masking technique is used the small detail differences in the silver image are not affected by the reduction in density range of the pattern. Indeed, use is made of the Mackie line effect (see Fig. 13) to emphasize the detail information. Figure 21 is an example of the type of reproduction obtained by this method (it should be noted that the image has been reversed by comparison with the representation conventionally used for single crystal electron diffraction patterns.)

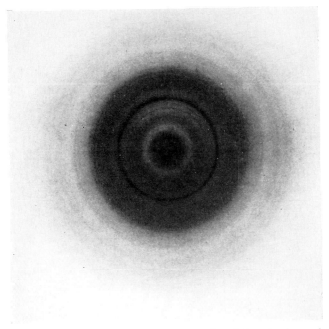

FIG. 18. An electron diffraction pattern reproduced by single unsharp mask technique.

C*

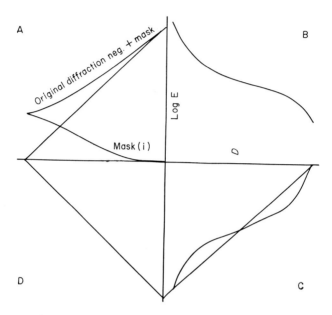

Fɪɢ. 19. Reproduction characteristics of single unsharp mask technique. In A the diffraction pattern is considered as the original, having linear density characteristics. The reduction of the diffraction pattern density range to that reproducible on printing paper (gradient B) is achieved by unsharp mask (i).

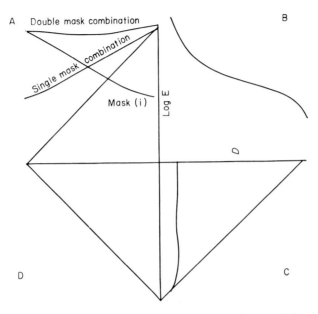

FIG. 20. By the addition of a further mask (A) the background density may be virtually removed leaving no gross density range. The unsharp masks however do not remove the fine detail of the diffraction lines.

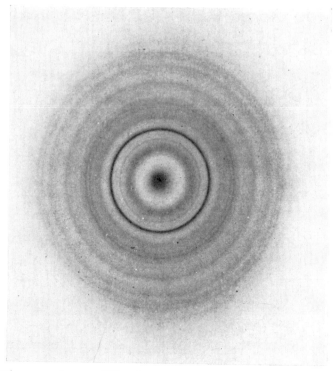

FIG. 21. The same electron diffraction pattern as shown in Fig. 18 reproduced by the double mask technique and approximating to the situation shown in Fig. 20.

This method does not give any information about the relative density of the background but no diffraction maxima are lost as a result of compression of density differences at the toe and shoulder of the printing paper characteristic curve.

ACKNOWLEDGEMENTS

I wish to thank Dr R. T. Murray for his permission to use Fig. 16 and the Editor of *Medical and Biological Illustration* for permission to use Figs 14, 18 and 21. Thanks are also due to Dr K. Little and Mr J. Fraser for their help and comments in the preparation of the manuscript.

REFERENCES

DRURY, D. J. (1972). *Med. biol. Illust.* **22**, 256-258.
MURRAY, R. T. (1966). *J. scient. Instrum.* **43**, 760.

3
Infrared photography, a versatile tool

H. LOU GIBSON

I. INTRODUCTION

Ever since Herschel discovered the infrared region of the solar spectrum, in 1800, technical, scientific and medical practitioners have been intrigued by its characteristics and aided by its properties. The capability of its being beamed as heating radiation was soon discovered for medical therapy and for technical purposes like paint drying. The fact that it could be focused into rays with special lenses, similarly to visible light, has led to numerous, current, heat-sensing and guidance systems. Its effect on botanical and other biological physiology has been widely studied.

By means of snooperscope devices infrared can be translated into visible images for 'seeing in the dark", and for visualizing infrared renditions. It is also possible to display heat patterns with certain phosphors and with cholesteric liquid crystals. Other thermographic methods display electronically produced images of various types of mechanical and biological heat patterns.

But the photographer not only wants to see but also to record. For this, black-and-white and color photographic emulsions have been devised which are sensitive to the "actinic" range of infrared from 700 to about 1350 nm. Camera work is done in the 700 to 900 nm range.

Spectroscopic, astronomical and other scientific applications utilize the full gamut of sensitivities.

Beyond the actinic range lies the heat range. The non-photographic methods mentioned above are pressed into service here, because it is not practical (even were it possible) to create emulsions for recording heat. The reason is that surroundings radiate so much ambient heat (which would fog the film) that it would be necessary to work with cameras and subjects held at temperatures around that of liquid air.

Infrared radiation can be classified into four broad ranges of increasingly longer wavelengths: The *actinic range*; which comprises the near-red part of the radiation produced by incandescent objects, such as the sun or a lamp filament. Such radiation can be reflected, transmitted, or emitted through luminescence,* by subjects that are not hot themselves. The *hot object range*; this radiation comes from nonincandescent subjects, such as heated flatirons, hot mill calenders, or an electrical component. These have temperatures around 400°C. The *calorific range*; this radiation is produced by objects with temperatures around those of boiling water and steam pipes (below about 200°C). It is nonactinic. The *warm range*; the human body and warm ground radiate in this range. It also is nonactinic. When you realize that the wavelength of radiation in this last category is around 9000 nm, it will be appreciated why recording such radiation on film is impossible. This chapter deals with work that can be carried out with ordinary cameras, in the actinic range from 700 to 900 nm. The applications involve the infrared images that can be recorded directly on the film. It is not practical here to go into the other techniques, but key references are given for those who wish to investigate further. However, two new techniques—infrared color photography and luminescence photography—are covered.

Infrared photography used to be done primarily with black-and-white emulsions. In 1942 a multi-layer, "false-color" film was devised for military uses in the detection of camouflage. This material translated an infrared image to a colored one, and combined the infrared resultant with a visible image component. Infrared color film is now available in 16 mm, 35 mm and sheet form. Starting around 1960, numerous applications for such a modified-color film have been found in all fields of infrared photography.

The photography of biological, green-light-excited, infrared lumines-

* This term refers to visible-light-excited infrared fluorescence. For photographic discussions, luminescence has been adopted in order to distinguish the phenomenon from ultraviolet-excited, visible fluorescence.

cence was first done in 1962. Some documentation work with ultraviolet excitation had been done prior to that.

It is not intended to treat the technical, working methods of infrared photography in detail. However, the basic principles are outlined in order to enable the photographer to evaluate the suitability of his equipment and facilities for using this photographic tool to advantage.

The main purpose of this chapter is to present a comprehensive discussion of outdoor and indoor applications. In this way the practitioner is offered a chance to guage the benefits of applying infrared photography in his own field.

The organized bibliography furnishes an entry into the voluminous literature on techniques and applications.

II. OUTDOOR APPLICATIONS

These depend upon the capability of infrared to pass through haze (not fog) with far less scattering than visible light and also upon the reflection characteristics of various entities in the terrain (Fig. 1). In particular, the renditions of foliage provide the key to many applications.

A. *Techniques*

Many projects require the use of elaborate aerial cameras. Nevertheless, the work that can be done with conventional cameras covers valuable scientific, pictorial and illustrative fields.

There are three basic techniques: high-altitude aerial and satellite photography; recording from light planes or from high places on the ground; and the photography of agricultural plots and single plants, from close to the ground.

Currently of great interest is the study of ecological factors and earth resources. The distribution of forests, crops and waste lands can be accurately mapped by cameras mounted in earth-orbiting satellites. Much information about the kinds of plants, rocks and soils, and standing and sub-surface water distributions can be obtained over large areas. Aerial photography with elaborate cameras from specially equipped planes is widely adopted and provides results showing greater specificity and detail. Much of the work is done at altitudes of about two miles.

Photography with ordinary cameras at lesser heights from light planes or from hills is often adopted for experimentation prior to launching a full-fledged aerial program. In that way, the suitability of infrared photography for the project in mind can be economically determined.

FIG. 1. A valuable property of infrared photography is its ability to record distant terrain through haze.

Also, some of the film and filter factors can be worked out ahead of time. In certain applications, when relatively small and accessible areas are involved, there may be no need for an elaborate aerial photographic program.

Ground photography is done mainly to back up the other investigations by finding out the disease and soil agencies that cause stress in plants. The records also serve as a check for the black-and-white tones and modified colors that can be expected as the signatures of specific crops and stress agencies.

In order to understand why infrared photography is effective, the renditions of healthy and diseased foliage have to be known. Discussion of such renditions is taken up next. Photography of botanical luminescence is done in the laboratory and is presented further on.

B. Healthy foliage

It is not the reflection of infrared by the chlorophylls and other leaf pigments that yields the results, as is often erroneously supposed. The epidermis and pigments of leaves are very transparent to infrared. Thus the radiation has free access to the parenchyma. By the same token, the green, yellow and infrared (but not red) radiations, which are strongly reflected from the mesophyll, readily emerge from the leaf to give it a green color and a bright characteristic in the infrared. Hence, foliage appears light-toned in an infrared photograph. The plant gets most of its warmth from its environment, not from direct-irradiation; and its energy for photosynthesis from visible light.

The infrared renditions of foliage in aerial photographs have been studied extensively. Deciduous trees and conifers can be readily differentiated by black-and-white infrared photography, but species within each group record to about the same tones. Hardwood and softwood stands can be easily identified.

It is with modified color infrared photography that the most informative and striking renditions are obtained. Deciduous trees record predominantly red, whereas conifers appear a bluish purple. There are a variety of colors in which fruit and nut trees are recorded—from pink (peach, almond) through red (pear), to reddish brown (walnut). Other healthy crops yield typical colors—e.g., oats, reddish; safflower, dark pink; alfalfa, red. Dormant plants may record in a greenish-brown color. These colors result from variations in the proportions of infrared and visible reflections.

The characteristic renditions made it possible to detect military camouflage by infrared photography. The color film was devised to emphasize the difference between natural and painted foliage. However, camouflage paints have been compounded that reflect visible and infrared in about the same proportions as leaves. This makes detection much more difficult.

C. *Unhealthy plants*

Many plants under stress from disease or insects, or from unsuitable soil and water conditions, can be detected by infrared photography because there is usually a loss of infrared reflectance from affected verdure. For example, potato streak virus damage appears darker in an infrared photograph than to the eye. Observations have been made on cherry gummosis and on cucumber lesions on tobacco. In the latter manifestation, the active spots do not record as clearly as does the residual damage.

It is likely that certain grain rusts cause the mesophyll tissues to become impacted and semi-transparent to infrared before there is a visible loss of green coloration. Infrared photography thereby provides early detection and localization. Fungus disease can be similarly located (and hence treated early) in citrus orchards. Oak-root fungus can be detected in young plum orchards and the affected trees then replaced with a resistant strain. Gross determinations of sub-surface pH can be made from the photographic appearance of plum foilage in an infrared survey—unsuitable areas can be treated or productivity assessed.

Infrared black-and-white and color photography are often utilized in crop surveys. More accurate information is obtainable from photographs, made from a height of two miles on *Phytophthora* infestations in navel oranges and potatoes, than is obtainable by experts walking through the same areas. The hyphae of powdery mildew brightens the tone of plants in the early stages of attack.

The value of infrared color photography also has been demonstrated in connection with the problem of surveying the approximately 55 million citrus trees in Florida. Trees under stress gradually lose their infrared reflectance. The reddish photographic rendition of healthy trees grades into magenta, purple and green as the loss of infrared reflectance progresses. Distinctive colors were obtained from the effects upon citrus trees caused by their principal diseases—footrot, advanced nematode infestation, very early Tristeza virus reaction, and manifestations of Psorosis, Xyloporosis and Exocortis viruses that had progressed beyond the mild stage.

In connection with the photographic detection of bark-beetle damage to ponderosa pine, black-and-white infrared photography was found ineffectual. Color photography and infrared color photography, however, is more successful. Both color methods yield good results. While the infrared color technique is better, especially when haze is present, more skill is needed in interpreting the records.

Differentiating tree species as well as tagging diseased individuals is another valuable advantage of using the infrared color technique as an aid for detecting forest diseases. Orange areas appear in conifers attacked by the pine beetle and the Douglas fir beetle; sucking insects produce damage that records as whitish areas on silver fir in Oregon. Much time is saved by studying infrared color transparencies, instead of ordinary ones. The infrared color record sharply delineates the conifers, so only the confines of such stands need be searched, instead of the entire photograph. When thousands of trees appear in aerial transparencies, it is important to narrow down the visual search to the kinds that could be infected.

The value of photography in all studies of foliage and verdure under stress lies in early and relatively easy detection of disease. Photography can also indicate remedial steps and make their application quick and efficient. These advantages are particularly beneficial when large orchard and agricultural areas or inaccessible forest regions must be studied.

D. Environmental studies

These can be carried out from the ground or from planes. Early papers discuss the advantages of infrared ground photography in this field. Applications cover the identification and appraisal of trees and smaller vegetation. Plants flourishing in ideal soils can be distinguished from the same plants growing under submarginal conditions. Useful records can generally be obtained from verdure up to 10 miles from the camera, and sometimes from as far as 50 miles.

Aerial photography has a bearing on many natural-science projects and some of the applications might be adapted for ground photography in biogeography. Water records almost black, damp areas photograph darker than dry ones. It is likely that studies in the ecology of areas adjacent to cultivation could benefit through indications of moisture conditions in bare ground.

It has been reported that physiological drought causes a lowering of infrared reflectance. Cotton is a good indicator plant for mapping regions of excess soil salinity. Pictures taken three weeks prior to normal harvesting time give the best indications. Infrared photography is best done in the early morning, when the plants have the highest turgidity.

Natural and polluted water resources have received extensive attention. Hydrological surveys show that even a few inches of clear water photograph very dark on infrared film. Infrared photography has been used to delineate the water lines of tidal country, and to map drainage and other land-development projects. Muddy water shows up in lighter tones than clear expanses, because of reflection from the suspended silt. It has been found that brownish, silted water may appear green in an infrared color transparency. Infrared film may be used to clearly delineate patches of floating plants and algae in turbid water areas, especially infrared color film. Small, hidden, jungle streams can be delineated by the slight color differences recorded in the adjacent trees. Muddy water drained or pumped into swamps often damages the trees to the extent of causing a dark infrared record.

Infrared photography, especially in color, is valuable for detecting sources and extents of polluted water. Many pollution problems arise because the sources are unknown, the consequences not observed soon enough, and the effects not appreciated by those authorities delegated to control such matters. Aerial infrared photography can detect critical areas and reduce field work by guiding technicians in taking laboratory samples. On infrared color film, clear water photographs black when a vertical viewpoint is selected. Water suffused with algae records red, and water with a low dissolved-oxygen level, milky. Infrared color film depicts changes in vegetation growing near outfalls of chemical exotics in a cyan hue, in contrast with the magenta-red of healthy flora. These early changes cannot be seen by the naked eye. An efficient sewage-disposal, trickling filter is likely to record black, whereas an odoriferous, over-loaded bed appears reddish.

Other features of terrain besides botanical features can be studied photographically. There are differences in the renditions of shale and limestone. Many rocks appear blue-gray in the modified-color transparency. Locations of springs can be detected from a great height. Topographic features of the earth's surface, the detection of alluvial drifts, and the differentiation of rock outcrops are greatly aided by infrared photography. Sterophotography is often employed.

In a different field it is practical to have recourse to the infrared photography of livestock. By means of the technique, it is even possible to sex the cattle and differentiate between Herefords and Hereford-Angus crosses. The counting of pigs, goats, sheep, cattle and horses can be greatly facilitated by the infrared techniques. Wild animal surveying is another application.

The changes produced by modern civilization are not the only ones that can be detected by infrared photography. Less marked, but often clear to the infrared camera, are the residual traces left in archaeological sites. Many crop and soil marks and other land scars have not yet disappeared to the infrared camera, even though they are indiscernible to the eye or fail to record on panchromatic film.

An exciting photoarchaeological find is shown in Fig. 2. An ancient, bastioned fortification was discovered in South Dakota by crop markings

FIG. 2. Aerial infrared photoarchaeological record made in 1965, of a previously only partially known village site along the Missouri River, 22 miles south of Pierre, South Dakota. The presence of bastions, their 200-ft spacing and other evidence indicate that the fortifications may have been built by Norse settlers about A.D. 1362. (Reproduced from an infrared color transparency. Courtesy of Carl H. Strandberg, Staff Engineer, Itek Data Analysis Center, Alexandria, Virginia.)

appearing in an infrared color transparency. The complete nature of this occupied area had been previously unknown. In the infrared color record, traces of later Indian settlement are superimposed over the earlier, apparently Scandinavian, remains. The illustration for Fig. 2 was obtained from a black-and-white internegative made from a modified color record.

E. Pictorial photography

Many dramatic pictorial infrared photographs are obtainable in black-and-white or color. Travel photography can often take advantage of the haze penetration afforded by black-and-white infrared photography. Infrared landscape photographs in black-and-white are characterized as follows: the sky is depicted almost black; clouds and snow are white; shadows and the shaded side of trees are dark, but usually show more detail than a panchromatic rendition; grass and leaves appear very light as though covered by snow; distant details are rendered with remarkable clarity. Infrared color photography records foliage in a striking red, flowers in modified colors and some types of stone in quite natural shades—all backed by a pleasing blue sky with white clouds in good contrast.

Outdoor fashion photography with infrared color film produces striking results. Fabrics appear in modified colors, whereas skin tones, though somewhat "cold," are almost normal. The photographic illustrator can often dramatize his subjects by making infrared pictures of them. This type of photography gives a good separation of the planes of buildings and darkens the sky to provide a contrasting background. Lightening the tones of trees often avoids "black holes" in the composition. A comparison between panchromatic and infrared rendering of architecture is shown in Fig. 3.

Infrared photographs taken outdoors in sunlight and then printed slightly darker than normal, strongly suggest that they were taken by moonlight. As a matter of fact, some of the "night" scenes in professional motion pictures are made in sunlight on infrared-sensitive film. Basically, well-exposed negatives are made and these are printed somewhat dark. Through this means, sunlight appears to be moonlight. The technique does not have the vogue it once had, however, because foliage is rendered somewhat light in tone. Also, more elaborate lighting units and fast films have simplified night cinematography with color and panchromatic films.

Fig. 3

III. EQUIPMENT

Conventional cameras and accessories are discussed here. Highly specialized equipment, such as aerial and snooperscope cameras, is described in the references.

A. Cameras

The view camera regularly used for ordinary photography can be used for infrared photography. Because much of the work, especially indoors, deals with small specimens, the camera should be adaptable for close-up photography.

A single-lens reflex camera with an automatic diaphragm is the most useful 35-mm equipment. It is well suited to hand-held operation with infrared color film. Also, when opaque, infrared-transmitting filters are placed over the lights instead of over the lens (as described further on), this camera also can be hand-held for black-and-white infrared photography. However, when such filters have to be placed over the lens, a camera with a viewfinder is needed. A red filter permits some visibility through the finder, but at low optic contrast.

If the camera has an automatic through-the-lens exposure meter, the meter should be turned off when an opaque filter is employed. Some work can be done, especially outdoors, with a red filter and with the meter in operation. The camera should be set for the film speed rating without a filter. However, a red filter will affect the spectral response of the meter and may indicate an incorrect exposure for automatic operation. Tests will indicate the need for setting a dummy film speed.

It is wise to be alert to a possible radiation leak through a leather bellows or the camera body, or through a plastic lens board, or through composition shutter blades. Should obscure streaks show up on negatives, such a shortcoming is a probable cause.

Most good camera lenses serve for infrared photography. Unless a lens has been especially achromatized for infrared photography, however, there will be a difference between the infrared-focus position and the

FIG. 3. Dramatic impact can often be introduced into architectural photographs by means of infrared photography. The infrared picture at the top was made with a Kodak Wratten Filter No. 87. The panchromatic comparison shows that even with a No. 15, orange, filter the results are neither as striking nor as three-dimensional. Notice how the infrared record has lightened the "black holes" of the conifers.

visual-focus position. Usually, this will give rise to no serious problems, yet it ought to be investigated. Some good lenses have a red dot on the focusing scale to indicate an average correction for infrared photography.

A lens of high quality is advisable in the field of document copying because of the fine detail often involved. And even though such subjects do not present depth-of-field problems, the lens should be stopped down to about f/11 in order to offset differences between visible-light and infrared performance. This aperture, or a smaller one, should be used for outdoor photography.

Usually, if the focusing is done on the near side of the region of interest, no correction need be made. In focusing it is customary to shift back and forth across the sharp-focus position. This action can be stopped just when the image of the plane focused upon goes slightly out of focus as the motion is increasing the lens-film distance toward what would be a nearer visual focus.

Sometimes a specific correction may have to be made. As a general rule, an average correction of 0·25% of the focal length should be added to the lens-film extension for infinity focus. For close-up photography at about $\frac{1}{4}$-scale, or at greater photomacrographic magnifications, the lens-film distance itself should be increased by this percentage after a sharp visual focus has been made. When a view-type camera can be focused by moving its back, it is relatively easy to measure the bellows draw for visual focus and to move the back away from the lens by the required amount. A resolution chart, on a card of a thickness found by tests, can be laid upon a document for aiding focus when the camera does not have a moving back.

Apart from these simple precautions, focusing is not unduly difficult. It should be noted that, even with accurate focus, infrared images are not quite as sharp as accurate panchromatic and color images. When infrared color film is used, focusing is done in the ordinary way, because it is a visible image that predominates in the modified-color transparency.

B. Filters

Since infrared emulsions are sensitive to the blue region of the spectrum as well as to part of the red and to the near infrared region, filters are needed for infrared records. Filter factors are given in manufacturers' data.

In an emergency, black-and-white photographs can be made with infrared-sensitive materials without a filter, but the rendering will be more like that of a blue-sensitive film. But some advantage can be taken of the sharp image obtained through blue sensitivity and the penetration obtained through infrared sensitivity.

The following Kodak Wratten Filters will absorb violet and blue for black-and-white infrared photography: No. 15—orange; No. 25—red; No. 29, No. 70—deep red; and No. 87, No. 88A, No. 87C—infrared, opaque visually. The orange and the red filters can be used when the camera has to be hand-held or when circumstances, like activity on the part of a live subject, make the adding of an opaque filter after focusing impractical. A wide range in the degree of sky darkening and haze penetration is possible through the selection of film and filter.

The Kodak Wratten Filter No. 89B has been designed for aerial photography. It produces records quite similar to the No. 25 Filter. However, it affords additional penetration of haze with only a slight increase in exposure time. For aerial photography, filters should be mounted in glass of optical quality; unmounted gelatin filters are likely to result in poor definition, but they are practical for ground photography. Camera filters for photographing infrared luminescence are covered in the section on that topic.

While Ektachrome Infrared Film does not call for the use of an opaque filter for the infrared color photographic technique, a Kodak Wratten Filter No. 12, minus blue, should be used over the camera lens. This filter absorbs the violet and blue to which the emulsions are sensitive. The color balance of the film is such that no other filter is normally needed outdoors, nor in biological work with artificial illumination of daylight quality.

The Eastman Kodak Company supplies infrared-interference filters for highly specialized techniques, manufactured to customer specifications on special order only. These filters come in three main types: short-wavelength pass (cut-off), long-wavelength pass (cut-on), and band pass (1·5 to 11·0 micrometers).

C. Lights

Photographic lights of all kinds have high emission in the infrared region of the spectrum. In most lighting setups the visible-light intensity does not have to be greater for infrared photography than it does for regular photography. Photographic exposure-meter readings for various setups with photoflood and similar lamps can be directly related. However, the fundamental exposure has to be based on exposure tests in order to obtain negatives of a desired quality.

The photoflood lamp is the most efficient incandescent source there is for such radiation. For a given intensity of actinic infrared, the photoflood proportionately emits less visible light than either a household service bulb or a heat lamp that is not filtered. The photoflood lamp is much cooler (for a given exposure level of infrared) than either of the other lamps. This is an important factor when lamphouses with infrared-filter windows are used or when heat can be harmful to the subject. Balanced against this efficiency is the relatively short burning life of photofloods.

It is practical to use 3200K photographic lamps in place of photofloods. They are about as efficient as photoflood lamps and have a somewhat longer life. Tungsten-halogen lamps are also suitable for many phases of infrared photography, provided infrared has not been filtered out.

Some lamp manufacturers coat a dark-red, infrared-transmitting envelope over photoflash lamps. This is feasible because they are used only once. Other sources are usually too hot for such treatment. Flashbulbs of this kind are designated "R". They are valuable when bright light has to be withheld from living subjects, as well as from the emulsion. For instance, they may be used for photographing eye responses or the actions of an animal in the dark. The use of the "R" flashbulbs would eliminate the need for special lamphouses with windows covered by large sheets of filter material. The practicality of changing bulbs for each exposure must be considered.

Infrared photoflash lamps currently manufactured are the General Electric 5R and the Toshiba Super 5R. Many photographic dealers do not stock these lamps, but they can order them from the manufacturer. The photographer may have to accept a minimum order quantity because of the relatively low demand for infrared lamps.

Guide numbers published for these bulbs apply to photography indoors. For outdoor work, it is necessary to open up the lens an additional f-stop, because there is practically no supplementary, fill-in illumination from surroundings.

Clear photoflash lamps should be used for routine studio work with animals. The optimum filtering is then done at the lens or over the lamp reflector.

In the photography of living subjects, electronic flash units have many advantages. Their benefits of coolness and short exposure time are extendible to infrared photography. The amount of infrared radiation emitted in electronic flashtube setups is comparable, exposurewise, to the intensities in photoflash setups that would be employed for photographing the same subjects. Another benefit from using these units is the fact that they are more readily obtainable with the compact reflectors, desirable for infrared photography, than is tungsten flood equipment. Preferably, they should be equipped with modeling bulbs. Low-voltage lamps have a higher proportion of infrared radiation than the high-voltage units.

Electronic flash units are by far the best sources for indoor infrared color photography. In addition to the advantages mentioned above, they provide consistent illumination of daylight quality. Also, filtering is simplified, since only the Kodak Wratten No. 12 Filter is needed.

D. *Backgrounds*

Painted walls, window shades and many of the backgrounds ordinarily used in regular photography can be utilized as backgrounds for infrared photography. Some pigments may photograph darker, lighter, or in a different color than their visual appearance, however. This can be checked by making photographic tests. The most reliable light-toned background for large subjects is a tightly stretched white sheet or a white wall, lighted to the same intensity as the subject. Most fairly dark blue and green pigments or dyes found in common cloth sheeting are suitable for yielding dark backgrounds. Green cloth is likely to record as purple in a modified color rendition.

Outdoors it is often advisable to isolate the rear part of a plant from the front part being photographed. A good all-purpose background for this is a smooth khaki blanket.

IV. INDOOR TECHNIQUES

There are numerous applications for infrared photography that can be done in studios and laboratories. Plants, minerals, animals, clinical patients, suspect documents, forensic objects, and paintings can often be examined advantageously by means of the black-and-white and color techniques. The one technical factor they all have in common is the need for even lighting.

A. *Direct lighting*

Direct lighting will be described first, because it requires nothing that is not already in the photographic department. In this method of lighting the lamps are aimed directly at the subject; no reflecting panels or diffusing media are employed. Special setups for indirect, diffuse lighting will be presented subsequently. One light on each side is sufficient for lighting small subjects. Four lights, two on each side, should be employed for those presenting areas larger than about 20 in². When pairs of lights are used in any application, they must all be of the same wattage, and in most instances, must be placed at equal distances from the subject.

Most lights provide a circular pattern of illumination, usually with a central zone of greatest intensity—the "hot spot". Therefore, lamps must be far enough away from the subject and be so directed as to spread the illumination evenly and completely over the appropriate area. As a safety measure against the illumination falling off at the edges of the field, it is advisable to spread the zones over an area somewhat larger than the region studied.

The same basic lighting can be used for all flat two-dimensional subjects. These include documents, paintings, flat mineral and fossil surfaces, cloth, wood sections and flattened leaves. One lamp on either side of the subject-lens axis usually suffices. The diameter of the reflectors should be from 8 to 12 in. Reflector photofloods are well suited to this application. In order to preclude specular reflections in the direction of the lens, the inside rim of each reflector should be on a line 45° from the surface of the subject. The reason for this is that the reflectors themselves are essentially part of the light source and could introduce specularity if not suitably angled. Figure 4 illustrates these principles. Direct lighting should always be used for flat (planar) originals.

When lighting three-dimensional specimens, it is vital to avoid, as much as possible, surface shadows from contrasting lighting, edge shadows, and reflections from improper placement of the lights. Thus, there are two requirements for the direct illumination employed—evenness and the correct lighting angles. A large percentage of the faults seen in unsuccessful infrared photographs can be traced to neglect of these principles. Even lighting calls for an adequate number of lights, an equal amount of illumination on both sides of the camera-subject axis, and a proper distribution of the lighting over the subject. Flat lighting is achieved by directing the lamps at the most suitable angle.

The lighting angle is usually defined as the one between the lamp-subject axis and the lens-subject axis. Obtaining correct angles is a matter of positioning the lights. In the horizontal plane (with the subject upright), the lighting angle, which is of course, the same on both sides of the camera, must be just great enough to illuminate the lateral aspects of the subject. It must not be so small as to cause a great deal of diffuse reflection in the camera direction.

The size of the horizontal angle adopted is governed by the shape of the surface being photographed. A convex surface usually necessitates a horizontal angle of about 55°, in contrast to the 45° arrangement for copying. On the other hand, a concave surface may require a horizontal angle of only about 40° to preclude the formation of an undesirable shadow at the bottom of the concavity. As a rough working rule, it can be taken that flat curves and plane surfaces will call for 45°. More acutely curved surfaces will require 55°, and concave surfaces 30 to 40°. Lighting requirements for subjects regular in shape are not so rigid as to be difficult to meet.

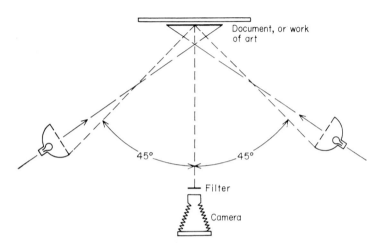

FIG. 4. The basic plan for the even copying of small documents in infrared. The same scheme serves for the direct lighting of most small, three-dimensional specimens to be studied by infrared.

When lights are aimed in any setup, each lamp ought to be turned on and directed separately. When the subject is longer than about 20 in, and four lamps are utilized, vertical angles should be provided by separating the lights vertically. The size of the vertical angle is not as critical as that of the horizontal, and should usually be the same above and below the camera-subject axis. However, when a specimen on a bench is being photographed, this is not usually practicable. Then it is often advantageous to place white paper under the specimen in order to reflect fill-in irradiation.

Tungsten illumination presents no problem in aiming the lights. Electronic flash units with modeling bulbs are also readily directed. To obtain suitable lighting directions with flashbulbs, however, it is first necessary to aim the lighting units at the proper angles with tungsten bulbs in place. These bulbs should then be replaced by the flashbulbs for the exposures. The flashbulbs can be fired from an improvised battery box with outlets for lamp plugs.

B. Diffuse lighting

Diffuse irradiation is mandatory for the clear recording of a complex shape like a plant. Also, clinical infrared photography is best done with a diffusion arrangement. Even specimens with simple shapes can be conveniently photographed by this method, especially when a great deal of work is done on a routine basis.

A diffusion cubicle can be made by hanging a white sheet in a "horse-shoe" around the subject. The height of the sheet varies from about 8 ft for patients to 4 ft for specimens on a bench. A two-way zippered slit is made in front of the cubicle in order to provide a port for the camera lens.

To illuminate this cubicle for color, and preferably (with live subjects) for black-and-white infrared photography, pairs of electronic flash lamps are needed. They should be located outside the cubicle, each at 45° to the lens axis for large subjects, or at 35° for close-ups. The lamps are positioned at camera height above the floor and 5 ft from the subject. In order to provide sufficient irradiation for practical lens apertures, each flashtube should be energized by 225 watt-seconds of power. The lamps ought not be placed closer to the sheets than 1 ft, or some unevenness in the illumination will result.

It should be noted that it is practical to place infrared gelatin filters over electronic flash lamps for black-and-white photography. Synchronized flash exposures can then be made under ambient room lighting when black-and-white film is used. Only a filter over the lens is needed for color work.

C. Transmission lighting

Thin sections of various types can be examined by the differential amount of infrared transmitted by them. The basic setup comprises an enclosure for the light and a masked window, or opening in a partition, over which the specimen is placed. Thick cardboard or thin metal can be used for the mask. The specimen should fit a hole in the mask tightly in order to preclude flare around the edges. When flat subjects are involved, the holes can be made a little smaller than the specimens.

Paintings can be photographed with transmitted infrared by trans-illuminating them. Should the work be done routinely, a large light-tight box or tunnel can be utilized. In the back of the tunnel there should be an adjustable opening large enough to present the area to be examined.

The front of the box should have a hinged door and a support for the camera. When the latter has been focused, the door is closed. The shutter can be operated by means of a long cable release extending through a small hole in the tunnel. When only an occasional painting is checked in this fashion, it might not be worthwhile to rig a tunnel. It would be practical to place the camera in one room and the lamp in the next, with the painting supported in the doorway between. Opaque curtains would serve to minimize the amount of illumination spilling over into the room having the camera. The painting could be transirradiated through the back of the canvas. A 500-W reflector photoflood, 6 ft from the picture, would serve. An electric fan should be used to keep the picture cool, because it is vital not to overheat the painting. Whenever there is the least possible danger of this, a method based on a flash technique must be worked out. This would be especially necessary for canvasses relined with wax.

D. *Handling specimens*

Obviously, the area of interest must be presented to the camera, but it should be pointed out that the main surface of most specimens ought to be perpendicular to the subject–lens axis. Animals may have to be restrained in order to accomplish this. In some experiments, anesthetization can be helpful; however, such an expedient might cause physiological changes that would invalidate the results of certain investigations. For recording the superficial circulation of furred animals, they have to be depilated.

The three-dimensional shapes of infrared subjects are almost never of consequence. When the area of interest is presented squarely toward the camera, depth-of-field requirements are minimized. Leaves can be flattened with thin glass if necessary. For close-up records, stems bearing whorled leaves may have to be trimmed to leave only the lateral blades.

Controls, like a healthy leaf or a luminescing standard, must often be included. Some special preparations may be needed depending on the nature of the information being sought. In working with gross, animal and human, anatomical specimens, a method of differentiating venous and arterial vessels involves injecting them with India ink and an aqueous suspension of red cinnabar. Infrared photography separates their tones with much more contrast than panchromatic photography does. Some fresh specimens present clearer detail when photographed under oil of wintergreen.

Thin sections of sedimental cores often lend themselves to photography

D

by transmitted infrared. Consolidated sediments are merely sectioned by conventional means. Unconsolidated material can be saturated with water, frozen, extruded, cut, thawed and then bound with water-soluble epoxy resin. Once set, sections are further trimmed to a suitable thickness for transillumination photography.

Certain micaceous rock specimens, like fossil-bearing Caithness flagstone and Cleveland shale, can be immersed in monobromonaphthalene. This improves the infrared contrast between the fossil and the matrix. This liquid has approximately the same refractive index as the mica platelets, so that strong specular reflections from the superficial rock grains are reduced and do not obscure the absorption of the infrared rays penetrating to the fossil. Polarizing filters can also reduce the glare of shiny facets.

E. Clinical subjects

The patient should be posed in the best position for steadiness and for adequate lighting of a specific area. In general, the procedures of ordinary clinical photography can be adopted. An area of interest that is relatively flat, like the male chest, should usually be presented at about 80° to the lens-subject axis. Adopting a little forward slant will minimize specular reflection from *slightly* convex surfaces under direct lighting. In general, rounded surfaces should be recorded perpendicularly.

The character and contour of the surfaces occasionally make localized highlights and dark shadows unavoidable in spite of careful lighting. If they obscure important detail, it is necessary to vary the position of the patient and to make enough photographs to provide a complete record of the detail desired.

When a patient is bedridden or in a wheelchair, the background surroundings are quite close to him. It is worthwhile to place the patient on a green cloth if good edge-lighting is desired and attainable. When a white sheet is the only feasible background, it should be made as smooth as possible; some shadows may have to be tolerated.

When infants are to be photographed, they can often be kept quiet by placing them at the mother's breast. This expedient has another advantage when the breast can be included in the photograph as it provides a subject of representative vascularity for comparison with the appearance of the rendition of the infant's condition.

F. Masking methods

These techniques offer a method of dodging that has the advantage of being automatic and also of permitting accentuation of very fine detail.

They are especially recommended for records that require the best possible emphasis of details which are faint or indistinct in the subject, or for negatives that present an excessive printing range. Masking is often used in making teaching slides and printed illustrations, in which the maximum of information should appear in a single record.

One masking procedure involves the use of a faint, diffuse, masking positive on film, held in contact with the negative during printing. The dark areas on the mask hold back, and thus lighten, the shadow areas in the negative; this is called an area mask. The negative-mask combination can be printed on a paper of higher contrast than would ordinarily be employed. This permits the emphasis of unmasked fine detail—which is diffused in the mask, so that it does not become covered up at the original negative.

A similar mask could also be made from another negative with an image of exactly the same size, but having some difference in image quality—such as that arising from differential filtration. The purpose of the mask made from the auxiliary negative is to subtract certain tones common to both from the main negative. This enables the photographer to print with greater emphasis any fine details that are solely or chiefly recorded in the main negative.

When such details exist solely in the main negative, a sharp subtraction mask can be made. When they also appear to some extent in the auxiliary negative, however, they had better be suppressed by diffusing the subtraction mask. Sometimes a diffuse negative mask made from an intermediate positive is effective. Use of such subtraction masks is frequently made in the examination of paintings and questioned documents, but can be applied to any subject exhibiting faint detail.

In order to provide a clear photographic rendition of covered signatures, sketches and other fine detail in paintings, subtractive masking methods are most often employed. The positive mask is made from a red-filter negative and is superimposed over an infrared negative in order to cancel out the general tone gradations common to both. This leaves the fine detail, present only in the infrared negative, unobscured for printing at high contrast. Thin-lined black crosses on small patches of white paper are temporarily attached to the corners of the painting. This is done not only to aid in registering the mask but also to ensure negatives made at the same magnification. The red-filter negative is made first. The camera is then refocused and an allowance, found by previous trial, is made to reduce the scale of the infrared negative to fit that of the red-filter negative.

G. Luminescence setups

In photographing infrared luminescence the basic principle involved is that of excluding infrared from the excitation radiation and barring visible light from the film. Then, any infrared that is imaged can come only from the luminescence excited by the visible light on the specimen.

Blue-green filters are needed over the light source and an opaque infrared filter is needed over the camera lens. The filters listed below can be used; the lamp filters do not have to be optically polished.

> 9780—Corning Glass Color Filter, C.S. No. 4-76, molded, 8 mm (blue-green).
>
> 3966—Corning Glass Color Filter (AKLO type), C.S. No. H.R. 1-59, molded and tempered, 4 mm (heat-absorbing).
>
> No. 87—Kodak Wratten Filter No. 87, gelatin, (infrared).

A 13% copper sulfate solution in a water cell has been used in place of the blue-green filters. It is not as efficient and is also rather clumsy, because an absolutely light-tight tunnel has to be built between it and the lamp. The glass filters, on the other hand, can be fitted into photographic spotlights or into light boxes. They must not leak visible light. The 3966 filter protects the 9780 glass from heat and it must be located between the 9780 glass and the light source. The diagram in Fig. 5 schematizes the setup.

When spotlights are used, the photography must be done in a completely dark room, and light baffles or heavy fireproof cloth on a wire frame must be used to prevent radiation from leaking out of the lamp ventilators. Should a continued program of luminescence photography be contemplated, especially when ultraviolet photography is also planned, it is much more convenient to build a light-tight box to hold the specimen. This will simplify the lighting problem greatly. Since exposure times become quite lengthy for faint emissions, aluminium, a fully infrared-opaque material, is more suitable as a construction material than wood. The glass filters (for ultraviolet or infrared photography) must be arranged in ports on two opposite sides of the box, and be fitted in light-tight recesses. However they must not be held so tightly that they crack when hot. A box is primarily useful for specimens, but it could be modified for investigating sections of paintings. For that purpose, the bottom could be made removable from the box so that the rest of the box could be placed snugly on the painting.

An extremely simple technique for specialized luminescence photography in forensic darkrooms consists of a pair of lighting units, each comprising a $\frac{1}{2}$-in plywood, non-ventilated, enclosure for six General

Electric F-6, T5-W fluorescent tubes. Should the box not be dense enough to retain infrared, the wood can be covered with aluminium paint, or with foil. The windows are 6-in squares of Corning 9788 glass. The tubes burn cool enough to obviate the need for heat-absorbing glass. Such a box also would be practical for investigating paintings, because

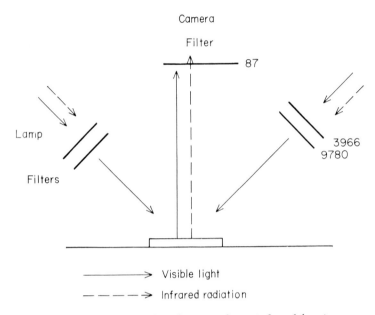

FIG. 5. The filter arrangement for photographing infrared luminescence.

there is no stray light. The room would have to be in complete darkness for the exposures.

With Kodak High Speed Infrared Film, an average exposure time is 45 s at f/5·6 when the lights are 15 in from the subject. This 9788 filter glass appears to be well suited to the investigation of questioned documents. However, for most specimen work, the 9780 filter glass provides a purer source of blue-green light, but exposure times are about 3 min at f/5·6 with two 500-W reflector lamps at 16 in from the subject. The ports in a specimen box should permit directing the lamps at 45°.

In other setups, an exposure meter and the gray side of a Kodak Neutral Test Card can be used in ascertaining exposures. A reading should be made under the blue-green illumination. This reading should then be treated as a tungsten reading. The exposure that would be given an ordinary infrared-reflection record, under such an intensity and with the film being used, should be calculated. The dummy exposure time so obtained must then be multiplied by 20,000 to yield the real exposure for the infrared-emission photograph when high-speed film is employed.

Any setup for photographing infrared luminescence should be tested by photographing a subject of sure emission, e.g., a tooth, bilirubin powder, or a green leaf can be employed. Another factor to check is the purity of the excitation. If even a small amount of radiation leaks around the filter or out of the lamp enclosures it can cause a false rendition because of the long exposures involved. A shiny ball bearing, or a spoon, should be placed alongside the specimen. It will pick up only faint, small infrared catchlights from the blue-green illumination, since only a very minute amount of infrared is passed by the excitation filters. Should bright, large, or multiple catchlights occur in the photograph, these would indicate that infrared radiation is coming from somewhere else in the setup, or through a cracked or very loosely fitted filter.

Luminescence can be photographed in photomacrographic and photomicrographic setups. The procedures for making photomacrographs described further on can be followed for recording the infrared luminescence of small specimens. Spotlights with small beams or the focusing lamps used in photomicrography are useful for lighting small areas. However, they must be enclosed or baffled to prevent stray light from escaping. The blue-green filters should be fitted tightly enough to eliminate light leaks.

Infrared luminescence can also be photographed in a photomicrographic setup. The excitation filters are placed in the light path between the lamp and substage condenser. The infrared filter (No. 87) is located at the eyepiece.

As a sample exposure, found for sectioned human dentin, the following factors were involved: X90, N.A. 0·35, Kohler illumination with a 500-W tungsten lamp—15 min with the high-speed infrared film.

It has been found that a beam splitter cannot be used. The exposures are so long that the eyepiece of this device is likely to focus an image of the dim room onto the film.

H. Photomicrography setups

Standard, polarizing and phase microscopes can be employed for infrared recording. The filters that would be utilized for ordinary camera work with the film to be used are placed in the light beam, ahead of the substage condenser.

Most microscope lamps serve for black-and-white, infrared photomicrography. A pulsed, xenon arc provides satisfactory illumination for infrared color film. Tungsten-halogen lamps have also proved suitable. Recently introduced, photomicrographic electronic flash units also are useful in color work.

Red or opaque filters are needed in the light beam for black-and-white photography. These are not necessary in the color technique, but, of course, the usual yellow filter is needed. Since infrared color film is quite fast, it may be necessary to reduce the light intensity with neutral density filters. The required amount of neutral density should be made up from carbon and silver filters. The density proportion should be two silver to one carbon in order to keep the color balance of the illumination adjusted to color film.

Other filter adjustments may have to be used for obtaining a reasonably neutral background in the color technique. For example, a Kodak Color Compensating Filter CC50R (red) with a xenon arc, and a CC50C2 (cyan) plus a CC20R with a tungsten-halogen lamp. Manufacturer's instructions indicate the color compensations needed to effect specific fine adjustments in the color balance of test results—they are different from those needed with ordinary color films.

Automatic exposure timers usually can be utilized. Filters should be in place, but a dummy film speed will have to be calibrated.

Focusing the microscope for infrared color photography is not difficult because no visually opaque filter is involved and much of the image is formed in the visible region. For black-and-white photomicrography more care is needed since the main image is solely an infrared one; microscope optics are not corrected for radiation in this region. In general, apochromatic objectives will yield a sharper image than achromats.

One method of focusing for black-and-white photomicrography involves the use of a Kodak Wratten Filter No. 29—red—in the light path. After careful visual focus is achieved through this filter, it is replaced by a No. 87 Filter—infrared.

Should the optical system of the individual microscope not lend itself closely enough to focusing by the above procedure, calibration with the fine adjustment must be made. This can be simplified by approximating the correction needed with the aid of visual determinations. A Kodak Wratten Filter No. 61—green—is placed in the illumination system; the visual focus is found; and the fine-adjustment reading is noted. These steps are repeated to find the index number required with the No. 29 Filter. The additional fine-adjustment shift, to be extended from the red index to achieve infrared focus, is then the difference between the green and red settings multiplied by 2 for apochromats, and by 1·4 for achromats. To avoid the effects of backlash, the adjustment knob should be turned each time, in the direction from green to red focus, as the index numbers are sought or set. Trial exposures can be made around the infrared index so found. From the results, it will be possible to arrive at an individual final focus correction. Each objective will have to be calibrated separately.

After the correction has been found, a filter (green or red) should be selected to be employed during the visual focusing of a given specimen. The choice will depend on which filter furnishes the focus more readily for the specimen being photographed. Thus, the infrared extension can be made from either the green or red index, but the number to be set must be established as indicated above. Of course, the filter used for focusing should be removed before the infrared filter is introduced for the exposure.

I. Photomacrography setups

Manufactured and improvised photomacrographic equipment can be utilized for infrared photography. The usual focusing and exposure compensating techniques are used. Filtering, lighting and transillumination are in accordance with infrared methods.

Infrared photomacrography often involves large tissue sections. They can be recorded by transmitted radiation by placing the infrared filter over the lens, or over the light source when the room can be darkened. Thick sections lend themselves to infrared-reflection photomacrography. Slide-mounted sections can be supported 1 in above a sheet of black paper. The specimens can be lighted by a spotlight on each side at 45°. Infrared filters are placed over the spotlights or the lens after the subjects are focused. Such an arrangement furnishes good illumination for infrared-reflection photomacrography of flat surfaces.

When the specimen is unmounted, and is uneven or rough, a cylinder of translucent white paper can be placed around it vertically; the enclosure is then illuminated from the outside by the spotlights. In this way, obscuring shadows can be avoided. Since the lens is quite close to the subject in photomacrography, the photographer may not notice that illumination could be striking the lens—a lens hood or improvised shield should be used to preclude this.

Because the lens is so close to the subject, it is better to filter the illumination if a darkened room and negligible stray light can be arranged. Then, there is no likelihood of jarring the setup by placing a filter over the lens after focusing and composing has been accomplished.

V. INDOOR APPLICATIONS

Shortly after infrared materials became readily available, two major applications opened up—examining documents and clinical infrared photography. The techniques were soon extended to the investigation of paintings, artifacts and forensic subjects, and to subjects in the natural sciences. For simplicity in planning setups for these applications, they can be roughly classified as two-dimensional, three-dimensional (inanimate) and biological (chiefly animate). Photomicrographic uses will be discussed separately.

The infrared copying techniques has been widely used for essentially two-dimensional subjects, and often in conjunction with other non-destructive methods of examination, such as ultraviolet photography and radiography. There are two broad categories of applications: investigating illegible documents—censured, deteriorated or forged, and examining paintings—genuine, altered or faked. Many of the applications described in early papers are no longer discussed in the literature because they have become routine. Since the publication of those papers, sensitized materials and processing solutions have been improved, but such changes affect the basic techniques described in them scarcely at all. However, new vistas are being opened up by the color and luminescence methods.

A. Copying documents

The most important application of infrared photography in copying is that of revealing indistinct writing. The text may have been made illegible by charring; deterioration as a result of age or the accumulation of dirt; obliteration by application of ink by a censor; invisible inks; deliberate chemical bleaching; or mechanical erasure and subsequent overwriting.

Inks, pigments and other materials that appear identical to the eye are frequently rendered quite differently by an infrared photograph. If an ink transparent to infrared is applied over one opaque to it, the underlying ink will show up in an infrared photograph. The original inks used in writing on documents that have become blackened may be revealed by infrared photography, although success will depend on the condition and reflectance of the paper or vellum. Typewriting that has been mechanically erased may show up in an infrared photograph by virtue of traces of carbon or dye left embedded in paper fibers. Chemically bleached writing often is decipherable by infrared photography if the product resulting

D*

from the reaction of the bleach with the ink absorbs more infrared radiation than the surrounding paper. Especially useful results have been obtained in resolving certain falsified documents by photographing infrared
luminescence induced by exposure to blue-green light or in some,
instances, to ultraviolet radiation. This technique should be tried whenever
reflection photography is not fruitful.

Infrared color photography is proving valuable in the differentiation
of ball-point inks, because of the wide variety of dyes used in their
composition. It is likely that older documents, like papyri and illuminated
manuscripts, lend themselves to this new method. Also, it has been
discovered that the leather upon which some of the Dead Sea scrolls were
inscribed luminesces strongly, even specimens blackened by age.

The main problem in investigating some of the documents just
described, and in making special subjects like palimpsests legible, lies in the
presence of two or more inks. When two inks are involved, the ink
applied last either has to be entirely transparent to infrared or has to have
some transparency and more infrared reflectance than the ink covered up.
Masking methods often help.

Information on the photographic behaviour of inks and pigments is
valuable in planning a procedure. The references given here include
typical experiments made along these lines. Among other discoveries, it
has been found that iron-gall, chromelogwood and osmium-pyrogallate
inks record dark, whereas most vegetable inks are transparent to infrared.

Masking methods offer intricate but invaluable means for separating
legends and imprints on documents when one or two sets of detail
interfere with another set. Masks are produced that differentiate
between wanted and unwanted information. Sometimes, making an
infrared negative mask is the only means of suppressing the unwanted
details.

Documents that have become charred by fire—and ancient and recent
subjects blackened by age, dirt or stains (Fig. 6)—can sometimes be
deciphered in an infrared print. Deciphering papyri and the investigation
of papers surviving wilful attempts to burn them are both aided by
infrared photography.

Sometimes, wear or fading will obliterate writing so that it can no
longer be seen with the naked eye or photographed with panchromatic
film. Yet traces may remain that can be picked up by infrared techniques.

Badly discolored, faded or dirt-covered photographs, daguerreotypes,
engravings, drawings, maps and other such items, have been successfully
photographed by infrared.

Fig. 6. Portion of a Dead Sea scroll so badly blackened by aging that the writing was absolutely illegible. *Left*: panchromatic-reflection photograph. *Right*: infrared-reflection photograph. (Courtesy of the Palestine Archaeological Museum.)

B. Examining paintings

Of prime importance in determining the value of a work of art are its rarity and the name of the painter. The scrupulous owner or purchaser insists that the work under consideration be genuine. As a result of this, a number of first-class laboratories have been founded privately or by museums and art galleries, in which particular attention is paid to the study of the characteristics of the material and technique of famous painters. They have become very competent in distinguishing between authentic works and copies, although in many cases their task is becoming increasingly difficult, because the forger is adapting his methods to keep pace with the improvements in analytical technique.

With chemical study and with x-ray and ultraviolet photography, infrared photography has taken its place as an important means of determining the authenticity of paintings.

Pigments vary in the way in which they transmit and reflect infrared, even though they look identical in color. Infrared photography, therefore, sometimes can be of use in detecting the presence of inpainting and other alterations, overpainting and in distinguishing between an original and a later copy. Important factors are the varnish and medium, which differ in their infrared transparency according to their nature and age. A painting whose varnish has darkened or deteriorated so much that detail can scarcely be seen, may be revealed by infrared photography.

Much of the work in the examination of paintings deals with primitive natural materials—like linseed and *Phytolacca clavigera* varnishes, *Semecarpus anacardium* pigments, and mineral colors—because they record differently from anilines and modern lacquers. The employment of infrared materials in copying old parchment maps under a thick layer of varnish has extended the amount of detail revealed and so has the penetration of varnish and dirt on paintings, icons and panels. Infrared photography offers advantages over ultraviolet photography because infrared rays do not cause varnish to fluoresce, as ultraviolet rays do.

Many of the uses for infrared photography in the examination of paintings depend on spectral differentiation as well as on penetration. Extensive investigations of the gray tones to which several modern pigments photographed—dry, with or without impurities, in various media, and on different surfaces—have been made. Differences were often detected photographically that did not appear upon spectrographic and other microchemical analyses; conversely, such analysis frequently shows differences undetected by photography. Currently, the value of infrared color photography in this respect is being appraised, with promising results. However, like the other techniques, the method is primarily useful for locating inpainting or for indicating chronological discrepancies. rather than for analyses.

Modern pigments, particularly those derived from aniline, can present a visual appearance similar to that of primitive pigments. In an infrared photograph, however, a marked difference may appear, which makes the establishment of chronology and the non-destructive detection of restoration quite simple.

The importance of photographically examining paintings before any restorative measures or cleaning procedures are begun is well established. The penetration of varnish, and even the penetration of thin layers of the warmer colors, often indicates the condition of the work. Also, there are instances involving inscriptions overpainted by the artist. Infrared photography can often provide conclusive information that proves the existence of such a legend and indicates the ground upon which it was painted, and thus justifies uncovering the text.

Works attributed to one artist are often found to carry hidden signatures of another or of a student. Sometimes the name of the patron can be uncovered. Most writers in this field discuss the value of analyzing the style of an artist with the help of infrared photography. One can detect the amount of preliminary sketching done on a canvas, as well as changes in composition made as the artist progressed with the painting. The great detail of the very complete tracings the American painter Johnson made on his canvases before beginning to paint was revealed in this way. In other instances, sketching, that would not have been done by the painter, has revealed the hand of a copyist. Other aspects of an artist's method of working can often be studied by infrared photography. In addition to the amount of sketching he did, the degree of undermodeling he applied can frequently be detected. Changes in the detail and composition are often revealed. Sometimes an abandoned effort is found under an entirely different painting.

The infrared transirradiation of paintings is often a valuable adjunct to reflection photography in revealing design sketching, signatures (especially those on the back of lined paintings) and other subsurface details. The luminescence technique is particularly valuable for indicating inpainting. (See Fig. 7.)

Masking methods are part of the curator's routine aids. Those who are mainly interested in signatures work with sharp masks. The script is generally absent on red-filter negatives and thus is not cancelled by sharp masks. Some workers, on the other hand, make diffuse masks. This is done for investigating fine details that appear to some extent in the red-filter negative as well as more strongly in the infrared negative.

C. Studying artifacts

Some of these objects could also be considered three-dimensional subjects instead of two-dimensional. They will be discussed here because many of them are quite flat, hence, copying lighting is almost always employed.

Fabrics are often studied by museum curators. Areas of restoration on tapestries can be detected because of differing infrared reflectances of primitive and aniline dyes. Also, the tarnishing of the silver component in gold thread in ornate textiles will sometimes leave traces recordable by infrared photography, even after the gold thread has been filched.

Infrared photography can serve as a valuable adjunct to radiography in dating, classifying and assembling prehistoric and protohistoric pottery fragments. Radiography reveals the nature of the clay body and vertical and horizontal radii of curvature; infrared photography indicates the character and direction of designs invisible to the eye. Color infrared photography shows promise in this field.

Infrared has been employed to penetrate the patina and saline encrustations covering a carbon-ink inscription on a calcareous stone fragment.

FIG. 7

Another experiment revealed a shell drawing hidden under a thick, resinous crust.

Infrared photography has proven invaluable in making writing and stencilled markings on the fabric coverings of American Civil War canteens legible. Both infrared-reflection and infrared-emission techniques contributed information unobtainable by other means. The understanding of the South American Chamula calendar board has been aided by infrared photography.

Infrared techniques can be used as part of the examination of dubious stamps. Forgeries of rare stamps or of current issues, the introduction or removal of cancellations, and the manipulation of surcharges, all leave evidence that can be detected photographically.

The photography of art and artifacts in caves and ruins could logically be classified as outdoor applications. Sometimes daylight is used as the source of illumination. However, the common use of portable, or installed, lighting equipment can just as logically make it a laboratory technique. Infrared color photography has contributed data on the chronology and sequential history of cave paintings in France. The possibility of and the nature of painted surfaces on early Grecian floors is being investigated.

Basically, the set up in Fig. 4 can be employed for both two- and three-dimensional subjects in this field, as well as for the objects next to be discussed. But the modifications for three-dimensional contours discussed under lighting must be taken into account. Special illumination is sometimes needed.

D. Forensic applications

In the field of law enforcement, infrared photography has numerous uses. These include detection and deciphering of erasures and forgeries; deciphering of charred documents or those which have become illegible as the result of age or abuse; differentiation between inks, dyes and pigments which are visually identical but which represent different compounds; detection of gunshot-powder burns, stains and irregularities in

FIG. 7. *Top*: panchromatic photograph of a restored painting. Areas marked with dots, in the lower record, were inpainted with modern pigments to visually match the older colors. *Bottom*: of all the ultraviolet and infrared techniques tried, the luminescence method showed the location of the retouching most clearly. (The diagonal line marks a region, to the right, from which the varnish had been removed.)

cloth; examination of cloth, fibers and hair which are dyed too dark to be easy to study by visible radiation; study of fingerprints; examination of the contents of sealed envelopes; detection of certain kinds of secret writing; the clinical determination of carbon monoxide impregnation of victims of gas poisoning; and photography in the dark.

Figure 8 indicates how infrared photography cleared up the cause of a

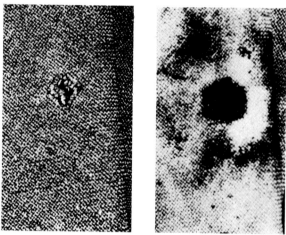

FIG. 8. From the visual appearance (left) of this garment it was not possible to determine the cause of the hole in it. The infrared photograph (right) reveals the powder and burn marks of a firearm. (Courtesy of Police Department, New York, New York.)

suspicious hole in a garment associated with a missing person. In another case, the sheath of a hunting knife furnished the name of an otherwise unidentified dead body. Letters on the sheath were too worn to be read, but they came up legibly in an infrared photograph.

For surveillance in the dark it is relatively simple to rig infrared photoflash bulbs, or to utilize them in flashguns, to make still photographs. Human subjects can be photographed without their realizing it. This is of special value in trapping burglars at safes, cash drawers, etc.

For photographic traps, cameras have to be preset and the flash fired by circuits triggered with infrared detectors. It is necessary, however, for the photographer to know where his subject is going to be. No lens filter is needed.

The use of coated flashbulbs entails some precaution when photographic traps are rigged. A dull red glow may be visible, especially if the subject happens to be looking in the direction of the flash. Visibility can be reduced by directing the flash-holder toward a light-toned wall or ceiling to provide bounce irradiation and to preclude direct viewing by the subject.*

The maximum working distance indoors for an infrared-coated No. 5R lamp, high speed infrared film and an F/3·5 lens is 60 ft. The approximate distance must be decided beforehand and the focusing scale set accordingly. The lens diaphragm must also be set according to a guide-number calculation involving this distance.

Should a sequence of photographs be required, a motor-driven camera (silenced in a blimp if necessary) and an electronic flash unit covered with the Kodak Wratten Filter No. 87C can be employed. The flash cannot be seen through this filter, but the unit should have at least 200 watt-seconds power, because this filter is quite dense.

E. Museum and laboratory specimens

Many art objects belong in this category and have already been covered, because most of them involve the two-dimensional copying technique. Again, fossils, coals and woods could be considered as biologic in character. However, photographically they are related and are treated here, along with minerals. The section on biological applications will be confined to living and recently alive subjects.

Several investigations have been conducted into the properties and identification of various woods. Among them, wedges of wood have been made to provide a transmission penetrameter. In another experiment, a cane clarinet reed was found to offer almost equal degrees of visible and infrared translucency. The compact structure of the reed was readily demonstrated by infrared photography, however. It is possible to penetrate a $\frac{1}{4}$-in hemlock knot by the reflection technique to the extent of showing the shadow of a screw 1/16-in below the surface, but not one 1/8-in below. In a cloudy amber bead, with pencil leads buried at various depths to provide a penetrameter, there was reflection, but little revealing penetration, due to scatter from the turbidity of the amber. Under transillumination the knot and the bead transmitted both visible light and infrared, the latter process being relatively stronger. The same was true of clear Baltic amber. Some visible, dark-toned, unrecognizable specks in the clear

---

* It should be noted that there are nonforensic uses for infrared flashbulbs in making photographs at low levels of illumination, where it is undesirable to distract the subject by a dazzling flash. Photography in theaters, or at formal ceremonies, such as weddings, can sometimes be done by infrared.

specimens disappeared in the infrared records. They were probably tiny insects or insect debris—chitin is quite transparent to infrared.

The hemlock knot luminesced, the glow was most intense in the dense center. Plastic wood, used to repair cracks in the knot, reflected infrared relatively stronger than it emitted infrared. This suggests a way to investigate restorations. The cloudy Baltic amber bead luminesced strongly, offering a possible means for detecting imitation amber.

It is possible to differentiate many coal samples by comparing their infrared luminescence and reflection characteristics. The following tabulation shows the luminescence (first) and reflection (second) intensities of several well-known coals and derivities.

Pittsburg Vitrain	Low	Intense
Pittsburg coal	High	Moderate
Anthracite	None	Intense
Lignite	None	Intense
Asphaltine, solid	High	Moderate
Asphaltine, in benzene	Very high	Low
Graphite	None	Moderate

Infrared-reflection photography has advantages in delineating certain fossils in addition to promise shown by the luminescence method. Most of the work reported deals with fossils associated with coal. The lignin layer can be penetrated. Other coal components provide not only permeability but also lend themselves to spectral differentiation. This is particularly true with paleobotanic specimens, where some fossilized leaves record in light tones like live leaves do.

Experiments with carbonaceous fossils showed that they photograph just as dark in a panchromatic record as in an infrared one. A fossil cockroach (*Etablattina* sp.) in underclay, for example, was just as clear (or indistinct) in both records. Some characteristics of certain matrices, however, may provide tone separation. For instance, specimens from the Green River formation are quite glaring visually; under infrared the very white areas are toned down. The procedure to adopt in these and in similar experiments, as is so often the case, is that of making a series of trial photographs. The potentiality of infrared photography often cannot be predicted.

In a series of experiments, the partially visible fossil shown in Fig. 9 was discovered to be transparent to infrared but luminesced strongly. Because of the well-known infrared transparency of chitin, some authorities believed the fossil might be a compressed exoskeleton. However,

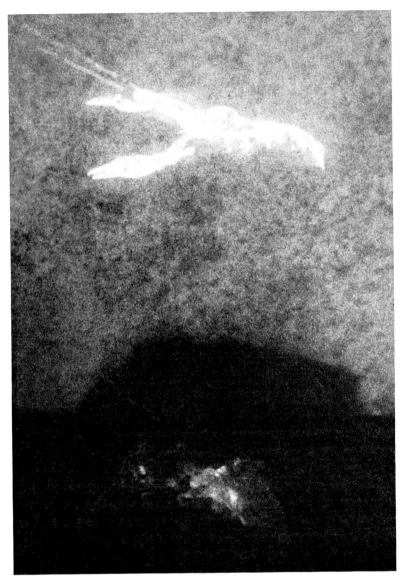

FIG. 9. This fossil crayfish, *Eryma leptodactylina*, in Jurassic (Solenhofen, Bavaria) limestone matrix, appeared visually to have a dark amber color, probably quite similar to that of the living specimen. The fossil was very transparent to incident infrared and brightly luminescent (here) under blue-green excitation. The small piece of rock was a greenockite specimen used as a "standard" in luminescence experiments.

experiments showed no luminescence from several of our contemporary insect and crustacean specimens. This suggests a mineral replica and also points to a nondestructive method of testing. It was also discovered that some fossil matrices and the weathered surface of an oil shale luminesced. Tar-pit matrix, however, did not.

A large amount of petrographic investigation of minerals is done with the microscope. However, the infrared photography of gross sections of sediments cut to less than 6 mm thick reveals definitive information on stratification, animal burrows and grain size. This is in addition to the information obtained by x-radiography and other methods. Slight differences in organic content are very susceptible to infrared detection. This method also has the advantage of being quick and simple.

By means of snooperscope equipment it has been determined that, while the infrared luminescence characteristics of most minerals were erratic, depended upon impurities, and varied with the source locality, one mineral—greenockite (cadmium sulphide), consistently fluoresced. This makes a piece of greenockite a useful standard for calibrating photographic techniques.

F. Technical uses

A variety of specialized industrial and commercial applications have been reported. These range from the clarity with which pore sites in rusted tin plate can be mapped through the rust surface by means of black-and-white infrared photography, to the detection of carbonaceous matter in lubricating oils, the inspection of welds and the study of reduction arcs.

Infrared photography and photomicrography find many uses in the textile industry. Dyes and dyeing can be investigated. Irregularities in weaving and dyeing dark fabrics are quite easy to detect by infrared because the technique usually renders dark colors lighter than they appear to the eye. Mixtures of fibers that accept color so that they cannot be detected visually can be revealed by infrared photography.

Photoengravers used to employ infrared materials in plate making for multicolor printing. However, since the advent of specialized emulsions for the graphic arts, infrared films are no longer needed.

Infrared-sensitive materials are valuable for studying the temperature distribution of hot bodies that are just below red heat—such as stoves, engine parts, high-pressure boilers, electrically heated appliances, cooling ingots and castings and insulation coverings. The range of temperatures which can be recorded is from about 250° to 500°C (482° to 932°F). Below this temperature range, the radiation is nonactinic; above it, some of the radiation is in the visible region.

On a single exposure it is possible to record temperatures within a 150°C (270°F) range. If an object's temperatures exceed this range, two or more negatives will be needed. A long exposure time will record the cooler parts and a short exposure, the hotter parts. Such direct photographs of the hot object itself depict the full extent of the heat pattern, provided the radiation is within the actinic range. Sometimes, as in studying the heat distribution of hot calender rolls, the equipment can be overheated temporarily in order to attain the actinic range.

The actual exposures will have to be determined by experiments, since they can vary from 4 min at f/5·6—with hot objects (275° to 350°C) and Kodak High Speed Infrared Films—to several minutes, or even hours, with slightly cooler objects. An exposure series made by doubling successive exposure times will usually serve to locate the proper exposure level.

Photography of hot objects must be done in a completely darkened room, otherwise, the photograph is obtained by reflected, not radiated, infrared. If a small amount of stray light is unavoidable, a satisfactory record can be obtained if the camera's lens is covered with a Kodak Wratten Filter No. 25 or 87 to avoid exposure by the blue component of the stray light. No filter is needed if total darkness is possible. Precautions should be taken to prevent the surroundings from burning if the object is to be heated for a long exposure.

Chemical reactions taking place in various regions of flames and other aspects of combustion research also can be studied by comparing panchromatic and infrared renditions. Incandescent regions in furnaces can be investigated for hot spots. A dense infrared filter cuts out the visible and part of the actinic range.

Nonactinic radiation can only be recorded by indirect methods. Technical literature should be consulted for manufacturers of such heat cameras.

While most commercial applications of infrared photography are made outdoors, two indoor ones may suggest other ideas. Natural and cultured pearls have been investigated by infrared photography. The two could be differentiated, but only by careful technique and exacting judgment. A method of photographing diamonds in order to make them appear attractive and convincing in black and white has been worked out.

G. Botanical subjects

The numerous manifestations of the disease and stress exhibited by plants have already been presented under outdoor applications. Nevertheless, further and confirming investigations can be done indoors. Closeups of leaves carrying black-spot fungus and numerous other bacterial or chloretic lesions are very informative. They can best be made indoors. Entire greenhouse plants can be photographed by diffuse illumination; the basic copying setup serves for leaves.

A series of experiments have been made with potato and tobacco leaves carrying streak diseases and virus X. Regardless of the causative virus, hardly visible lesions on necrosing potato leaves could be readily recorded by black-and-white infrared photography. They could not be detected by panchromatic photography. In contrast, infected tobacco leaves behaved in the opposite way—they were detectable by panchromatic but not by infrared photography. The lesions of tobacco ringspot did lend themselves to infrared recording. Upon investigation, it was found that necrotic areas involving empty cells devoid of chlorophyll permitted infrared to be reflected from the leaf structure, just like healthy leaves. When disease fills the spaces of the destroyed cells with pectic substances, with tannin and other breakdown products, infrared is absorbed and thus prevented from reaching the reflective cell walls.

An unusually high degree of infrared absorption was found in a black, rotted area on a cactus plant. The cause of the black rot was not known. However, it is known that the gills of mushrooms are opaque to infrared. The finding does suggest that the rot might have been due to a fungus rather than to a virus or bacterium. The absorption was several orders greater than that of graphite, which is considered to be a good absorber of infrared.

Because of their water content, leaves begin to absorb infrared at wavelengths longer than 900 nm. Leaf lesions can sometimes be mapped and differentiated most clearly by photographing dried leaves. The healthy parts of the dried leaf maintain their infrared reflection and emission characteristics. The same is true for dried, extracted chlorophyll.

It has long been known that chlorophyll luminesces. It had once been thought that the phenomenon accounted for the bright rendition of leaves in infrared photographs. The exposure times (page 90) required for emission photography discounts this supposition.

Plant components with no chlorophyll do not luminesce, flower petals, for example. It is also interesting to note that sclerophyllic leaves do not luminesce as brightly as softer ones. In other experiments it has been found that the yellowish pigments in the stems of *Equisetum arvense* do not luminesce like those (green) of *E. hymenale*. However, the green foliage of *E. arvense* does. Solvents that leach the chlorophyll from parts of a leaf produce depleted areas that do not luminesce, although the remaining tissues reflect infrared.

A method has been devised for photographing and calculating the degree of infrared phosphorescence in substances exhibiting an appreciable persistence. A reversible fatigue effect in the infrared fluorescence of chlorophyll in the leaves of a living plant has been noted. Recorded by photographing infrared luminescence, certain anomalies in the mechanism of photosynthesis exhibited by several colonies of green algae, *Chlamydomonas reinhardi*, have been demonstrated. Under specific conditions the colonies exhibited an enhanced fluorescence in the infrared when excited by wavelengths shorter than 600 nm.

H. Zoological findings

Some phases of photographing laboratory and veterinary animals call for the techniques of clinical infrared photography, because when the animal is depilated its skin or body can be photographed by the same infrared techniques that are used to photograph clinical subjects. Other aspects of zoological infrared photography will now be explored, including the recording of human and animal gross specimens and substances.

It has been discovered that fossil sepia (from *Acanthoteuthis* sp., Oxford clay) and pigment from the present-day *Sepia officinalis* are both opaque to infrared. Other pigments found to record dark are the spots on frogs and the black stripes on mackerel by black-and-white infrared photography. Many green caterpillars photograph to the same tone as leaves in a black-and-white infrared photograph, yet record in a different hue in a color infrared photograph.

Infrared radiation can penetrate amniotic membranes to reveal details in animal fetuses without the need for deranging the specimen. Data on infrared transmission by other animal organs have been published, and key papers are given in the references.

By means of black-and-white infrared films developed in a "chromagenic" developer, informative color photographs of a sea-horse and a tsetse fly have been produced. The infrared negatives were put in juxtaposition with Kodacolor negatives for printing onto photographic color paper. The infrared records provided internal details because of the penetration of chitin; the color negatives supplied the surface details. The combination offered much more information than could be obtained from either type of record alone.

Combined infrared recording and radiography has yielded an unusual application of black-and-white infrared photography. By placing biological specimens (large moth and frog) upon films in a light-tight box, "contact prints" were made. The radiations used were infrared and diagnostic x-rays. The resulting photograph was quite like a grenz-ray radiograph, although some of the surface details that were recorded would be absent in a radiograph. The technique could be useful on occasions when a soft x-ray tube is not available. The harder x-radiation delineates the dense regions like bones, and the infrared radiation produces detail in the soft tissues and the surface.

Black-and-white, color and luminescence techniques have been valuable for investigating gross anatomical specimens. For example, partly through penetration and partly by virtue of infrared absorption, silicotic nodules can be distinguished from the reddish brown areas of tissues in fixed lung sections. Other investigators have introduced infrared-absorbing materials into the circulatory systems of human and animal specimens for various clinical and anatomical researches. India ink is opaque; red cinnabar is strongly reflective; infrared photography separates their tones with much more contrast than does panchromatic photography.

Just as a regular medical photograph in color usually imparts more pertinent information than its black-and-white counterpart, so do modified color records often surpass black-and-white ones. For example, infrared color photography can differentiate silver sulfide deposits and melanin granules in a microscope slide made from a papillary body of a patient with localized argyria. These substances were otherwise indistinguishable.

The external aspect of the optic sclera records blue in the color infrared record. This is also true of coloboma in fundus photography. In order to investigate the probable biological substance producing this blueness, pure cholesterol (as one of the scleral constituents) was photographed—it recorded a pale blue. However, when cross-sections of normal veins and arteries (obtained in a liver specimen) were compared with atherosclerotic vessels, and with a fixed, sectional eyeball, no blueness showed in the vessels. The diseased vessels were then photographed beside tendons from normal heart valves, the latter were strongly blue in the results.

This suggests that it is the collagen or fibrous content of the sclera that yields the blue color. The blueness in the records of these white subjects indicates chiefly the presence of scattering and infrared absorption.

Biological specimens exhibiting infrared fluorescence under blue-green excitation have been explored. It was possible to show differences in gallstones and their striations. In particular, bilirubin was found to luminesce very strongly. Much analytical work has been done by means of studying visible fluorescence excited by ultraviolet and blue light. It is likely that further data can be obtained from records of infrared luminescence. (See Fig. 10.) The following tabulation compares infrared-reflection intensities with infrared-luminescence brightness.

Specimen	Reflectance	Luminescence
Bilirubin powder	Moderate	Strong
Biliverdin powder	Trace	None
Cholesterol	Strong	Trace
Thiamine	Strong	Trace
Uric acid	Strong	Trace
Tricalcium phosphate	Strong	None
Apatite (hydroxy)	Moderate	None
Human tooth (old)	Moderate	Strong
Bone (cortical, old)	Strong	Moderate
Bone (cortical, fresh)	Moderate	Weak
Bone (cancellous, fresh)	Moderate	Trace
Artery wall	Weak	Weak
Artery lining (atherosclerotic)	Weak	Strong
Adrenal medulla	Moderate	Trace
Adrenal cortex	Moderate	Strong

Information of this nature gives the investigator one more tool for carrying out various researches. For example, infrared, ultraviolet and x-ray techniques were utilized for studying an early Indian mandible (ca. A.D. 600, Jersey County, Illinois). It was thought to contain teeth filled by a primitive dentist. The conclusion was that dental work had been done and that the most likely filling material was fish bone.

The black-and-white renditions of sectioned, recently extracted, human teeth and living teeth in the mouth have been noted. In general, enamel photographs darker than dentin; a precarious chalky degeneration reverses these tones. With healthy living teeth the condition of the incisal edge can be noted, it photographs almost white. In the record of normal

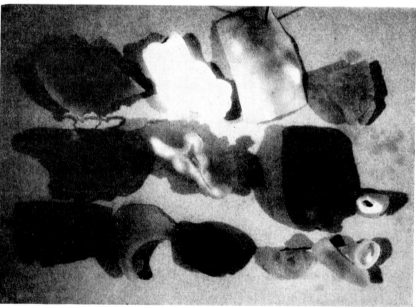

FIG. 10. Infrared reflection and luminescence of biological specimens. From top left: vertebral bone, impacted human teeth, atherosclerotic aorta (intimal surface), spleen—thyroid, adrenal, kidney, atherosclerotic coronary artery—myocardium, aorta (external surface), myocardium (another patient), normal coronary arteries (3 specimens). (See tabulation on page 109 for salient features.)

teeth brightness increases evenly as the thickness of the dentin increases. Uneven areas of thin enamel appear light in tone.

I. Photography in the dark

In addition to the surveillance photography described under forensic applications, the behaviour of animals and people can be studied without disturbing them. Also, significant pupillary actions can be recorded without an interfering light intensity, which could cause distraction or unwanted pupillary accommodation.

In contrast to the camera-trap applications involving still photography most human behavioural studies require cinematographic records to be meaningful. Here too, a hidden camera is used. A typical experimental setup has been described, which was arranged in a room 20 by 13 ft, with a 10-ft ceiling, and seating 25 people. Nine bullet-type light fixtures, in three rows, were mounted on the ceiling. To establish a suitable lighting these lights, with ordinary service bulbs in them, were aimed and fixed in a position to provide even illumination over the prospective motion picture audience. The reflectors were directed at $45°$ downward into the faces of the viewers to preclude contrasty shadows of overhead lighting. For the cinematography, 150-W projector-flood lamps were utilized. These were covered with infrared filter material. No filter was used over the camera lens; in this way, both the infrared radiation and the light from the projector reflected from the screen contributed to the exposure. Audience reactions to various films were recorded in the project.

Another branch of investigation is the photography of the behaviour of laboratory or wild animals in the dark. Some of this investigation can be done with panchromatic photography by intermittent flashes. However, one is never sure that the visible flashes do not disturb the subjects. (Elaborate snooperscope cameras have been devised for photographing animals outdoors in the dark.)

Time-lapse equipment is often used in the laboratory when a series of stills, say 1 s apart, suffices. Sometimes the animals themselves trigger electronic flash units only when they are in the camera field. Cinematographic setups are needed to record sustained actions. Feeding, fighting and mating habits of animals and fish have been studied in this way. And so has the flight of bats in the dark.

J. Pupillography

Recording the size and reaction of the pupil under various stimuli is another field implemented by infrared photography. The method has been employed to study numerous physical and physiological effects in human and animal subjects. Dark adaptation, visibility curves, accommodation, response to flashes, the inadequate and auditory stimuli and the effects of drugs and fatigue are among the phenomena investigated. Much of the recording was carried out with motion-picture cameras to produce a series of single-frame, still records. There are now available spring-driven 35-mm cameras accepting rolls of films for 250 exposures; these can add convenient refinements to some of the earlier setups. Too, exposures were often long, new workers could well take advantage of fast, modern infrared emulsions and the speed, convenience and coolness of electronic flash units.

VI. CLINICAL APPLICATIONS

In the early thirties, the penetrating property of infrared radiation through human tissues was well known from academic experiments to determine this factor—mainly with instruments, but with some photography. Then photography took another direction, that of investigating its value in obtaining clinical data and in diagnosis, particularly in dermatology and vascular medicine. Now, medical infrared photography serves as a valuable laboratory aid and, by itself, offers diagnostic evidence in certain conditions.

A. Penetration

It is generally agreed that infrared can penetrate human tissues to the depth of 3 cm. However, photographs cannot be made to this depth because 3 cm of translucent barrier would be interposed between subject and image. Instrument readings and photography show that the skin of all races reflects actinic infrared to about the same degree. But instrument determinations cannot indicate the depth from which an image can be obtained.

The author made some simple infrared photographic experiments to determine this. He photographed the closed eye and compared the results with tests made of pencil leads inserted under the prepuce. The pupil did not appear through the dense tarsal plates. However, pencil leads clearly recorded through the taut prepuce.

In general photographic practice it will be found that infrared radiation between 700 and 900 nm can photographically penetrate the skin to a depth of about 3 mm. The translucency of tissues, the thickness of overlaying fat and detail size govern delineation and tone value in the reflected subject matter.

The interpretation of infrared records in many disciplines is somewhat limited by the difficulty in establishing norms and by the lack of statistical data for defining pathognomic signs or keys to identification. For example, it is difficult to specify a "normal" venous pattern. This will be appreciated upon noting the wide variety in the patterns exhibited by healthy and pathologic female breasts shown in the literature.

In any application involving comparable or serial records, standardization with respect to the following should be established: time of day with respect to eating, menstrual cycle, medication, emotional state, fatigue, allergy and room temperature. Idiosyncrasies and salient features of the medical history might also have to be taken into account.

B. *Dermatological uses*

Work in this field has been both experimental and clinical—to determine infrared penetration of the skin and to study lesions.

The visible color of human skin in health and disease has been investigated widely. Indications are that a technique permitting the additional visualization of an infrared characteristic can be of unusual value in research and possibly in diagnosis.

The absorption of melanin must be mainly in the visible region, because melanin granules on photomicrographic slides transmit actinic infrared. This is evidenced by the fact that melanotic tissue sections, and the black melanophores in frog skin, record red in infrared color transparencies made by transmission photomicrography, demonstrating translucency to infrared. It has generally been assumed that black skin photographs light-toned by infrared because melanin reflects infrared. However, the findings obtained by infrared color photography indicate that this is not so. The mechanism must be that of a high infrared transmittance to the underlying, or intermixed, tissue. These reflect the infrared back through the almost "transparent" melanin granules. Thus, as far as infrared photography of the skin is affected the melanin particles might as well be a thin layer of transmittant, matte particles—with high absorption in the visible range of the spectrum, but little absorption in the infrared.

Keratin in hair has a low transmittance through the length of a stubble element; when a hair is at some distance above the skin, lateral transmittance is not augmented by an embedding in a reflecting medium. For these reasons hair records dark, even though there is some transverse infrared penetration in a photomicrographic setup. When sparse dark hair lies very close to the body infrared does reflect off the skin to become partially transmitted through the hair, which records reddish in infrared color photography but very dark in black and white. The male chest should be shaved to permit recording a venous pattern.

Amongst dermatological conditions studied are the vascular bed under varicose and other dermatological lesions; healing under deep-seated lesions, such as those of lupus vulgaris, eczema and remittent varicose ulcers; superficial lesions, like those of psoriasis; some pigmentary conditions; and the infrared delineation of "removed" tattoo patterns obliterated to visual examination. The translation colors of the modified-color technique permits differentiation between pigmented nevii of the fingernail and splinter hemorrhages in the nail bed.

Melanin has been studied in patients with vitiligo. In this condition demelanization results from the inability of melanocytes to form melanin pigment in response to pigmentogenic stimuli. The skin pattern does not show up in a black-and-white record. But the infrared translation color for melanin, which varies from a light reddish brown to a dark brown (quite similar to that observed visually except that it is always more red), permits mapping the affected areas. Skin not containing appreciable melanin appears as a pale, cold white. Black skin shows the red translation color of melanin.

Healthy, mature nipples record reddish, but in a patient with advanced infiltrating ductal carcinoma, the affected nipple recorded blue-gray. It is not possible to state how soon in the progress of the disease this grayish color would manifest itself. Further investigation should be of value because the difference was scarcely noticeable to the eye.

Other skin pigments enter into the appearance of skin colors and their infrared renditions. The carotenoids do not contribute to skin color as recorded by infrared. Moreover, even with their high concentration in xanthodermia they only contribute a slight buff to the translated skin color. Because xanthodermia may be confused with "jaundice" or "anemia" infrared color photography may be expected to be of some ancillary value in differentiating the conditions by virtue of recording "jaundice" as dark brown. Oxyhemoglobin and reduced hemoglobin, the remaining two pigments contributing to normal skin color, show specific translation colors of greenish yellow and reddish brown, respectively.

Several of the pigmentary disturbances encountered in human skin have been explored. Argyria, which varies in skin coloration from deep brown to blue, results most frequently from the ingestion of silver nitrate or from the application of it to mucous membranes. It also results from the use of various colloidal silver compounds. Occasionally, argyria may result in workers employed in the manufacture of silver nitrate. In a patient with argyria the grayness observed in the skin is intensified in the infrared record, but there is little added from the diagnostic point of view. Hemochromatosis or "bronze diabetes" is a disturbance of metabolism characterized by the deposition of hemosiderin and hemofucsin in various organs of the body and to the skin. In one patient studied with this condition, the infrared color record had little to add as an aid to diagnosis. One patient, on Atrabrine medication, with discoid lupus erythematosus, was photographed with color infrared film. The translation color was similar to that observed visually. Nevertheless, because infrared color photography is a contrasty technique, affected areas can be mapped with greater clarity than that obtainable by ordinary color photography.

Other lesions also lend themselves to this emphasis. The mottled pattern of congenital phlebectasia can be clearly delineated for easy study by modified color infrared photography; the faint lesions in non-suntanned areas, particularly, are made clearly evident. It is possible to emphasize faint lesions of scleroderma. From the results obtainable by studying the superficial and invisible deep manifestations of hemorrhage in hemophiliacs, it would seem that bruises could be detected and mapped photographically from the medico-legal standpoint.

Allergy and tuberculin skin tests and the effects of artificial stimuli on the circulation are related to dermatological investigations. For example, photomacrographs have been made of the nailfold for tracing the effects of epinephrine upon normal and hypertensive subjects. Such studies are also related to those involving the recording of venous patterns.

C. Blood characteristics

The renditions of the superficial venous system have provided many applications for clinical infrared photography. But before one can evaluate them the infrared characteristics of blood must be understood. It has been discovered that mesenteric, venous, guinea pig blood, *in vivo* in a non-oxidizing nitrogen atmosphere, records lighter in black-and-white tones than does arterial blood. (See Fig. 11.) By infrared color photography venous blood recorded red-brown; arterial blood, green-yellow.

Venous circulation near the surface of the body is more superficial and flows through larger vessels than its arterial counterpart. This accounts for the early findings of workers who photographed the superficial venous patterns of patients but did not record arterial patterns. They assumed that arterial blood reflected too much infrared to be recorded. This is now known to be untrue.

To test the mesenteric findings further, a patient with small veins extremely close to the surface of the skin was studied. Renditions in

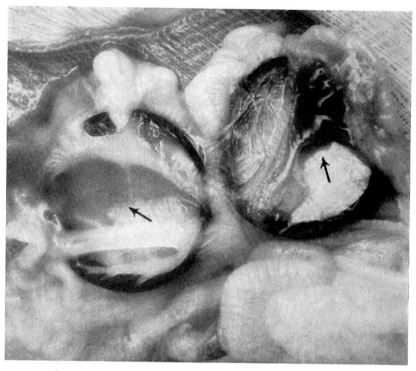

FIG. 11. Infrared reflection photograph of the mesentery of a guinea pig exposed and photographed in a nitrogen atmosphere in order to prevent oxidation of the small pools of blood from punctured vessels. *Left arrow*: (lighter pool) venous blood. *Right arrow*: (darker pool) arterial blood.

conformity with those findings were obtained. Veins and arteries could not be distinguished in black and white but the veins recorded redder in the color photograph. Under a small scattering strip of Parafilm the veins appeared and recorded as a dark blue—just like they do when laying under scattering skin tissues of moderate thickness.

These photographic renditions of blood are in conformity with technical data. Spectrophotometric reflection curves for whole blood with oxyhemoglobin and with completely reduced hemoglobin indicate that the photographed colors should be slightly greenish yellow and reddish brown, as was observed in the photographs of the guinea pig mesentery. Again, living, unstained red blood cells yielded a characteristic color in photomicrographs ($\times 200$) made on infrared color film, depending on their oxygen concentration. This suggests a method for studying some of the mechanisms of oxygen transfer in the vicinity of the capillaries.

Still left unexplained is the blueness of the color infrared photographic record of veins at the normal distance under the skin. A clue is provided by the fact that blue sky records blue with camouflage-detection film. Visually this blue is the result of scattering by minute atmospheric particles. Both the visual blueness of superficial veins and the color infrared rendering can be explained on the basis of the veins being embedded in the translucent layers of the body tissues. The same blueness is exhibited by melanoses under thin layers. To demonstrate further the effect of scattering layers, veins in the prepuce were found to record blue through the external skin, and the same veins appeared reddish brown through the internal, transitional, more transparent epithelium that presents itself when the prepuce is reflected.

D. Circulatory patterns

By "milking" the blood out of large superficial veins, it is possible to demonstrate that it is the blood in the veins that provides the pattern, not the veins themselves. This furnishes the means for the delineation of circulatory patterns in the infrared phlebogram. The property has been used to detect normal changes in venous patterns, such as those caused by pregnancy. Specific pathological conditions investigated with a technique involving phlebograms are discussed under their own headings.

Certain anatomical studies have been aided by means of infrared phlebograms but such records need careful interpretation. For example, there is the difficulty of defining an anatomical norm for the vascular system of the mammary glands. In face of this, an ingenious norm has been worked out for the subsequent detection of possible changes. This involves periodically photographing young women prior to the age when pathologic manifestations are likely.

Although it is generally agreed that the veins are more noticeable in the infrared photograph than they are visually, the pictures must not be expected always to show a striking network of veins. Indeed, it is a mistake to be disappointed when the pattern is not boldly delineated. Its distinctness depends on the thickness of the overlaying skin, on the degree of venous engorgement, on the condition of the vein walls and on the nearness of the veins to the surface (which depends on the anatomical

E

location). Conditions that reduce or obscure the venous pattern include the following: a relatively thick layer of subcutaneous fat, the thickened walls of tortuous varicose veins and the depth of large veins in most regions of the back. In evaluating results, the following points should be studied: the shape of the venous pattern itself, its distinctness or strength and changes in this respect in serial photographs and the number and length of veins visualized.

When a transient engorgement of the vessels is involved, the extensions of branching patterns should be studied carefully. Sometimes it is difficult to evaluate the dark tone-values of large, isolated veins such as those in the forearm, whereas changes in a pattern can be readily detected. This is strikingly borne out in Fig. 12. A prominent vein on each thigh appears in both records. The obvious venous engorgement exhibited in the right-hand photograph is clear from the extension of the pattern. Two veins in the groin, however, show mainly an intensification—an effect, which in the absence of other evidence, could be attributed to a change in printing contrast.

These two records illustrate the value of infrared photography in detecting changes that were not discernible visually. They document a previously unreported physiological phenomenon. The subject, a healthy 12-year-old girl, exhibited a marked engorgement of her superficial veins that reached a peak 45 min after eating lunch. This was manifested again in two years. Four years later the effect was still detectable, but post-pubertal subcutaneous fat masked the intensity. Four other subjects—8, 13, 22, and 54 years old—were tested; only the 13-year-old (boy) showed a slight, but noticeable, positive postprandial effect.

The girl (Fig. 12) had not reached the menarche when the phenomenon was first discovered. There are diabetic members in her family. Since the investigation was primarily a photographic, not clinical, one, it was not deemed judicious to elicit other details of her medical history. One other observation may be worth considering. The author had previously photographed patients who had had a history of nephritis. They showed overall anterior venous networks that were unusually well-delineated and closely integrated. In contrast, most men and boys show such definite patterns around the groin only; most women and girls exhibit veins in the same region and also around the breasts when developed. It has not been possible, however, to make a statistical study to determine conclusively whether or not the above phenomenon has diagnostic significance or how variable it may be in manifestation.

Of course, such limited investigations cannot be conclusive. Neverthe-

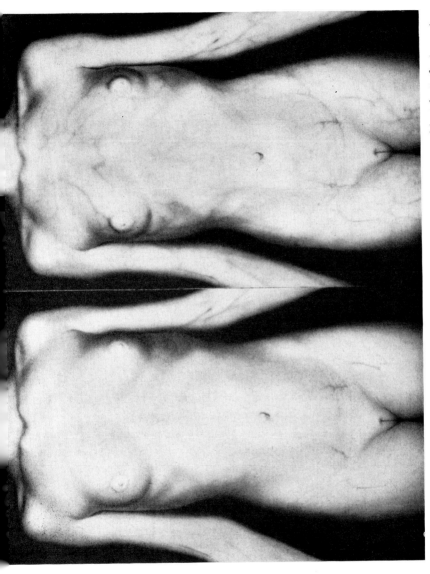

FIG. 12. Infrared photographs of torso and upper extremities of a 12-year-old girl. *Left*: intensity of venous pattern present before lunch and in the late afternoon. *Right*: engorged venous pattern photographed 45 min after lunch.

less, in view of the fact that a regression in the size of orolabial blood vessels in diabetics when they are treated has been observed there may be a promising avenue of investigation here. Vascular changes in diabetes are well known.

The postprandial finding prompted another investigation. A diabetic girl, under treatment, and her asymptomatic brother were studied. The girl showed a slight postprandial regression of venous intensity whereas the boy had a definite intensification. This recent work is cited at length because it is indicative of the many intriguing avenues of exploration still open to infrared photographers. Of course, a vast amount of investigation already has been done over the years in other fields in order to determine the value of recording the patterns of the superficial venous system. Notable fields are the study of liver pathology and varicose veins.

Infrared photography has been shown to offer opportunities for study of varicosities. In connection with the cure of varicose veins by means of sclerosing injections, the prognosis after such injections, and the question of true or false recurrences, infrared recording shows to some extent the stasis which cannot be recognized clinically. Small and tortuous vessels present over the back of the thigh, for example, may be imperceptible to the eye or to touch. Yet many of them can be varicose and ready to dilate.

In addition to the use of this technique to map the course and number of varicose and thrombotic veins, infrared photography has been used in the treatment of lesions resulting from venous stasis, like varicose ulcers. The technique provides an insight into one aspect of the status of the environmental tissues because it indicates the degree of oxygen depletion of venous blood in the ulcer floor and in adjoining veins. In this way, it is possible to obtain some estimation of the probable healing tendency of the ulcers and thus to facilitate choice of treatment. It is logical to assume that information could be gathered regarding the condition of recipient areas for skin grafts.

In connection with thrombotic conditions, the signs for the diagnosis of primary axillary thrombosis include the presence of numerous prominent superficial veins of the affected side, as shown by infrared photography. After a thrombosis the technique can demonstrate whether recanalization takes place or whether the development of a collateral circulation ensues.

Manifestations of vena cava obstruction can often be demonstrated by electronic flash infrared photography. A rapid, cephalad blood return from the groin can be recorded by milking a prominant abdominal vein upward, photographing the result and then immediately making another photograph to record the rapid, aberrant, upward return.

In addition to varicose, thrombotic and phlebitic conditions infrared photographs of the superficial circulatory system have aided the study of cases of pericardial effusion, para-nitroaniline intoxication; congenital heart diseases involving cyanosis, venous and arterial clusters near the surface of oral mucosa, the circulation in clubbed fingers; the effects of aneurysm and neurotrauma. Some work has been done to investigate the effects of neurogenic tonus or other conditions of the dorsal musculature upon the circulatory pattern of the back. Infrared venography has been used to evaluate the effectiveness of vessel anastomoses postsurgically.

E. Liver pathology

Several published accounts of the use of infrared photography deal with attempts to develop a differential diagnostic aid relative to cirrhosis and carcinosis of the liver and other hepatic conditions. One fact in the literature stands out as being of major significance in this respect. In incipient cirrhosis there may be no recognizable collateral circulation whereas the presence of a well-developed collateral venous pattern in advanced liver disease indicates or confirms, for all practical purposes, the presence of cirrhosis.

An excellent physiologic and pathologic anatomic basis supports this distinction. It has been conclusively demonstrated that there is a tremendous decrease from normal in the number of available venous channels passing through a cirrhotic liver. This change reflects directly the specific nature of the cirrhotic disease process as contrasted, for example, with the development of metastatic tumor nodules within an otherwise architecturally unaltered liver. If obstruction of the portal system develops progressively over a long period of time there will be stasis within the drainage area and a concomitant development of a collateral venous circulation in the abdominal wall, in which newly formed anastomoses are prominent. Incidentally, experience indicates that once this new vein bed is developed, the removal of ascitic fluid will at most only slightly diminish the infrared venous pattern.

Many workers agree that infrared photography offers a better means for demonstrating the collateral venous circulation in the abdominal wall than is afforded by any usual clinical method. Early diagnosis of portal cirrhosis of the liver is extremely difficult and at times impossible. The absence of an enlarged network of superficial veins of the abdominal wall does not rule out the disease in the early stages. However, in cases which otherwise appear as advanced cirrhosis the absence of enlarged veins of the abdominal wall does rule out this disease. Metastatic carcinoma of the liver, diffuse abdominal carcinomatosis and gumma of the liver show no increase in superficial veins on infrared photographs. Photographic demonstration is thus a valuable aid in the differential diagnosis of portal cirrhosis of the liver.

F. Tumours

Since infrared photography is capable of detecting diffusions of venous blood under the skin, it is very helpful in the diagnosis of vascular tumors. It can indicate intracutaneous or subcutaneous vascular tumors covered with normal skin, in which the presence or absence of excess vascularity cannot be positively demonstrated by inspection, palpation, provoked local congestion or even transillumination. The technique has made it possible to rule out suspected hemangioma when actually a lymphangioma was involved.

Early malignant neoplasms on or near the body surface can be expected to show exaggerated and possible abnormal markings in the surrounding zone, indicative of the invariable increase in blood supply to tumor regions. In this field, therefore, the technique is an additional tool in establishing the presence of a possible neoplasm, of course, it cannot encroach on biopsy as a diagnostic procedure. Its usefulness in determining the primarily vascular nature of an otherwise-known, superficial neoplasm is beyond question.

With regard to malignant melanoma a somewhat different application is valuable. Once the obvious lesion is removed, the healed site and that over the lymph nodes draining it, as well as all melanotic moles on the body, can well be photographed on infrared film. This procedure should be repeated every six months. Pigmentation recurring subsuperficially at the postoperative site or elsewhere is detectable earlier by infrared black-and-white photography than by visual observation. The same can be anticipated with infrared color photography; because such a tumour would lie in a scattering medium it would record dark blue.

The clinical condition of benign melanosis may actually be pre-cancerous melanosis. Photography with regular color film and infrared color film, repeated at intervals, would reveal any significant changes that might occur. Black-and-white infrared photography is not useful in delineating superficial melanosis, particularly on the sclera.

G. Breast pathology

The early detection of breast cancer from the character of the venous pattern has received a great deal of attention. An intensified pattern appears early. However, because a "normal" breast pattern cannot be defined, it may be impossible to discover a venous change from one infrared photograph. For this reason it has been suggested that young women should have infrared breast phlebograms made regularly. Changes in individual patterns would provide a valuable alerting signal. To statistically evaluate such serial photography there is a need for extensive surveys. The government of Finland has started a program to survey one million women for breast cancer. Their project involves the use of a thermographic camera for a record of superficial heat patterns, infrared photography for a map of venous patterns and mammographic x-ray records. As yet it is too early for reporting official results of correlating this information over a period of time. It should be noted that it is feasible to begin photographic surveys at an earlier age than that usually selected for radiographic examination.

In all photographic applications based on the evaluation of infrared venous patterns the records must be correlated with, and interpreted in the light of, physical findings. This approach will prevent disappointments which sometimes arise from the overoptimistic expectation that the photograph is going to reveal everything about the case. In that way only can the full benefit of the technique be gained.

H. Dental uses

The fine, visible, vascular networks in the normal oral mucosa seldom appear in an infrared photograph because they are embedded in a capillary background of similar reflectance. Some of the engorged venous branchings, however, can be mapped. Sometimes a strong network pattern appears in the alveolar mucosa of diabetics.

Invisible as well as visible venous trunks throughout most of the mouth can be clearly depicted, but the normal dorsum of the tongue and the hard palate are too heavily stratified for sufficient penetration. It is likely that oral dermatological lesions lend themselves to infrared photographic study. Pathological disturbances in the vascular system can be detected and recorded to provide a diagnostic aid and a means for investigation.

I. Ophthalmology

The penetration of infrared photography has been employed with striking results in photographing the anterior segments of the eye. Typical studies involve parenchymatous keratitis, corneal dystrophy, corneal leucoma and mature senile cataract. In these cases corneal opacities prevent examination of the underlying structures by any other clinical means.

Work has also been done to aid in the treatment of interstitial keratitis, sclerosing keratitis, and trachoma, as well as surveys prior to optic iridectomy. The technique is valuable for enabling the surgeon to gain a knowledge of the size, shape and location of the pupil in order to determine the advisability of corneal transplantation. Infrared records have been used to differentiate between atrophied and normal tissues in the iris.

Work with infrared color film is proving fruitful, especially with the retinal camera. It has been found that a vitreous humor clouded with blood could be penetrated to provide a record of the fundus, which revealed detail too indistinct to observe visually. Infrared color photography of retinitis pigmentosa through a medium dense cataract yielded much more detail that could be seen or photographed by a regular color technique. Almost imperceptible regions affected by an arterial occlusion can be delineated sharply in the clear eye by means of infrared color film. Diabetic retinopathy can be readily mapped. Melanotic lesions become strongly emphasized in the infrared color record; they record reddish when present in the retinal layers, and blue when located in the choroid. The technique of infrared absorption angiography can be applied to the study of choroidal circulation and ocular dynamics.

On the external eye, scleral melanosis can be distinguished from associated vascularities with infrared color photography, since they record red and blue, respectively. Such a melanotic lesion disappears in the black-and-white infrared photograph. Conjunctival vessels are delineated in yellow, whereas they can scarcely be recorded at all in the black-and-white technique.

VII. PHOTOMICROGRAPHIC FIELD

Photography through the microscope cuts across most of the applications discussed in this chapter. Investigation into the applications and techniques of infrared photomicrography was done early. The later literature sometimes uses the records without going into fundamentals of the technique. Also, microradiography with soft x-rays serves to reveal details in many specimens once penetrated by means of infrared photography. However, new avenues have been opened up by the use of the infrared color film. There are still fields in which infrared photography can be found simple and useful.

A. Early work

An early investigation dealt with Lower Silurian graptolites. It was found that even the carbonized chitin of these hydrozoon remains could be penetrated by infrared to show detail. Many other carbonized fossil remains, such as fish scales and animal hairs, also lend themselves to infrared photography. Insect carapaces and fossil pollen grains are transparent to infrared, while bitumen matrix is opaque. It is possible to deduce data on the formation temperature of coals from the infrared photomicrographic renditions of rosin structure.

The keratin of human and other hairs and the dark chitin of insects and other arthropods can be penetrated by infrared radiation. Invisible or scarcely visible cellular detail in present-day plant structures, such as rhizoids and sporangia, become distinct in the infrared photomicrograph. Pigments in chloroplasts absorb visible light but pass infrared. New detail has been recorded in plant chromosomes.

In animal histology the fine structures of the nucleus are among the subjects that can be depicted in the additional detail yielded by the technique. The method can be applied to delineating neurohistological sections stained with silver nitrate. Brownish and reddish areas in kidney sections can be easily penetrated.

Photomicrographs have been made of muscle, kidney and bone sections by omitting the usual infrared filter, but using infrared film. Such photographs combine a sharp image in the blue with an infrared image. Visually opaque melanin deposits in eye sections, cut through the iris, can be recorded (with an infrared filter in place) to show otherwise unobserveable detail. The luminescence and reflection characteristics of tooth sections have been studied (Fig. 13). In all these applications, black-and-white infrared photography provided information not obtainable visually or by other photographic means.

B. Modified-color uses

Infrared color photomicrography has introduced many new applications because it combines infrared penetration and specific color renditions. Though they both appear black visually in a tissue section, silver sulfide and melanin granules can be distinguished in the infrared color transparency. Other applications for the technique include the detection of autoradiographic silver and the differentiation of inclusions in lung sections. Living oxygenated red blood cells at × 200, with infrared color film, yield a color compatible with the reflected color of arterial blood *in vivo*. Possibilities for studying oxygen transfer in a thin capillary bed are thus afforded by infrared color photomicrography and cine-photomicrography. When the records are made at moderate magnification to preclude diffraction and depth-of-field color fringes, a difference in color

E*

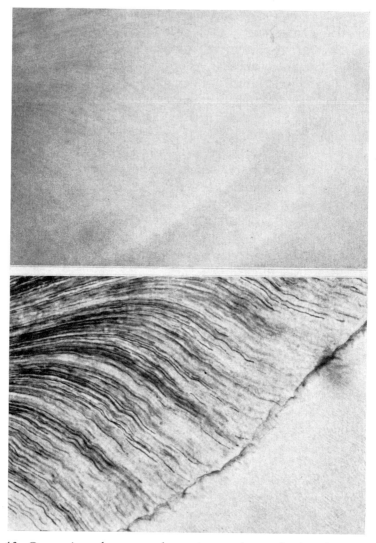

FIG. 13. Comparison between photomicrographs made by the infrared-emission (*upper*) and infrared-transmission (*lower*) techniques. The specimen is a sectioned human tooth photographed at × 90. Dentin possesses marked structural variations in density, as shown by infrared transmission, yet the emission intensities are quite homogeneous.

should be noticeable between oxygenated and nonoxygenated red blood cells.

Modified color photography can be of great assistance in histology. The photographs offer valuable new information on differentiating biologic pigments, tissue structures, inclusions and histological stains. Living and dead unstained bacteria are recorded in a contrasting red. They were well separated from other materials, such as earth particles and organic structures. The technique could be useful in extra-terrestrial investigations into the presence of bacteria. Infrared color photomicrography increases the contrast and color differentiation in metachromatically stained tissues containing mucinous material. The possibility of introducing an infrared-absorbing metal, such as silver, tungsten, copper, iron or osmium, into the tissues opens further applications.

As in the other fields treated in this chapter, the unique capabilities of the various infrared photographic techniques should be considered. They are valuable additions to the investigator's armamentarium.

ACKNOWLEDGEMENT

The author and the publisher appreciate the courtesy of the Eastman Kodak Company in allowing them to modify and republish some of the material and illustrations from copyrighted Kodak publications that were prepared by the author when he was a member of the Company's editorial staff. No part of this chapter may be reproduced without the written permission of the publisher and the Eastman Kodak Company.

REFERENCES

The references given here offer the reader complete technical, photographic information. In addition, key papers provide background information on applications, and most of them have extensive bibliographies. Notes with some of these references indicate special fields. The topics of these books and papers are classified in the same order as the table of contents. Their titles are indicative of content. Numbered references inserted indicate works on broad subjects that also include the topic to a useful extent.

CLARK, W. and GIBSON, H. L. (1976). "Photography by Infrared." 3rd Ed. John Wiley and Sons, New York. (In preparation.) (All applications, including thermography.)*

ANON. "Applied Infrared Photography." (M-28.) (1972). Eastman Kodak, Rochester, New York. (All outdoor and indoor techniques except clinical.)*

Techniques (outdoor)

1. ANON. (1950). "Photography as an Aid to Scientific Work." Ilford, London.
2. ANON. (1969). "Photointerpretation and Its Uses." (M-42.) Eastman Kodak, Rochester, New York.
3. ANON. (1974). "Photography from Lightplanes and Helicopters." (M-5.) Eastman Kodak, Rochester, New York.
4. ANON. (1974). "Kodak Data for Aerial Photography." (M-29.) Eastman Kodak, Rochester, New York.
5. ENGEL, C. E. (ed.) (1968). "Photography for the Scientist." Academic Press, London and New York.
6. LANCTOT, G. H. (1968). Experiments in infrared color. *PSA Jl* **34**, 16, 19.
7. ST. JOSEPH, J. K. S. (ed.) (1966). "The Uses of Air Photography." John Baker, London.
8. STRANDBERG, C. H. (1967). Photoarchaeology. (1967). *Photogramm. Engng* **33**, 1152-1157.
9. STRANDBERG, C. H. (1967). "Aerial Discovery Manual." John Wiley and Sons, New York.
10. THOMPSON, M. M. *et. al.* (1966). "Manual of Photogrammetry." 3rd Ed. **I, II**. *Am. Soc. Photogramm.*
11. WEBER, H. (1967). A primer on infra-red. *Camera 35* **11**, 64, 79-80.

Healthy foliage (7, 9)

12. COLWELL, R. N., ESTES, J. E., TIEDEMAN, C. E. and FLEMING, J. E. (1966). The usefulness of thermal infrared and related imagery in the evaluation of agricultural resources. Report of the University of California **1**, 11. (Includes livestock.)
13. FRICKE, W. and VOLGER, K. (1965). Falschfarben-photographie für die Luftbild-interpretation. *Umschau* **65**, 441-442.
14. SPURR, S. H. (1960). "Photogrammetry and Photointerpretation." 2nd Ed. The Ronald Company, New York.
15. STELLINGWERF, D. A. (1966). "Practical Applications of Aerial Photographs in Forestry and other Vegetable Studies." Series B, No. 36, International Training Center for Aerial Survey. ITC Publications, Delft.

Unhealthy plants (9, 12, 13, 14, 15)

16. BAWDEN, F. C. (1933). Infra-red photography and plant virus diseases. *Nature, Lond.* **132**, 168.

* Because these books deal with all topics at great length, they will not be inserted in the topical outline.

17. CIESLA, W. M., BELL, J. C. JR. and CURLIN, J. W. (1967). Color photos and the southern pine beetle. *Photogramm. Engng* **33**, 882-888.
18. FRITZ, N. L. (1965). Film sees new world of color. *Citrus World* **2**, No. 2, 11-12, 26.
19. FRITZ, N. L. (1967). Optimum methods for using infrared-sensitive color film. *Photogramm. Engng* **33**, 1128-1138.
20. GIBSON, H. L. (1967). Strong infrared absorption by rotted cactus pulp. *J. biol. photogr. Ass.* **35**, 120-125.
21. HELLER, R. C. *et. al.* (1966). The use of multispectral sensing techniques to detect ponderosa pine trees under stress from insect or pathogenic organisms. Annual Progress Report, Pacific Southwest Forest and Range Experiment Station, U.S. Dept. of Agriculture.
22. JACKSON, R. (1964). Detection of plant disease symptoms by infrared. *J. biol. photogr. Ass.* **32**, 45-58.
23. NORMAN, G. G. and FRITZ, N. L. (1965). Infrared photography as an indicator of disease and decline in citrus trees. *Proc. Florida St. hort. Soc.* **78**, 59-63.

Environmental studies (9, 14)
24. BEAVER, B. and WOOD, J. (1973). Aerial infrared locates solid ground over mine. *Civ. Engr-ASCE* **43**, 62-63.
25. COLWELL, R. N. (1967). Remote sensing as a means of determining ecological conditions. *BioScience* **17**, 444-449 (and cover).
26. LATTMAN, L. H. (1963). Geologic interpretation of airborne infrared imagery. *Photogramm. Engng* **22**, 83-87.
27. PARRY, J. T. and TURNER, H. (1971). Infrared photos for drainage analysis. *Photogramm Engng* **37**, 1031-1038. (Hydrology.)
28. STRANDBERG, C. H. (1964). An aerial water quality reconnaissance system. *Photogramm. Engng* **30**, 46-54.
29. WHITE, E. E. and HAYES, R. J. (1961). The use of stereo-color photography for soil profile studies. *Photogr. J.* **101**, 211-215.
30. WILSON, R C. (1960). "Manual of Photographic Interpretation." George Banta, Menasha. (Includes archaeology.)
31. WOBBER, F. J. (1971). Imaging techniques for oil-pollution survey purposes. *Phot. Applications* **6-4**, 16-23. (Ecology, photography.)

Equipment (1, 5, 10)
Indoor techniques
Lighting (5)
32. GIBSON, H. L. (1945). Infrared photography of patients (with an evaluation by S. Milnes Bouton, Jr). *Med. Radiogr. Photogr.* **21**, 72-86.
33. GIBSON, H. L. (1964). Diffuse lighting for clinical infrared photography. *Med. Radiogr. Photogr.* **40**, 38-40.
34. GIBSON, H. L. (1966). A white cubicle for diffuse illumination in infrared and general biological photography. *J. biol. photogr. Ass.* **34**, 23-28.

35. RHOADS, D. C. and STANLEY, D. J. (1966). Transmitted infrared radiation: a simple method for studying sedimentary-structures. *J. Sedim. Petrol.* **36**, 1144-1149.

36. THOLL, J. (1951). Infrared photography of documents. *JPSA* **17B**, Part 1, 10-13.

Handling subjects (20, 22, 32, 35, 36)
Masking methods

37. GOSLING, J. W. (1962). Photographic separation of colored imprints by masking techniques. *Identification News* **12**, 4-10.

38. LOOSE, L. (1958). Nouveau procédé de tirage infrarouge par masquage. *Bull. Inst. r. Patrimoine Arti.* **1**, 85-93.

39. NICKEL, H. L. (1960). Infrarot-kontrastaufnahmen von Gemälden. *Wiss. Aschr. Univ. Halle* **9**, 421-424.

Luminescence setups

40. BARNES, D. F. (1958). Infra-red luminescence of minerals. *Geology Survey Bulletin 1052-C*. United States Government Printing Office, Washington. (Visual study only.)

41. GIBSON, H. L. (1962). The photography of infrared luminescence. Part I. *Med. biol. Illust.* **12**, 155-166. (Technique.)

42. GIBSON, H. L. (1963). The photography of infrared luminescence. Part II. *Med. biol. Illust.* **13**, 18-26. (Results, fatigue.)

43. GIBSON, H. L. (1963). The photography of infrared luminescence. Part III. *Med. biol. Illust.* **13**, 89-90. (Decay curves.)

44. GIBSON, H. L. (1963). Photographing ultraviolet and infrared luminescence. *Dent. Radiogr. Photogr.* **36**, 34-39.

45. LAZAREV, D. and ERSATOV, D. P. (1954). Infrared luminescence in reproduction techniques. *Dokl. Akad. Nauk SSSR* **96**, 281-282. (In Russian.)

46. SOMERFORD, A. W. (1961). Technique of infrared luminescence photography. *Identification News* **11**, 4-6, 10.

47. ZYUSHKIN, N. M. (1960). Photography of luminescence in reproduction techniques. *Zh. nauch prikl. Fotogr. Kinema* **5**, 274-279. (In Russian.)

Photomicrography (5, 44)

48. CASIDA, L. E. JR. (1968). Infrared color photography: selective demonstration of bacteria. *Science, N.Y.* **159**, 199-200.

49. FOWLER, F. W., JR. and HARLOW, W. M. (1940). Infrared photomicrography reveals plant cell-wall structure. *Paper Ind. Paper Wld* **21**, 1159-1160.

50. KLINGNER, F. E. (1934). Erfahrungen bei Mikroaufnahmen von kohlenden Unschlitten mit ultraroten Strahlen. *Mintan. Rund.* **26**, 1-4.

51. LOVELAND, R. P. (1970). "Photomicrography." **2**. John Wiley and Sons, New York.

52. MASSOPUST, L. C. (1934). Infra-red photography in anatomy; some experimental observations. *Anat. Rec.* **61**, 71-79.

53. Prát, S. (1935). Demonstration of photomicrographs of chromosomes made in infra-red rays. *Proc. Zesde Intern. Botan. Cong.* **2**, 24.

54. Shillaber, C. P. (1949). "Photomicrography in Theory and Practice." John Wiley and Sons, New York.

Photomacrography (35, 41, 44)

55. Gibson, H. L. (1970). "Close-up Photography and Photomacrography." Eastman Kodak, Rochester, New York. (Gives theoretical and working data, but no infrared.)

56. Gibson, H. L. (1971). Multispectrum investigation of prehistoric teeth. *Dent. Radiogr. Photogr.* **44**, 57-64.

Indoor applications
Documents (5, 36, 37, 45, 46, 47)

57. Bendikson, L. (1932). Phototechnical problems: some results obtained at the Huntington Library. *Libr. J.* **57**, 789-794.

58. Bendikson, L. (1933). Charred documents. *Libr. J.* **58**, 243-244.

59. Harrison, W. R. (1958). "Suspect Documents." Sweet and Maxwell, London.

60. Mitchell, C. A. (1937). The evidence of inks and pencil pigments. *J. Proc. Inst. Chem. Gt. Br.* **2**, 150-151.

61. O'Hara, C. E. and Osterburg, J. W. (1949). "An Introduction to Criminalistics." MacMillan, New York.

Paintings (38, 39)

62. Bridgman, C. F. and Gibson, H. L. (1963). Infra-red luminescence in the photographic examination of paintings and other art objects. *Stud. Conserv.* **8**, 77-83. (Includes pigment studies.)

63. Coremans, P. (1938). Les rayons infra-rouges; nature; leurs applications dans les musées. *Bull. Musées r. Art. Hist.* **6**, 87-91.

64. Farnsworth, M. (1938). Infra-red absorption of paint materials. *Tech. Stud. Commonw. exp. Bldg Stn* **2**, 88-98. (Fogg Museum of Art.)

65. Hours-Miedan, M. (1957). "A la Découverte de la Peinture par les Methodes Physiques." Arts et Metiers Graphiques, Paris.

66. Hultzen, G. (1934). Det infarödkänsliga materialets anvandning vid reproducktionsarbetet. *Nord. Tidskr. Fotog.* **18**, 170-172.

67. Keck, S. (1941). A use of infra-red photography in the study of technique. *Tech. Stud. Commonw. exp. Bldg Stn* **9**, 145-152. (Fogg Museum of Art.)

68. Lyon, R. A. (1934). Infra-red radiations aid examination of paintings. *Tech. Stud.* **2**, 203-212. (Fogg Museum of Art.)

69. Wehlte, G. (1955). Gemäldeuntersuchung im Infrarot. *Maltechnik* **61**, 52-58.

70. Wehlte, G. (1971). Infrarot-Farbfilm. *Maltechnik* **77**, 14-19.

Artifacts (5, 54, 62)

71. Matthews, S. K. (1968). "Photography in Archaeology and Art." John Baker, London.

72. MILANESI, Q. (1963). Proposta di una facile metodica ausiliaria per lo studio delle ceramiche di epoca preistorica e protostorica. *Riv. Sci. preist.* **18**, 287-293.

Forensic subjects (37, 46, 60, 61)

73. ANON. (1972). "Photographic Surveillance Techniques for Law Enforcement Agencies." (M-8.) Eastman Kodak, Rochester, New York.

Laboratory specimens (34, 35, 42, 55, 56)

74. DELAY, A. and LECOMTE, J. (1943). La photographie infrarouge et la pérméabilité des bois. *Sci. Inds photogr.* **14**, 56-60.

75. EGGERT, J. (1936). La photographie au service de la paléontologie. Procès-Verbaux, Rapports et Mémoires, IX Congress International Photographie (Paris 1935), 737-747.

76. EMERSON, H. J. (1941). Stamp forger beware! *Photo Technique* **3**, 42-45.

77. FRIEDEL, R. A. and GIBSON, H. L. (1964). Infra-red and ultraviolet visible spectrometry. Internal Report U.S. Dept. of Interior, Bureau of Mines **30**, J1. (Coals.)

78. HARRIS, J. E. and LATHAM, E. (1951). Infra-red photography of fossils. *Med. biol. Illust.* **1**, 130-135.

79. PRÁT, S. (1936). Botanical photography with infra-red light. *J. biol. photogr. Ass.* **4**, 191-201.

80. KUMMEL, B. and RAUP, D. M. (eds) (1965). "Handbook of Paleontological Techniques." W. H. Freeman, San Francisco.

Technical uses (74)

81. BERAL, L. (1949). Photographic techniques in combustion research. *Photogr. J.* **89B**, 98-107.

82. BOOTHROYD, G. (1961). Photographic technique for the determination of metal cutting temperatures. *Br. J. appl. Phys.* **12**, 238-242.

83. WATERS, L. A. (1934). Further experiments in infra-red. *Camera Mag.* **48**, 233-238. (Diamonds.)

84. WEBER, K. and SAVIC, M. L. (1934). Die photographische Unterscheidung der natürlichen Perlen von gezüchteten. *Phot. Lorr.* **70**, 10-11.

85. YAJIMA, T., SHIMIZU, F. and SHIMODA, K. (1962). High-speed photography using a ruby optical laser. *Applied Optics* **1**, 770-771.

Botanical specimens (5, 41, 42, 43, 49)

86. GARNIER, J. (1967). Une méthode de détection, par photographie, de souches d'algues vertes émettant *in vivo* une fluorescence anormale. *C. r. hebd. Seanc. Acad. Sci., Paris* **265**, 874-877.

87. MECKE, VON R. and BALDWIN, W. C. G. (1937). Warum erscheinen die Blatter im ultraroten Licht hell? *Naturwissenschaften* **25**, 305-307.

88. TONZIG, S. and VITERBI, E. (1935). La fotografia die vegetali mediante le radiazioni infrarosse. *Atti Congr. Intern. Ellectro-Radio-Biologia* **1**, 459-463.

Zoological findings
89. DELATIL, P. (1961). Color photography as an instrument of scientific observation and measurement (with technical data by I. Kitrosser). *Camera, Luzern*, **40**, 29-56. (Chromagenic.)
90. GIBSON, H. L., *Buckley*, W. R. and WHITMORE, K. E. (1965). New vistas in infrared photography. *J. biol. photogr. Ass.* **33**, 1-33. (Includes color.)
91. JEWETT, D. A. and DUKELOW, W. R. (1972). Infrared photolaparographic techniques for ovulation studies in primates. *J. med. Primatol.* **1**, 193-195.
92. MASSOPUST, L. C. (1936). Simultaneous infra-red roentgen photography. *Radiology* **27**, 663-666.
93. MITCHELL, C. A. (1935). The use of infra-red rays in the examination of inks and pigments. *Analyst*, **60**, 454-461.
94. SWINDLE, P. F. (1935). The architecture of the blood vascular networks in erectile and secretory lining of the nasal passages. *Ann. Otol. Rhinol. Lar.* **44**, 913-932.
95. YAMADA, T. (1933). Biological researches on the infrared rays. III: Absorption of infrared rays by animal tissues. *Acta Sch. med. Univ. Kioto*, **16**, 237-239.

Photography in the dark
96. FACTO, L. A. and CATRON, D. V. (1961). Time lapse cinematography as a method of studying animal behaviour and ration preferences. *J. biol. photogr. Ass.* **29**, 113-123.
97. GREENHILL, L. P. (1955). The recording of audience reactions by infra-red photography. Technical Report—SPECDEVCEN **269**, 7-56 For Special Devices Center, United States Government.
98. GREENHILL, L. P. (1962). The use of infra-red-memomotion photography in research on human behaviour. *Forschungsfilm* **4**, 349-352.
99. KANTOR, B. R. (1955). Infrared motion-picture technique in observing audience reactions. *J. Soc. Motion Pict. Telev. Engrs* **64**, 626-628.
100. MORRIS, R. B. and SPENCER, D. A. (1940). Dazzle-free photoflash photography. *Br. J. Photogr.* **87**, 288-289.
101. RIECK, J. (1964). Bild- und Ton-Zeitdehnung. *Kinotech. Umsch.* **18**, 277-278. (Animals.)
102. WULFECK, J. W. (1955). Infra-red photography of the so-called third Purkinje image. *J. opt. Soc. Am.* **45**, 928-930.

Pupillography (5)
103. FUGATE, J. M. (1954). A masking technique for isolating the pupillary response to focused light. *J. opt. Soc. Am.* **44**, 771-779.
104. HESS, E. H. (1965). Attitude and pupil size. *Scient. Am.* **212**, 36-54.
105. LOEWENFELD, I. E. (1958). Mechanism of reflex dilation of the pupil; historical review and experimental analysis. *Doc. Ophthal.* **12**, 190-448. (Includes animals.)

106. LOWENSTEIN, O. (1956). Pupillography. *A.M.A. Archs Ophthal.* **55**, 565-571.

107. LOWENSTEIN, O. and FRIEDMAN, E. D. (1942). Pupillographic studies—I. Present state of pupillography; its method and diagnostic significance. *Archs Ophthal.* **27**, 969-993.

108. LOWENSTEIN, O. and LOEWENFELD, I. E. (1950). Mutual role of sympathetic and parasympathetic in shaping of the pupillary reflex to light. 1950, *A.M.A. Archs Neurol. Psychiatry* **64**, 341-377.

109. LOWENSTEIN, O. and LOEWENFELD, I. E. (1950). Role of sympathetic and parasympathetic systems in reflex dilation of the pupil. *A.M.A. Archs, Neurol. Psychiatry* **64**, 313-340. (Includes animals.)

Clinical applications (5, 32, 90, 143, 147, 155)

110. GIBSON, H. L. (1973). "Medical Photography, Clinical, Ultraviolet, and Infrared." Eastman Kodak, Rochester, New York. (Comprehensive on techniques and applications).*

Penetration (90)

111. BUCKLEY, W. R. and GRUM, F. (1964). Reflection spectrophotometry III, Absorption characteristics and color of human skin. *A.M.A. Archs Derm.* **89**, 110-116.

112. CARTWRIGHT, H. C. (1930). Infrared transmission of the flesh. *J. opt. Soc. Am.* **20**, 81-84.

113. DENT, R. V. (1941). The photographic aspect of light reflection from human skin. *J. Lab. clin. Med.* **26**, 1852-1862.

114. GIBSON, H. L. (1967). Medical infrared color photography. Part 2. *Visual Med.* **2** (3), 43-51.

115. HARDY, J. D. and MUNSCHENHEIM, C. (1936). Radiation of heat from the human body. V. The transmission of infrared radiation through the skin. *J. Clin. Invest.* **15**, 1-9.

Dermatological uses (114)

116. BEAN, W. B. (1958). "Vascular spiders and related lesions of the skin." Charles C. Thomas, Springfield.

117. BECKER, S. W. (1933). Vitiligo, a clinical and histologic study, with a consideration of pinta. *Arch. Derm. Syph.* **28**, 497-504.

118. BUCKLEY, W. R. and GRUM, F. (1961). Reflection spetrophotometry, use in evaluation of skin pigmentary disturbances. *A.M.A. Archs. Derm.* **83**, 249-261.

119. EDWARDS, E. A. and DUNTLEY, S. Q. (1939). The pigments and color of living human skin. *Am. J. Anat.* **65**, 1-33.

120. GIBSON, H. L. (1967). Medical infrared color photography. Part 1. *Visual Med.* **2** (2), 43-50.

121. HAXTHAUSEN, H. (1933). Infrared photography of subcutaneous veins:

* See Footnote, page 128.

demonstration of concealed varices in ulcer and eczema of the leg. *Br. J. Derm.* **45**, 506-511.

122. JÖRG, M. (1938). Über weitere Anwendungen der Ultrarotphotographie in Kriminalistik und Medizin. *Phot. Korr.* **74**, 148-150. (Tattoos.)

123. MASSOPUST, L. C. (1934). Infrared photography. *Radiogr. clin. Photogr.* **10** (4), 2-6.

124. PAYNE, R. T. (1934). Infrared photography of the superficial venous system. *Lancet* **1**, 234-236.

125. PRADER, F. (1941). Unterhautaufnahme und Kutantest. *Z. angew. Photogr. Wiss. Tech.* **3**, 62-64.

126. ZIMMERMANN, C. (1936). Aufnahmen auf Agfa-infrarot-platten in der Wissenschaft lichmedizinischen Photographie. *Agfa RöntgBl.* **6**, 26-32.

Blood characteristics (90, 120)

127. CHOROMOKOS, E., KOGURE, K. and DAVID, N. (1969). Infrared absorption angiography. *J. biol. photogr. Ass.* **37**, 100-104.

128. DAYSOG, A., DOBSON, H. L. and BRENNAN, J. C. (1961). Renal glomerular and vascular lesions in prediabetics and in diabetes mellitus, a study based on renal biopsies. *Ann. intern. Med.* **54**, 672-684.

129. DITZEL, J. and CAMERINI-DAVOLOS, R. (1958). Reversibility of venular dialation and congestion in diabetic subjects over a period of hours. *Proc. Soc. exp. Biol. Med.* **97**, 475-477.

130. GREISMAN, S. E. (1952). The reactivity of the capillary bed of the nailfold to circulating epinephrine and non-epinephrine in patients with normal blood pressure and with essential hypertension. *J. Clin. Invest.* **31**, 782-788.

131. HANDELSMAN, M. B., MORRIONE, T. G. and GHITMAN, B. (1962). Skin vascular alterations in diabetes mellitus. *Arch. intern. Med.* **110**, 70-77.

132. MERKELBACH, O. (1939). Das infrarote Spektrum von Hämoglobin, von Blutfarbstoffderivaten und von Pigment. (Dopalilanin) *Z. angew. Photogr. Wiss. Tech.* **1**, 33-42.

133. WAGNER, W. W. JR and FILLEY, G. F. (1965). Microscopic observation of the lung *in vivo*. *Vascular Diseases* **2**, 229-241.

134. WAGNER, W. W. JR, BARKER, D. B. and FILLEY, G. F. (1967). A photographic method for quantitating blood flow in the pulmonary micro-circulation. *J. biol. photogr. Ass.* **35**, 95-108.

Circulatory patterns (52, 90, 114, 121, 124, 128, 130, 131)

135. BARKER, N. W. and JULIN, L. A. (1934). Demonstration of superficial veins by infrared photography. *Proc. Staff Meet. Mayo Clin.* **9**, 68-70.

136. BENJAMIN, A. (1967). Uses of infrared film in diagnosis. *Med. Trib.* **8** (5).

137. BLAKEMORE, A. H. and LORD, J. W. JR (1945). A nonsuture method of blood vessel anastomosis. Part II. *J. Am. med. Ass.* **127**, 685-748.

138. Bowes, K. (1950). Clinical aspects of infrared photography. *Photogr. J.* **90B**, 63-65.

139. Charr, R. and Swenson, P. C. (1946). Clubbed fingers. *Am. J. Radiol.* **55**, 325-330.

140. Eggert, J. (1935). Fortschritte und Grenzleistungen in der infrarot Photographie. *Veroff. wiss. Photo-lab. Agfa* **4**, 101-118.

141. Epstein, B. S. (1939). Infrared photographic demonstration of the superficial venous pattern in congenital heart disease with cyanosis. *Am. Heart J.* **18**, 282-289.

142. Friedman, J., Lite, T. and Fischler, H. A. (1958). Infrared photography of the oral mucosa. *N.Y. J. Dent.* **28**, 7-13.

143. Gibson, H. L. (1960). "The Photography of Patients." 2nd Ed. Charles C. Thomas, Springfield. (Includes basic photography.)

144. Gibson, H. L. (1961). Postprandial intensification of venous pattern. *Med. Radiogr. Photogr.* **37**, 16-18.

145. Hinshaw, H. D. and Rutledge, D. I. (1942). Lesions in the superior mediastinum which interfere with venous circulation. *J. Lab. clin. Med.* **27**, 908-916.

146. Kaplan, T. (1938). Thrombosis of the axillary vein; report of five cases with comments on etiology, pathology and diagnosis. *J. Am. med. Ass.* **110**, 2059-2064.

147. Linssen, E. E. (ed.) (1961). "Medical Photography in Practice." Fountain Press, London. (Includes general medical photography.)

148. Massopust, L. C. (1936). Infrared photographic study of the changing pattern of the superficial veins in a case of human pregnancy. *Surgery Gynec. Obstet.* **63**, 86-89.

149. Massopust, L. C. (1947). An application of infrared photography. *Med. Radiogr. Photogr.* **23**, 23.

150. Massopust, L. C. (1952). Infrared Photography in Medicine." Charles C. Thomas, Springfield. (Includes data on specimens.)

151. Missal, M. E., Robinson, J. A. and Tatum, R. W. (1965). Inferior vena cava obstruction. *Ann. intern. Med.* **62**, 133-161.

152. Shpiner, L. B. (1947). Anteriovenous aneurysm of the axillary artery and vein caused by a gunshot wound. *Milit. Surg.* **101**, 23-26.

153. Stewart, H. J., Crance, N. F. and Deitrick, J. W. (1938). Studies of the circulation in pericardial effusion. *Am. Heart J.* **16**, 189-197.

154. Thompson, L. R. (1951). Photographs, infrared photographs and transillumination diagrams illustrating diagnosis and treatment of the cervix uteri. *Am. J. Surg.* **81**, 503-507.

155. Wagner, G. (1965). "Infrarot Fotographie." Verlag Die Schönen Bücher, Stuttgart. (General topics included.)

156. Wilson, E. E. (1937). The changes in infrared photographs taken during the treatment of varicose veins. *Am. J. Surg.* **37**, 470-474.

157. ZEHNDER, M. (1938). Die Claudicatio venosa der oberen Extremitaten als Symptoms. *Arch. klin. Chir.* **192**, 354-382.
158. ZIMMERMAN, L. M. and RATTNER, H. (1935). Infrared photography of sub-cutaneous veins. *Am. J. Surg.* **27**, 502.

Liver pathology (32, 90)

159. JANKELSON, I. R. and BAKER, H. (1938). Infrared photography of abdominal wall in portal cirrhosis of liver. *Am. J. dig. Dis.* **5**, 414-418.
160. JANKELSON, I. R., ZAMCHECK, N. and BAKER, H. (1954). Symposium on cirrhosis of liver. Correlation between needle biopsy of the liver and infrared photography of the abdomen in cirrhosis of the liver. *Am. J. Gastroent. N.Y.* **21**, 9-17.
161. JONES, E. (1935). Demonstration of collateral venous circulation in the abdominal wall by means of infrared photography. *Am. J. med. Sci.* **190**, 478-485.
162. ROMANOV, U. D. and SVERDLOV, B. D. (1963). Infrared photography for detection of deep collateral vessels of the anterior abdominal wall in disorders of portal circulation. *Terap. Arkh.* **35**, 30-34. (In Russian.)
163. TURBA, G. and TAVAZZI, L. (1962). Infrared studies of the superficial venous circulation of the abdomen in cirrhosis of the liver. *Panminerva Med.* **4**, 442-443.
164. WAYBURN, E. (1942). Infrared photography of the abdominal wall. *Am. J. dig. dis.* **9**, 392-394.

Tumors (90, 122, 149)

165. ALDIS, A. S. and MARSHALL, R. J. (1963). Metastatic melanoma, detection by infrared recording. *Med. biol. Illust.* **13**, 2-4.
166. REHBOK, D. J. (1939). Venous pattern in a case of mediastinal tumor. *Radiogr. clin. Photogr.* **15**, 31.
167. RONCHESE, F. (1937). Infrared photography in the diagnosis of vascular tumors. *Am. J. Surg.* **37**, 475-477.

Breast pathology (32, 90, 114, 120, 143)

168. GORMAN, W. A. and HIRSCHEIMER, A. (1939). A study of the superficial venous pattern in pregnant and non-pregnant women by infrared photography. *Surgery Gynec. Obstet.* **68**, 54-62.
169. KAUFMAN, P. A. (1956). Subcutaneous phlebitis of the breast and chest wall. *Ann. Surg.* **144**, 847-853.
170. MASSOPUST, L. C. (1948). Infrared photographic study of the superficial veins of the thorax in relation to breast tumors; a preliminary report. *Surgery Gynec. Obstet.* **86**, 54-58.
171. MASSOPUST, L. C. and GARDNER, W. D. (1950). Infrared photographic studies of the superficial thoracic veins in the female; anatomical considerations. *Surgery Gynec. Obstet.* **91**, 717-727.
172. MASSOPUST, L. C. and GARDNER, W. D. (1953). The infrared phlebogram in the diagnosis of breast complaints. *Surgery Gynec. Obstet.* **97**, 619-626.

173. ROSENBLOOM, M. A. (1953). Infrared photography of the female breast; preliminary report on a survey of the vascular patterns of normal breasts with possible application to cancer detection. *Obstet. Gynec. N.Y.* **2**, 603-610.

Dental uses (44, 56, 142)

174. DE MENT, J. and CULBERTSON, R. (1951). Comparative photography in dental science. *Dent. Radiogr. Photogr.* **24**, 28-34.
175. KRANZ, P. P. (1957). "Chirurgie des praktischen Zahnarztes." Johann A. Bart, Leipzig.

Ophthalmology (90, 114; See also Pupillography)

176. DEKKING, H. M. (1934). Infrarotphotographie des Auges. II. Mitteilung: das Pigment. *Arch. f. Ophthal.* **133**, 20-25.
177. DIAZ-CANEJA, E. (1936). Quelques résultats de l'exploration du fond de l'oeil sous la lumière infra-rouge. *Bull. Mém. Soc. f. Ophthal.* **49**, 193-211.
178. FELDMAN, J. B. (1936). A review of infrared photography with reference to its value in ophthalmology. *Archs Ophth. N.Y.* **15**, 435-442.
179. FLOWER, R. W. (1972). Infrared absorption angiography of the choroid and some observation on the effects of high intraocular pressures. *Am. J. Ophthal.* **74**, 4.
180. GIBSON, H. L. (1965). Further data on the use of infrared color film. *J. biol. photogr. Ass.* **33**, 155-166.
181. KLEEFELD, G. (1935). Exploration photographique du segment antérieur de l'oeil au moyen des rayons infra-rouges. *Soc. Franc. Ophthalmol.* **48**, 79.
182. KUGELBERG, I. (1934). Der Augenhintergrund in infrarotem Licht. *Acta ophthal.* **12**, 179-190.
183. KULVIN, S., STAUFFER, L., KOGURE, K. and DAVID, N. J. (1934). Fundus angiography in man by intracarotid administration of dye. *S. Med. J.* **63**, 9.
184. MANN, W. A. JR. (1935). Infrared photography of the eye. *Archs Ophthal. N.Y.* **13**, 985-991.
185. OGG, A. J. (1958). Examination of the eye with infrared radiation. *Br. J. Ophthal.* **42**, 306-310. (Snooperscope.)

Photomicrographicfield (90, 120, 133; see also Photomicrography)

186. BINKIN, J. (1933). Mikrophotographie mit infraroten Strahlen. *diss. Basel.*
187. BLAIR, D. M. and DAVIES, F. (1933). A method of differentiating ganglion cells and their study by infrared photography. *Lancet* **225**, 1, 1113-1114.
188. BLAIR, D. M. and DAVIES, F. (1933). Infrared plates in neurohistological illustration. *Lancet* **225**, II, 801.
189. CALZAVARA, E. and BERTRAND, I. (1927). L'infra-rouge en cytologie. 1927, *Annls Anat. path. Anat. norm. méd.-chir.* **5**, 461-473.
190. NOMARSKI, G. (1955). Microscopie dans l'infrarouge. *Revue Opt. théor. instrum.* **34**, 29-41.

191. PREISSECKER, E. (1931): Über Mikrophotographie im infraroten Licht. *Wien klin. Wschr.* **2**, 1458-1460.

Thermography (147)

192. ASTHEIMER, R. W. (1969). Infrared to visible image translation devices. *Photogr. Sci. Engng* **13**, 127-133.

193. BARNES, R. B. and COHEN, J. G. (1963). Clinical thermography. *J. Am. med. Ass.* **185**, 949-952.

194. BARNES, R. B. (1968). Diagnostic thermography. *Applied Optics,* **7**, 1673.

195. BENJAMIN, A. (1968). Liquid crystal photography. *Visual/Sonic Medicine* **3**, 10-12.

196. CADE, C. M. (1961). New advances in infrared. *Ind. comml. Photogr.* **10**, 68, 99, J1.

197. COHEN, J. G. (1967). Medical thermography. *Scient. Am.* **221**, 94-102.

198. COLWELL, R. N. (1973). Remote sensing as an aid to the management of earth resources. *Am. Scient.* **61**, 175-183. (Includes satellites, radar recording and photography.)

199. CORNWALL, W. S. (1972). "Thermography: A Bibliography." Eastman Kodak, Rochester. (Extensive; medical, dental, and veterinary.)

200. CRISSEY, J. T., FERGASEN, J. L. and BETTENHAUSEN, J. M. (1965). Cutaneous thermography with liquid crystals. *J. invest. Derm.* **45**, 329-333.

201. ENGEL, C. E. (1959). Modern developments in infrared recording. *Discovery* **20**, 392-396.

202. FERGASON, J. L. (1968). Liquid crystals in non-destructive testing. *Applied Optics* **7**, 1729-1737.

203. HARDING, W. R., HILSUM, C. and NORTHROP, D. C. (1958). A new thermal image-converter. *Nature, Lond.* **181**, 691.

204. LAWSON, R. (1957). Thermography. A new tool in the investigation of breast lesions. *Can. Servs med. J.* **13**, 517-524.

205. LAWSON, R. (1958). A new infrared imaging device. *Can. med. Ass. J.* **79**, 402-403.

206. LAWSON, R. N. and ALT, L. L. (1965). Skin temperature recording with phosphors: a new technique. *Can. med. Ass. J.* **92**, 255.

207. LAWSON, R. N. and CHUGHATI, M. S. (1963). Breast cancer and body temperature. *Can. med. Ass. J.* **88**, 68-70.

208. LAWSON, R. N., WLODEK, G. B. and WEBSTER, D. R. (1961). Thermographic assessment of burns and frostbite. *Can. med. Ass. J.* **84**, 1129-1131.

209. OSBORNE, R. F. (1967). Thermography in industry. *Optical Spectra*, 3rd quarter.

210. SAMUELS, B. I., DOWDY, A. J. and LECKY, J. W. (1972). Parathyroid thermography. *Radiology* **104**, 575-578.

211. STRANDNESS, D. E. JR. (1967). Liquid crystals monitor skin temperature. *Rassegna* **44**, 16. (Medical review, English edition.)

212. WHIPPLE, H. E. (ed.) (1964). Thermography and its clinical applications. *Ann. N.Y. Acad. Sci.* **121**, 1-304.

213. WILLIAMS, K. L. and CADE, C. M. (1964). Pictorial recording of body temperature. *Med. biol. Illust.* **14**, 105-112.

214. WILLIAMS, K. L., WILLIAMS, F. J. L. and HANDLEY, R. S. (1961). Infrared thermometry in diagnosis of breast disease. *Lancet* **258**, II, 1378-1381.

215. WOODMANSEE, W. *et al.* Cholesteric liquid crystals applied to skin temperature visualization. 1965, *Proceedings of the 18th Annual Conference on Engineering in Medicine and Biology*, Philadelphia: The Conference Committee for the 18th Annual Conference on Engineering and Biology. (Herman P. Schwan, Chairman, Moore School of Electrical Engineering, University of Pennsylvania, Philadelphia, Penna. 19104.)

216. ZIRVAS, C. (1956). Ultrarotdiagnose und Herdgeschehen. *Neues Zahnhk.* **3**, 17.

4
Photography in paediatrics

GEORGE W. ROGERS

I. INTRODUCTION

Paediatrics is the branch of medicine devoted to the care and treatment of sick children from a few hours old to approximately 12 years of age. There are many diseases specific to children which vary in degree and form, while some conditions are also common to adults. Although many diseases may develop in a child, those which are congenital in origin (i.e., present at birth) are considered of great importance. Ever since the early days of photography the value of recording medical and, in particular, paediatric conditions has been realised as a useful means of advancing the subject. Photographs are taken not only to record the patient for future reference but also in some cases as an aid to diagnosis and treatment. A large percentage of photographs taken are produced in the form of colour transparencies for teaching purposes in under-graduate and post-graduate studies and for teaching nursing staff. Much of the research today relies upon photographs to support the material for publications.

Photography of sick children presents a number of special problems not normally met with when photographing adult patients. These are summarized as follows:

(a) Special patient handling technique.
(b) Specialised equipment.
(c) Extra safety precautions.
(d) Problems of standardization—a child starts his life a matter of inches in length and grows to normal adult height.

In order for this contribution to be useful and complete in itself, it was considered necessary to include certain practices which are common to both adult and child patient photography. Reference is made to other work where overlap occurs, and brief discussion of the common areas is included to give the *basic* requirements only.

Successful paediatric photography is achieved by a combination of patience and skill, developed by experience. Without a genuine concern for the welfare of each child and a natural love of children, results will be found inadequate.

II. THE PATIENT

Patients in a childrens' hospital range in age from birth to approximately 12 years. Occasionally older teenagers are seen as part of a follow-up programme. The special needs and capabilities of each patient depend

on his age, state of health, upbringing, education and social background.

A. Babies

Small babies, especially neonates (babies from birth to one month) are
frequently photographed in the ward, often in incubators. The very
young baby may need assistance in breathing, is prone to infection and
must be kept warm. Occasionally the baby can be moved from the
incubator for brief periods for the photographs to be taken, but this is not
always possible for medical reasons.

B. Young children

The small child has more independence and awareness of his environment. The first contact with this patient is usually made in the waiting-
room, and the success of this initial meeting can affect all subsequent
photography.

A check must be made to see if the child has been photographed before.
This is often the case and a brief study of the records may indicate further
points to consider. For example, the child may be shown crying or
incompletely undressed, reminding the photographer of past difficulties.

It is advisable to warn the child if the position required for photography
is likely to hurt him. When possible, he should take up this position himself. If retractors are needed, for example, the child is encouraged to hold
them.

Reassurance that the photographer will not himself touch the child
and a calm unhurried approach by all adults present help the child to relax.
Children soon detect tension in the atmosphere and their intelligence
should never be underestimated.

Small children cannot keep still for long, so the necessary pictures must
be taken quickly; a hand-held camera and electronic flash make this
possible. It is usual to demonstrate the flash being fired, before taking
photographs. This allows the child to see what happens from a distance
before he becomes involved and is usually greeted with interest.

A challenge may encourage co-operation. For example "Can you stand
up as straight as a soldier?" Occasionally, if a child has been spoilt and is
petulant or being awkward, annoyance on the photographer's part may
produce a satisfactory result because it is unexpected.

An example may serve to illustrate the point. A small child arrived at
the hospital to stay for a few days to have tests for a suspected serious
condition. Within a few hours of arrival and after several tests, he was

sent for a number of photographs including full-body views. On removal of several items of clothing it became obvious that he would no longer be willing to co-operate. The session was therefore abandoned and the mother was told that a further attempt would be made the following day, by which time he would be more accustomed to the hospital. While the mother was re-dressing the child, the photographer talked to him about his little toy car that he had brought with him. A friendship between the photographer and child thus resulted from this short conversation. At this point his co-operation seemed highly probable, but the temptation to try again that day was resisted. Photographs were taken the following day with complete success, because of the relationship established.

C. *Older children*

An older child is normally independent and co-operative. He will respond to a friendly atmosphere and should be treated in an adult manner.

He may easily be embarrassed on undressing, at the idea of being photographed naked, or at the thought of other people seeing the pictures. He is often less embarrassed in the presence of a nurse than with his own parent.

A school-girl should always have a chaperone and may prefer a female photographer when she has to remove clothing. The very quiet, withdrawn child is often the most upset and may need extra attention and reassurance. Asking a nervous child questions helps to take his mind off himself.

D. *Parents*

The patient should not be discussed while present, if he is old enough to understand what is being said. Due to their worry and concern, the parents may often forget that the child is listening.

Photographs are part of the patient's confidential records and are not released from the department files except with official sanction. Patients or parents may be eager to obtain a copy and it is difficult to resist a request from a parent especially if the request is made on compassionate grounds. Photographs are sometimes given to parents with the written authority of the consultant in charge, for therapeutic purposes. This is done in cases of obesity, to encourage the parents to maintain their child's diet, by reminding them of his original appearance.

E. *Safety*

The photographic studio contains a quantity of electrical apparatus which is all potentially dangerous. Studio electronic flash units are particularly so, because of the very high voltages used. Great care should be taken by all staff to ensure that no child has an accident by touching wiring or electrical sockets. Lighting cables can be held by chains suspended from the ceiling and electrical sockets, instead of being placed on the walls, can be fixed to overhead conduit piping, so that they are out of the child's reach. Lamps placed directly over the patient should be *very* secure and all loose parts, such as detachable reflectors, should either be permanently fixed in some way, or should have a safety device to prevent them falling if accidentally knocked. The floor should be kept clean and free of any object which may cause injury since children frequently walk around in bare feet.

Any dressings that have to be removed must only be touched by the accompanying nurse. If the patient has to lie down on a high bed or sit on a rotating stool, he should be held by an assistant, to prevent any possibility of him falling off.

All medical photographers should have a basic knowledge of first aid and all departments should keep a first-aid box. Staff should memorize the telephone numbers to ring in case of cardiac arrest, casualty or fire.

The child must be watched at all times because an accident can occur in seconds. Even quite small babies can move themselves a short distance by kicking and toddlers have boundless curiosity. Most older children, especially boys, have enquiring minds where equipment is concerned, and all children are quick to touch something that interests them.

F. Conclusion

To the photographer, a child may be just another patient, but visiting a photographic department may be an important occasion and lasting memory for the child concerned. Successful handling of children comes chiefly with experience. A good relationship between photographer and patient is as important as photographic expertise and plays a valuable part in the overall treatment of the sick child.

III. PHOTOGRAPHIC PRACTICE

A. Terminology and standardization

1. Terminology. Correct standardization with respect to anatomical positioning relies on a basic knowledge of anatomy and its terminology. Much of this information, which is of practical use to medical photographers, is contained in the works of Armstrong (1964), Pauchet and Dupret (1968) and the drawing by Turlington (1957) shows anatomical planes and positions. More specific information related to standard positioning and terminology in the photography of patients is given by Eckhoff (1952), Mason (1960), Hansell and Ollerenshaw (1962), Duguid and Ollerenshaw (1962), Mason (1964), Hertl (1964), Whitley (1970) and Rogers (1971).

The following anatomical terms are just a few of the more common ones met with, in both adult and paediatric photography:

"Anatomical position". This is a position in which the body stands upright facing the observer with feet slightly apart, arms hanging at the sides with palms facing forwards, and head erect. Dupertuis and Tanner (1950) recommend a modification to this position for routine photogra-metric anthropometry (see Fig. 1).

Median plane. This imaginary vertical plane passes through the body from front to back and from the top of the head to the ground between the feet, dividing the body equally into a left and right half.

Coronal plane. This is a vertical plane at right angles to the median plane, dividing the body into front and back.

Medial. Towards the midline.

Superior. Above or upper.

Inferior. Below or lower.

Anterior. In front.

Posterior. Behind or back.

Lateral. To the side or furthest away from the mid-line.

Distal. Farther away from the centre or source (opposite to proximal).

Proximal. Nearest the trunk or centre of the body (opposite to distal).

Dorsal. Relating to the back (dorsum).

Dorsum of the hand. The back of the hand.

Dorsum of the foot. The upper part of the foot.

Ventral. To the front. (Latin, *venter* belly).

Prone. Lying with face downward.

Supine. Lying on the back (face upwards).

Abduction. Movement away from the median plane, e.g., arms moved away from the sides of the body.

Adduction. Movement in towards the median plane, e.g., arms moved in to the sides of the body.

Flexion. Bending, either backwards or forwards, e.g., flexion of the toes implies bending of the toes (backwards) towards the soles of the feet, whereas flexion of the back means bending (forward) towards the front of the body.

Extension. Straightening (opposite to flexion).

Standard views, to illustrate a particular condition, are still subject to the dictates of local demand and ideas. Recommendations have been put forward by a number of workers, some of whom are mentioned at the

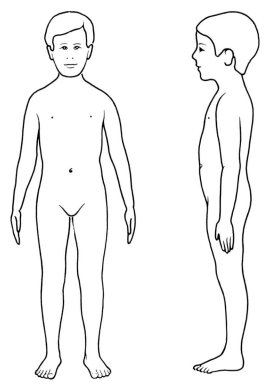

FIG. 1. This diagram shows the position recommended for full-length photography of child patients. The palms face in towards the side of the body for the anterior view and the arms and hands are held touching the sides in the lateral. Children find this position easier to adopt (it is also more natural) than the "Anatomical position".

beginning of this section, but as yet no national or preferably international standards have been published. For this reason "minimum recommended" views are given for each condition mentioned in section IV. The following are just a few of those most commonly taken in paediatric photography and the numbers given in brackets refer to those illustrated in Fig. 2 which

PHOTOGRAPHIC STANDARDISATION CHART

Please indicate by serial number, positions required   also (L) or (R) as applicable

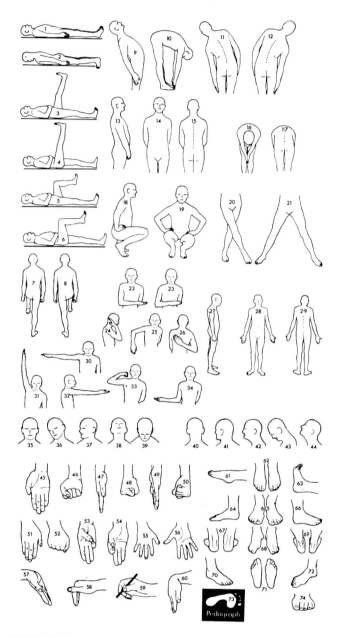

STANDARD POSITIONS

MEDICAL PHOTOGRAPHIC DEPARTMENT
INSTITUTE OF ORTHOPÆDICS
ROYAL . NATIONAL ORTHOPÆDIC HOSPITAL

FIG. 2.

shows the "Photographic Standardization Chart" drawn up by Whitley (1970).

(a) *Anterior posterior* (numbers 28 and 35) abbreviated "AP" = front view.

(b) *Posterior anterior* (numbers 29 and 40) abbreviated "PA" = back view.

(c) *Lateral* (numbers 27 and 42) abbreviated "LAT" = true side view (90° to the median plane); sometimes called a profile.

The aspect is indicated by the prefix right or left (R. or L.). Thus a request for a "left lateral" view (L.LAT) would require the patient to turn to *his* right so that his left side faces the camera.

(d) *45° view.* A position exactly half-way between a front view and a true lateral (45° to median plane). The term "45° view" should be used in place of the commonly used misleading names such as "oblique", "half-face", "$\frac{3}{4}$-view" and "semi-side" face.

Most conditions met with in paediatric photography can be fully demonstrated by one or more of the above positions which generally relate to the whole body, trunk and head. Terms used more specifically for the photography of other parts of the body are discussed by the authors mentioned at the beginning of this section.

(e) *Infra-nasal.* This is an anterior close-up view of the nose, with the head tipped upwards and backwards at an angle of 45° so that the nostril shape and upper lip formation may be demonstrated. (See p. 160 and p. 165.

2. Standardization. At one time lengthy notes and laborious measurements were taken by the clinician at the time of examination in order to provide a clinical record of a condition. Photographs in many cases now replace these early methods, and in addition offer more accurate and comprehensive information. However, some degree of standardization with respect to scale, positioning and lighting, is essential if these routine records are to be of value.

An important point not often fully appreciated is that standardization in paediatric photography may form the basis and even dictate the needs

---

FIG. 2. The "Photographic Standardization Chart" reprinted from *Medical and Biological Illustration* by courtesy of R. J. Whitely and the editors (B.M.A.). This type of chart simplifies requests for standard photographic views since the clinician need only write the appropriate reference numbers on the photographic card. This particular chart was designed for orthopaedic purposes, but modifications can be made to suit other specializations.

of photographing the adult. This is so because any child who is photographed, may at some later stage in adolescent or adult life be photographed again, and comparisons may be required to show development since childhood. Useful comparisons cannot be made if accurate standard records of known scale were not taken originally, although in the author's experience, clinicians have sometimes been misled and on some occasions, have even drawn conclusions from photographs which were clearly non-comparable.

Many problems of standardization of scale can be overcome by taking photographs at fixed ratios of reproduction in relation to a specific body area. This method requires that the focal length of the lens and the negative size remain identical for all follow-up pictures and that this information is accurately recorded on each occasion for future reference. This is a popular system which is not only easy to use but is also consistently accurate.

One such system is that described by Duguid (1969) in which the body is divided into regions according to their relative size and each region is reproduced to a fixed image scale in relation to the size of print, slide or negative used. However, paediatric photography requires a modified approach in order to achieve useful comparative records. Since the child grows rapidly (normal birth length is about 20 in compared with a normal 12-year-old at about 56 in in height) it is impracticable to reproduce photographs to a set scale routinely, as this would in some cases require enormous differences in the degree of enlargement. In practice, all clinical photographs are taken at set ratios and the camera settings noted on the request card for future reference. In most cases that are photographed in black and white, the region of interest is simply enlarged to fill the print area. On occasions when accurate comparative enlargements are required, precise scaling is accomplished by reference to the camera settings recorded on the request card. Measuring scales are included in all full-length views (see III.B), and in other cases where it is known in advance that accurate comparisons are needed. Ideally when a scale is introduced as a means of subsequent measurement of the subject, it is best recorded in the same negative as the subject. An exception to this is when the rule cannot easily be located in the exact plane of focus, such as is experienced when taking anterior facial views. The scale may then be recorded as a second negative at *exactly* the same magnification ratio by photographing a transparent rule held in front of a transilluminated background. The two resultant negatives are subsequently printed on the same sheet of paper, thus avoiding inaccuracy due to disproportionate changes in paper size. (Since this method is recommended only for roll or 35-mm film, changes in the size of consecutive frames in a roll of film are minimal compared to changes that may take place with separate sheets of film.) The composite print is made by enlarging the rule to a predetermined size, with the negative masked so that the rule is positioned in the bottom $\frac{1}{2}$ in of the printing paper. The film is then advanced and the negative masked so that the facial view is printed in the upper area of the paper. An example is shown in Fig. 3. Recent advances in extensive cranio-facial surgery have created a need for pre- and post-operative photographs to be reproduced to scale for assessment purposes, and the above method is employed routinely in these cases. These include the conditions, Crouzon's disease, Apert's syndrome and Hypertelorism (see IV). Precise scaling is occasionally required for cases which involve surgical movement of the jaw to correct abnormal protrusion and retrusion. (see IV, Prognathism.) For these, lateral facial views are taken to include a rule in the same negative. The rule is held perpendicularly, close to the nose-tip, at the exact mid-line of the face. The photograph is reproduced to exactly the same size by reference to the rule which is included in each print to check accuracy of scale when the prints are dry. Several prints are made for the surgeon to cut up and reposition so that he may obtain an impression of the amount of movement required to correct the abnormality. Another method which is now used in preference, is to make a tracing from accurate cephalometric soft-tissue x-ray profiles. This tracing of the soft-tissue outline is placed on the enlarger baseboard and the lateral photograph enlarged to fit exactly. It is important when taking these photographs to ensure the patient is in a relaxed ("at rest") position.

All scales and measuring devices should now be in the metric system. However, because records extend back over many years it has been decided to include both metric and inch and feet scales for at least another 10 years. By this time it should be possible to use only metric units, since conversion will probably be required in comparatively few cases.

B. Basic technique

1. Full-length. Full-length photographs are required to illustrate many paediatric conditions. These may indicate the general state of health, degree of deformity and stature of the patient.

Photographs may be taken either with the child standing or lying down. A portable platform on which the patient stands, is fitted with a removable vertical measuring scale so that his height is recorded in the negative. On occasions a "normal" child photographed alongside the patient, helps to contrast their differences by providing a comparison. This is demonstrated

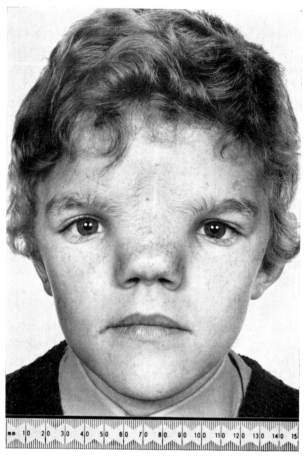

FIG. 3. Pre-operative Hypertelorism. Millimetre scales are used in cases of Hypertelorism, Apert's Syndrome and Crouzon's disease for assessing post-operative results. The scale is photographed on the next frame of film at exactly the same magnification and subsequently printed on the same sheet of paper.

by Fig. 4. The child is positioned close to the scale thus avoiding waste of space in the final prints, so that several views may be placed together on the same mount. Full-length views are normally taken with the patient in the "anatomical position". However, it has become standard practice to photograph child patients with the palms facing in towards the body as shown in Fig. 1. The child is asked to stand up straight "like a soldier" with arms to the side and he is then asked to slightly move his arms away from his side. The child generally responds to this instruction if at the

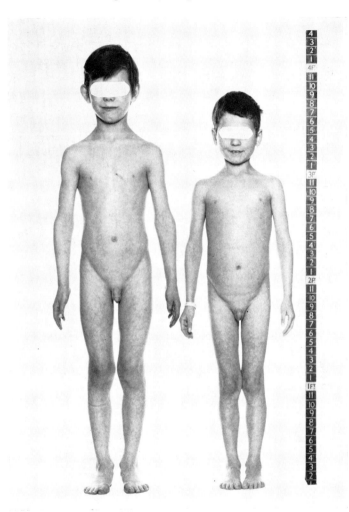

FIG. 4. A normal child may be used as a control. In this case, the boys are twins; *left:* normal, *right:* coeliac disease, $8\frac{3}{4}$ years of age.

same time the photographer demonstrates the action. In fact the child treats it as a game and usually enjoys helping in this way.

Young children, especially toddlers, require helping and are usually encouraged to hold on to the measuring pole with one hand whilst an assistant (usually a nurse or parent) holds the other. Some assistance is also necessary with certain older children suffering from nervous complaints and others who may be physically handicapped. A fall from the standing platform which is approximately 12 in from the ground, could cause injury, and for this reason the assistant should remain close to the child throughout photography. Few conditions are adequately demonstrated by an anterior view alone, and on most occasions a lateral is taken in addition. For the lateral view, the child is again asked to stand up "like a soldier" but with arms held straight down *touching the sides* and with feet together (see Fig. 1). Few children are able to keep both legs "in line" when their feet are parted, whereas when they are placed together, only the leg nearest the camera is reproduced, giving a clean outline.

Posterior views are routinely taken for conditions such as obesity and lipodystrophy. Since the child faces away from the camera it is usual for him to close the eyes, thus avoiding unnecessary exposure to the flash-illuminated background (see III.E). Instructions given from the camera position are avoided, otherwise the patient is distracted and liable to move or turn round. He is usually accurately positioned by the photographer and then asked to stand still for the photograph whilst the photographer returns to his "taking" position. Some conditions require anterior, posterior and both lateral views to be taken and scoliosis, for example, requires the above four views each to be taken with the patient *both* standing up straight and bending in an attempt to touch the toes without bending the knees. A long focal length lens is used (see III.D) in the majority of cases, although tall patients necessitate the use of a standard lens, due to the limited studio length.

Two lamps are used to illuminate full-lengths and these are on most occasions placed one directly above the other to produce an effect similar to that given by one lamp. The lower lamp is directed down slightly towards the patient's feet and the other is pointed more towards the upper part of the body. This method is suitable with a white background, gives adequate coverage of the whole body and generally results in a small shadow underneath the patient's chin. (See Fig. 4.)

Babies and children whose conditions prevent them standing, are photographed from above whilst they lie on the floor. They are suitably cushioned beneath with blankets, on top of which is placed a *rubber* sheet (so that laundry is kept to a minimum), covered by a white cotton sheet, replaced at frequent intervals. The measuring scale is removed from the standing platform and placed beside the child for length measurement. The patient is left to adopt his normal posture whilst laying on his back, although it is often found necessary for an assistant to hold the feet of a small child so that his length may be accurately recorded. Lateral views often require assistance in holding the child on his side to prevent him rolling on to his back or front. This usually involves the placing of one

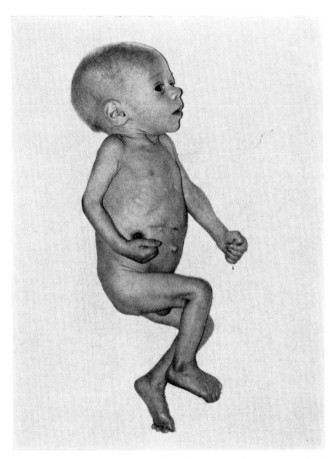

FIG. 5. Even illumination of a whole body is given by a portable flash head. When held resting on the lens-hood, it produces a thin unobtrusive black line (shadow) around the subject.

hand in the small of the back. When difficulties arise the child may be placed on a clinical couch, lying on his back, and the lateral view obtained in this way. This method may be preferable, for instance when the profile of the abdomen is the main area of interest.

Dressings are only removed by the nurse accompanying the child provided that ward sister has given her approval. On arrival at the studio it is often discovered that a child has a urine bag attached, and it is usual to suggest that pictures are postponed until the following day, since urine collection is usually of no more than 24 h duration.

On occasions it may be necessary to take pictures with the bag in position in which case it is concealed as much as possible by folding underneath the child as appropriate. On rare occasions where photographs of the genitalia are required the bag is briefly removed provided that authority has been given.

Since the lamps and cameras are positioned above the child, extreme care is necessary to ensure every item is securely connected and unlikely to fall on the patient (see II.E). In order to gain full coverage from head to toe, a pair of step-ladders are kept at hand for this purpose. For most cases a long focal lens is used on each camera since many of the children unable stand are usually quite small and the longer focal length gives greater working distances and less distortion.

Full-length photographs of children lying on the floor are normally taken with two lamps positioned directly over the child, one each side and close to the camera lens. Location photographs may be taken with a single electronic flash head resting on the top of the lens-hood (see Fig. 5).

2. Head. (a) Full-face and head. The face is probably photographed more often than any other part of the body (Rogers, 1969). An important contributory factor is that many paediatric conditions, especially those of congenital origin, have a typical facial appearance. In some of these cases an initial diagnosis can often be made from the face alone. One such example is that of lipodystrophy (see IV). Many of these typical facies were illustrated by Martin (1961a) and a selection are reprinted in Fig. 6.

Cleft lip and palate deformities and naevi represent two of the most common conditions referred for facial views. Nearly all disorders affecting the face can be fully demonstrated by an anterior, 45°, or lateral view or

---

FIG. 6. A selection of photographs from "Some Facies in the Diseases of Childhood", reprinted from *Medical and Biological Illustration* by courtesy of Derek Martin and the editors (B.M.A.) These conditions are mentioned in the text (section IV): (a) Congenital Ptosis; (b) Ocular Hypertelorism; (c) Neuroblastoma; (d) Prognathism; (e) Cretinism; (f) Gargoylism (Hunter-Hurler Syndrome); (g) Microcephaly; (h) Oxycephaly (Crouzon's Disease); (i) As (h); (j) Mongolism; (k) Turner's Syndrome; (l) Lipodystrophy; (m) Achondroplasia; (n) Adenoma Sebaceum in Epiloia; (o) Treacher–Collin's Syndrome; (p) Acrocephalosyndactyly (Apert's Syndrome); (q) Progeria.

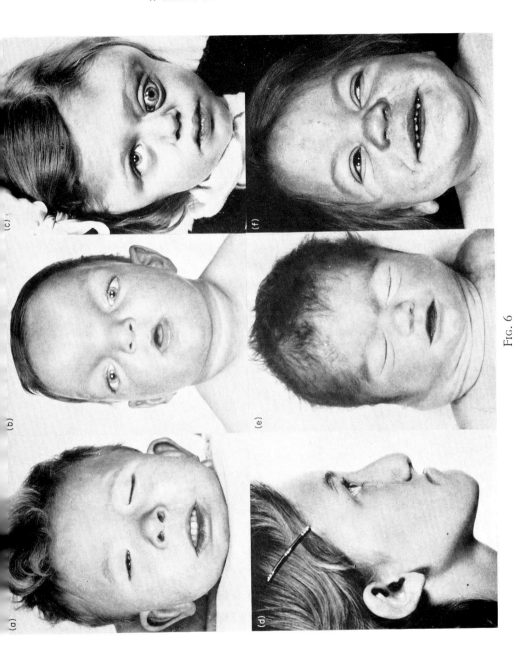

FIG. 6

F*

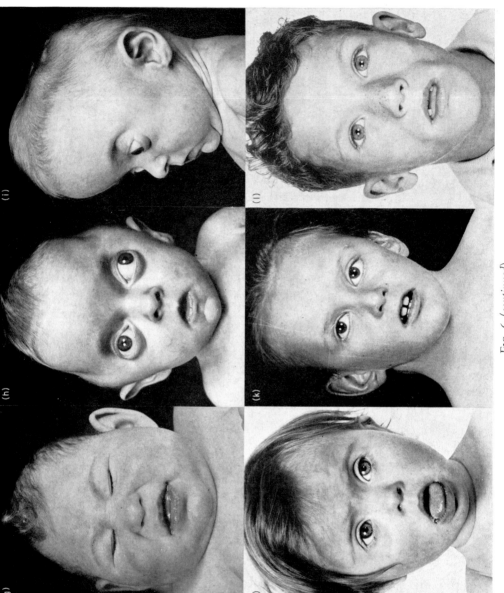

FIG. 6 (continued)

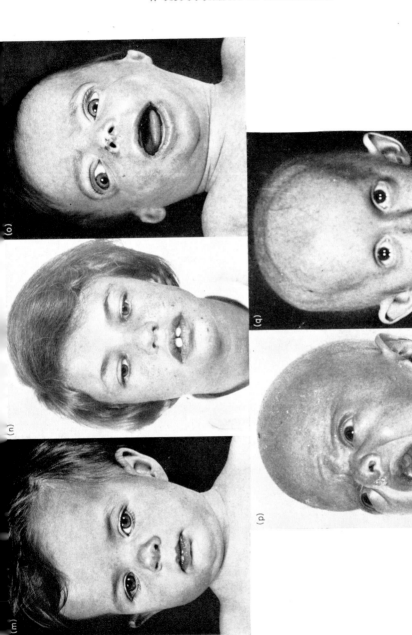

Fig. 6 (continued)

by a combination of these views (Rogers, 1971). Eckhoff (1952) recommends these views as standard, but suggests that the "three-quarter position" (45° view) may be omitted in times of economy. The relative merits of "full-face" and "profile" views are comprehensively discussed by Hertl (1964). A large number of medical conditions are more clearly demonstrated by taking lateral views in addition to the anterior aspect. These often provide a better and more striking record (see Fig. 7). An

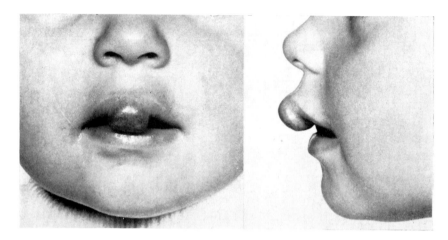

Fig. 7. Haemangioma of the lip. A more complete picture is obtained by taking a lateral view in addition to an anterior. This often gives a more striking demonstration of the condition.

additional "infra-nasal" view is sometimes included to demonstrate certain nasal deformities requiring correction, such as is common in cleft-lip cases (see p. 165).

With facial views it is usual to include the top of the head down to just below the chin and occasionally the neck, where this is involved. Both lateral aspects are routinely taken in the majority of cases to provide comparative records, since many unilateral conditions may involve the unaffected side over a period. When only one lateral is taken, this should be the *left* side, to accord with anthropological custom, whenever there is a choice. It is important that facial views are taken with the child relaxed as far as possible in order to avoid a distortion of his natural appearance due to changes of facial expression. Exceptions to this are when separate photographs are taken of the child smiling and at rest, to show facial paralysis. Certain malocclusion cases also require an additional range of views and these are discussed elsewhere by the author (Rogers, 1971).

Posterior views of the head may be required in addition, to show deformities affecting the shape of the skull. Many of these conditions are of congenital origin and include hydrocephalus and craniosynostosis among those most commonly photographed.

Occasionally superior views showing the skull shape are required. For this view the child is placed on a clinical couch in the supine position with feet furthermost from the camera. A suitable pad is placed under the neck posteriorly to raise the back of the head clear of the couch. This allows the whole skull circumference to be demonstrated. In some cases this additional view gives valuable information not recorded by other views and Fig. 8, showing the condition of scaphocephaly, demonstrates this point.

Ideally, no clothing (example, collars, ties, etc.) should appear in the final picture; unfortunately this is unavoidable in a number of cases.

In order to obtain general views of the head the child may be seated on a couch. Babies and young children appear comforted by the large firm support it gives, and they are placed at approximately the same height as the photographer. This allows for direct communication with the patient up to the point of exposure, giving the photographer a greater amount of control over the subject. With older children a rotating stool is used. Care should be taken to see that infirm (or adventurous) children are safe on this type of seat. With the co-operation of the child, easy centering of the face and head is obtained, and in seconds rotation provides an accurate lateral view. Hairgrips are used where necessary to hold back the hair from the sides of the face and forehead.

Two lamps are used on most occasions when photographing the whole head. Anterior and posterior views are taken with the lamps positioned one each side of and close to the camera lens. Lateral views are taken with one lamp positioned on the opposite side of the lens to the direction in which the patient faces. The second lamp is placed on the opposite side to the first at 45° to the camera and is directed towards the patient's face. This positioning reduces the dark shadow in the orbit which often results from using both lamps at equal distance and angle to the patient.

(b) *Eyes*. Hansell (1957) deals comprehensively with many of the problems and special techniques required for eye photography. Some of the more common situations met with in practice are briefly discussed below.

The full face is included in those conditions where involvement of the eye is secondary to the basic condition or where inclusion of the rest of the face would result in a more complete picture. For instance, in Crouzon's disease there is a marked bilateral protrusion of the eyeballs (exophthalmos)

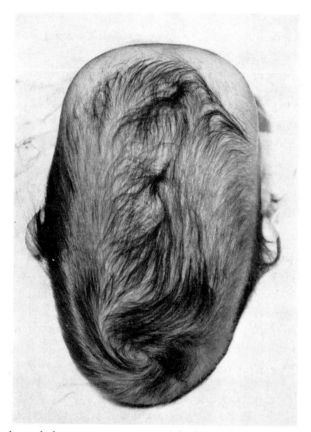

FIG. 8. Scaphocephaly. A superior view of the head gives important additional information not shown in anterior, posterior or lateral views. This view is also useful for demonstration of facial asymmetries.

and this is clearly demonstrated in full-face anterior and lateral views, without the need for separate close-ups of the eyes.

Close-up views of an individual eye including the immediate surrounding area are commonly taken to illustrate ptosis, epicanthus, small naevi and other lesions. Where lesions extend on to the upper lid, it is often necessary to take two photographs; one with the eye closed and one with it open, since the lid may partially cover up the lesion when the eye is open.

Squint cases are illustrated by taking photographs of both eyes together in the *"nine positions of gaze"* and these are shown in Fig. 9. Mason (1964) also mentions the use of these standard ophthalmic positions to demonstrate ocular paralysis in the conditions of myasthenia gravis and hyperthyroidism. For these views the child's head is held from behind (usually by the parent) with one hand placed firmly each side of the head to restrict movement. A small, interesting, brightly coloured squeaker toy is used for the purpose of directing the child's attention. This is held by the photographer, first immediately on top of the lens-hood for the frontal view (occasionally children are able to look straight into the camera lens instead). It is then held at arm's length in the other eight positions of gaze. Since the camera is hand-held, this requires a certain amount of dexterity on the part of the photographer. In practice, however, this is fairly easy to achieve and is always preferred to using unskilled assistance, especially as the photographer is the person best able to decide the exact point at which the picture should be taken. The tendency for the upper lids to drop when the child looks down is avoided if the assistant places one finger on each lid to hold them in position. Most individual views are taken with the child seated either on a rotating stool or clinical couch. A special head-rest (with chin support) suitable for eye photography, as described by Lunnon (1952), is used when photographing older children who are able to co-operate. This device may be clamped to a table (or any convenient support), and placed directly in front of the child at a convenient height. Younger children are preferably photographed whilst seated in a children's dental chair when a number of standard views are to be taken. Unlike the head-rest mentioned earlier, surprisingly few children are frightened by the chair, and once positioned, generally remain still throughout the photographic session.

Whenever possible, only one lamp should be used for eye photography so that the lamp reflection can be positioned away from the involved area. In practice, it is often necessary to use two lamps in order to ensure even illumination, especially when dealing with a child who finds it difficult to remain still. On most occasions, the two lamp reflexes in the eyes, have detracted little from the main area of interest, as can be seen in Fig. 9.

Many paediatric conditions, especially neurological disorders, cause abnormal movements of the eyes. These are recorded by cinematography and are discussed in section III.L. Retinal photography is briefly mentioned in section III.C.

(c) *Nose.* Most deformities of the nose are adequately demonstrated by views taken to include the whole head. Anterior and both lateral aspects

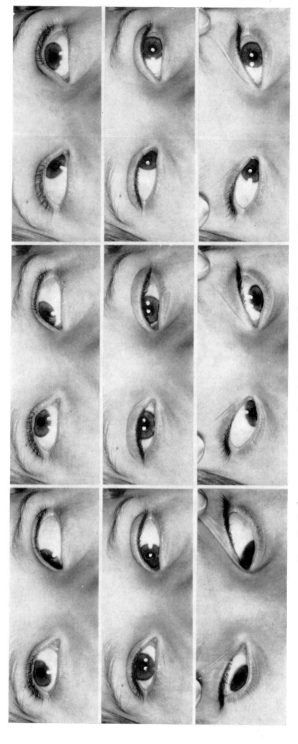

Fig. 9. Left convergent squint. The standard "nine positions" of gaze.

are usually photographed. Since the nostrils are commonly affected, an additional close-up view is routinely taken to show the nostril shape and upper lip formation. This anterior view includes an area from the chin to the eyes and is taken with the child's head tilted back 45°. In order to simplify requests for this view it has been given the name "infra-nasal" and is illustrated by Fig. 10.

There are three basic methods of achieving this position and each depends upon the likely co-operation of the child. One method used for babies is to place them in a sitting up position on the edge of the clinical couch to face the camera. They are firmly held from behind by an assistant (usually the parent) and then tipped back until the correct position is obtained. Care should be taken to provide support for the neck.

Some infants may not respond to this method, in which case they are placed supine on the couch and photographed from above, whilst their head is held by the assistant. The photographer stands on a small stool to gain the necessary height for correct positioning. Older children are seated on a stool and encouraged to look at a point on the ceiling; minor adjustments being made to the camera position to obtain the required angle.

Conditions most commonly photographed to show nasal deformities are cleft-lip (with associated cleft-palate) and haemangiomas (usually cavernous). Other conditions include those due to trauma, nasal encephaloceles and various congenital defects.

(d) *Mouth.* The majority of conditions affecting the mouth and surrounding areas are clearly shown in an anterior full-face view. *Extra-oral* close ups are occasionally taken of local skin lesions, but more frequently *intra-oral* views are required. These are mainly taken to show certain palatal defects; most common of which is the condition cleft-palate (with associated cleft-lip).

Children able to co-operate are photographed while seated. With younger patients, intra-oral photographs are usually obtained with the patient supine, his head held on one side, face towards the camera. A small stool is kept conveniently at hand so that the photographer may gain a higher viewpoint, from above the child, when necessary.

Since most patients are sent direct from out-patients immediately after examination by the clinician, they frequently expect a similar "*investigation*" by the photographer. Many of them are therefore initially reluctant to open their mouths, and a variety of methods are tried in order to encourage them to do so. Clear photographs of the palate are achieved with young patients in one of three ways; these being when the child laughs, yawns or cries. First of all an attempt is made to encourage the patient to laugh by tickling him. The mother is very often helpful since she knows

(a)

(b)

(c)

(d)

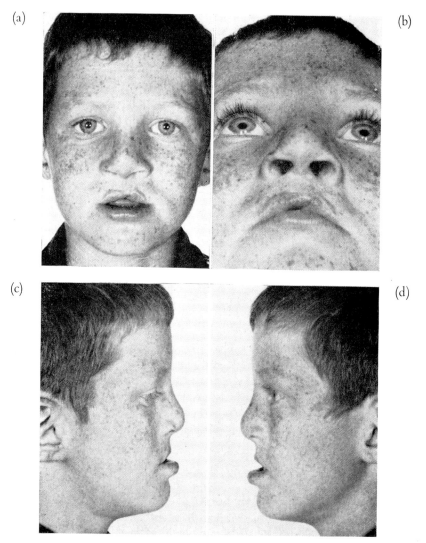

FIG. 10. Post-operative cleft-lip and palate for nasal correction. These are the four standard views taken: (a) Anterior; (b) Infranasal; (c) Right lateral; (d) Left lateral.

the child's most sensitive areas. The majority of successful palatal pictures are achieved by this method. Many babies have frequent yawning sessions and the author is often surprised at the number of successful pictures gained in this way. The child is usually captured whilst he is in the middle of a yawn and much depends upon the speed of the photographer in seizing the opportunity. The third method is used only when the first two fail. Fortunately the child is crying in less than 25% of those cases photographed and the majority of these are babies in the first few months of life, who cry as a natural reaction to being passively posed. In the remainder of cases the child's head is held firmly by the parent. This often produces an immediate response in which the child opens his mouth to cry whilst attempting to release himself. The photograph is quickly taken since few opportunities are repeated.

Another method described by Evatt (1961), in which an assistant gently pinches the nostrils together immediately before exposure, is resorted to on rare occasions. It is important to realize that on no occasion should a child be "forced" beyond certain limits in order to obtain these views (see II).

Intra-oral views are normally taken with a ring flash and extra-oral views are often best illuminated by a single lamp placed directly above the camera lens.

(e) *Teeth.* Many of the dental cases photographed are treated by orthodontics and oral surgery. Since these types of treatment almost always involve changes in facial appearance, anterior and lateral views to include the whole face are taken, both before and after treatment. Some stages in between require these views when the change is significant or when demonstrating new techniques.

Complete standardization is essential for routine comparative studies, since it is common for surgeons to rely upon these photographs as an aid to their treatment. A particular method of scaling is used in some cases prior to mandibular and maxillary surgery (see p. 151).

Conditions such as inflamation of the gums (gingivitis), cysts, and those due to trauma (example: fractured incisors) represent a small percentage of cases photographed. Usually intra-oral views are taken to record changes and movement of the teeth and supporting structures. These movements are effected either by surgical means or by the use of orthodontic appliances. Many types of appliances, which may be either fixed or removable, are placed in the mouth, and some adjusted at intervals to bring about a movement. Clear views of the teeth are obtained by retracting the lips. Numerous retractors have been designed for this purpose and a number of different types are illustrated by Rogers (1971).

A special type of retractor has been developed for lateral views of the teeth since standard types do not hold back the lip sufficiently. One of these retractors is inserted in the side furthest from the camera and a standard one used for the nearer side. At the present time, black acrylic ones are used, due entirely to local preference of the clinicians. Retractors should be clinically clean before use.

Most patients who are given either of the above treatments are school-children and many of them are able to co-operate with the photographer. It is usual to ask the patient to hold the retractors once the photographer has placed them in position. Thus, when the child is asked to first pull the retractors forward and then pull out to the side (to bring the lips clear of the teeth), he more readily accepts the small amount of self-inflicted discomfort. Rubber bands are always removed from appliances before photographs are taken.

For orthodontic cases, a standard set of intra-oral views, with lips retracted, are taken on each visit. These are an anterior (buccal-aspect), and both right and left 45° views, all taken with the teeth in occlusion (i.e., biting together). The anterior view is then repeated with the teeth slightly apart to show the edge shape of the upper and lower incisors.

Cases undergoing maxillary or mandibular surgery (to move the position of the upper or lower jaw) require both anterior and lateral views to be taken with the teeth in occlusion. These patients are always photo-graphed before surgery, post-operatively with fixed splints in position, and again to show the final result. On each of these occasions full-face views are also taken.

A number of more specialized standard views have been designed for the systematic recording of other conditions such as that of malocclusion. These are discussed elsewhere by the author (Rogers, 1971) and therefore, are not repeated in this chapter. Other techniques of intra-oral photography are discussed by Jones (1961), Callender (1966) and Adams (1968).

Surface-silvered mirrors allow reflected views to be taken to show the back surface (lingual aspect) and biting surface (occlusal aspect) of the teeth. Unlike ordinary mirrors, this type does not give a double image, but care should be taken in handling as they are easily marked. The mirror is warmed before insertion in the mouth to prevent condensation, caused by the patient's breath, from clouding up the mirror image. A new type of mirror has become available (Sansom, 1965) which has reflective qualities equal to that of the finest surface-silvered optical mirror. It consists of a thin, transparent plastic sheet of polyester film on which is vacuum-coated a very thin layer of aluminium. This mirror is extremely light in weight, virtually unbreakable and can be cut to size from a larger sheet. Perhaps its biggest advantage is that it is virtually non–misting. When using a mirror, it is important to show it in the picture because the reflected image is laterally reversed. This can of course be corrected at the printing stage or when mounting the slide.

Most views of the teeth are taken using a ring flash as sole illuminant, but for lateral views, the same lighting procedure as is used for lateral facial views, is adopted (see p. 161).

(f) *Ears*. Photographs of the ear are most common in cases of protruding or "bat ears" and accessory auricles. These, and other ear deformities are discussed in section IV. Many conditions require anterior (AP) and posterior (PA) views to include the whole head and a lateral close-up of each ear. Both left and right laterals are required for comparison, even when only one side is affected. The above four views form the basis for standardization and others are added where necessary. In cases of accessory auricles it is usual to take a close-up view of the affected side only. Hairgrips are used to hold hair away from the ear and an elastic band is fastened round long hair to produce a semi "pony-tail" when taking the posterior view. Close-up views of the ear are normally illuminated by a single lamp.

3. *Trunk*. A number of conditions are illustrated by photography of the trunk. These most commonly include congenital deformities, especially those affecting the chest, lower trunk and spinal column. Others include skin conditions (e.g., naevi) and those due to trauma (e.g., burns). Many patients are photographed in the studio, although frequent visits to the wards are required for neonates and others suffering from serious complaints. In practice the trunk may be conveniently divided into three areas usually photographed. These are the anterior, posterior and lower trunk.

(a) *Anterior trunk*. The anterior upper trunk is frequently photographed to show certain breast abnormalities, such as precocious breast development and, less often, gynaecomastia. Standard views for photography of the breast are discussed by Hansell and Ollerenshaw (1962). In paediatrics, the greatest need is to show the absence or presence of the breast and to what extent it protrudes. A satisfactory demonstration of such conditions is achieved by an anterior and both lateral views. It is important to realize that the child is often very sensitive about a deformity and care should be taken to avoid unnecessary embarrassment. Certain abnormalities of the chest may require both right and left 45° views to be taken in addition to anterior and lateral aspects. These are often required when depressions or protruberances of the chest wall are present, such as in those cases of pectus carcinatum (pigeon chest) and pectus excavatum (funnel chest). Thus a

three-dimensional impression is given by the 45° view in addition to the
contour, and extent of protrusion provided by the lateral aspect. Each
view gives valuable information to the clinician in follow-up studies, even
though the 45° view taken alone gives a good impression of the deformity
and is usually the one chosen for textbook demonstration of these cases.
Most of these deformities are photographed in the studio with the patient
standing, preferably on a raised platform (such as is used for full-length
views) so that the child is brought to a height where the photographer is
able to operate more effectively. Clothing is removed down to the waist
and photographs are taken to include the neck (just below the chin) and
down as far as the umbilicus. The arms are not normally included in the
picture and are therefore abducted, so that a clear view may be taken.
Certain conditions, however, may require the arms to be included, as is
found with some burns cases when demonstrating muscle contractures of
the arms and shoulders. Anterior and posterior views of the trunk are
then taken both with the arms *slightly* abducted and also fully abducted
to show the "muscle pull" and limit of movement caused by the condition.
Additional close-up views may be required to show the contraction.

Older children unable to stand are occasionally photographed whilst
they sit on a stool or chair. To avoid the natural tendency to slouch
forward, which would result in a distorted record of the condition, they
are encouraged to sit up with their back resting against the back of a chair.
The latter is camouflaged with a sheet that matches the background.
Smaller children and babies are preferably photographed in the recumbent
position. Sometimes it may be desirable to place the child on a clinical
couch and for the parent to hold him in position. This often gives comfort
to the fractious child, frightened by photographic paraphernalia, and on
occasions provides more control in the precise positioning of very young
babies.

(*b*) *Posterior trunk.* Many of those conditions affecting the posterior
trunk include protruding deformities such as meningoceles, myelo-
meningoceles and teratomas. These require both posterior and lateral
aspects to be photographed. Detail of the deformity and the extent of the
area affected is shown by the posterior view, and the lateral shows the
degree of protrusion, as illustrated by Fig. 11. Most other conditions which
commonly include skin lesions and hairy patches, being non-protruding,
need a posterior view only. Of the more serious conditions, some of
which are mentioned above, most are photographed pre-operatively on
the ward whilst they are nursed in an incubator (see III.I). Post-operative
follow-up records are mainly photographed in the studio with the patient

either sitting or recumbent, dependent upon the age and co-operation of the child.

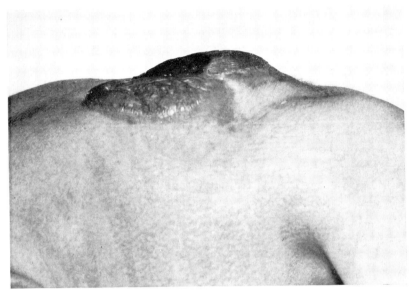

FIG. 11. Meningocele. A lateral view shows the extent of protrusion and is usually taken in addition to the posterior aspect.

(c) *Lower trunk.* A number of conditions require an anterior view of the lower trunk and these are most often achieved by supporting the patient on the edge of the clinical couch with his legs abducted. The area photographed extends from the umbilicus to and slightly beyond the perineum and often requires two separate photographs. For instance, in cases of extrophy of the bladder two anterior views are considered necessary; one with the child sitting upright, taken slightly superiorly and the second with the patient inclined backwards, taken slightly inferiorly to include the anus. Genital anomalies such as those of hypospadias, require a close-up view to show the external urinary meatus. A pointer may be used to show the exact opening in those cases where this is not clearly visible. Disposable rubber gloves are always used when holding the penis to show the deformity. It is fairly common for the parent to act as assistant in these cases and this proves useful in gaining co-operation of the child who is comforted by the familiar face.

A lateral close-up is occasionally needed to show the degree of chordee (bending of the penis) which is common in cases of *perineal* hypospadias.

Other genital anomalies, such as those of intersex and of vaginal agenesis, require two separate close-up views of the genitalia. These are taken with the patient in a recumbent position with legs abducted and knees flexed. One view is taken with the skin held back on either side of the genitalia to show detail of the deformity and the second taken to show the deformity as it normally appears, when undisturbed. It has now become usual practise to photograph the majority of cases in the anaesthetic room prior to surgery whilst they are anaesthetized as this avoids embarrassment to the patient.

Anterior and posterior trunk views are on most occasions illuminated by two lamps placed one each side of, and close to, the camera lens. Occasionally a 4 : 1 lighting ratio is used in addition, to provide extra contrast in order to show up certain deformities. Lower trunk views, especially close-ups, often need only a single lamp for illumination, and this is usually placed directly over the lens-hood.

4. Upper limbs. Of those conditions affecting the upper limbs, many are congenital and others are due to trauma, usually as a result of burns and scalds. In a number of cases full-length or trunk views to include the upper limbs are all that are required.

The most common types of upper limb deformities that are sent for photographs, are those affecting the hand. Conditions such as syndactyly, polydactyly, Dupuytren's contracture and absent, deformed, or accessory digits represent by far the greatest proportion of these cases. Standardization of views is particularly important, since many of the conditions require long-term follow-up records. Eckhoff (1952) demonstrates many of the standard views required from the plastic surgeon's point of view, and those demonstrated by Whitley (1970) are shown in Fig. 2. Lateral views taken from both the radial or thumb side and from the ulnar or little finger side may be required to illustrate some conditions such as Dupuytren's contracture. Of those cases photographed, few require views other than dorsal and palmar aspects. Where possible, these are obtained by seating the child on a low stool (the standing platform for full-length views is a useful height for this). A horizontal board attached to a portable stand is used for children able to co-operate. The board is covered with a white cotton sheet to provide a clear background, and is adjusted for height so that the board just clears the knees of the patient when placed directly in front of him.

Photographs usually include both hands together, even when only one hand is affected, and the hands are held flat against the board and photographed from above. In palmar views it is usually necessary for the forearms to be fully supinated with the elbows abducted in order to get the fingers and thumbs flat. This view often creates difficulty and it is sometimes necessary for an assistant to hold down the wrists. Dorsal views however present few problems.

Fingernails are photographed by the same method employed for the hand, except that three separate views are taken. These are: one close-up of both thumbnails together, and separate views of each hand to include the four fingernails. This is necessary because when the fingernails lie flat the thumbnails are at approximately 45°.

When photographing babies and infants, a great amount of improvisation is necessary. No hard and fast rules can be applied, since each situation generally requires a different solution. The most common difficulty is that of getting the hand in the correct position with fingers extended, since many young patients are either unable or unwilling to straighten them. In these cases it is usual to photograph each hand separately. Most infants do not respond to the method suggested by Evatt (1961) in which a sheet of glass is placed gently over the hand to keep the fingers straight. It is, however, possible to use this method with some babies, but more often, successful pictures are obtained if the assistant (usually the mother) holds the baby's wrist and straightens his fingers immediately prior to exposure. A clean background giving a good contrast without undue shadowing is achieved by placing a folded, small, white sheet over the patient's lap, and holding his hands against it. Success or failure depends to a great extent on the attitude of the patient, the help of the mother, and the ingenuity of the photographer; good luck also plays an important role!

Most photographs of the hand are taken from above, with one lamp placed immediately over the camera lens-hood.

5. *Lower limbs.* The foot is by far the most common area photographed in those conditions where the lower limbs are involved. The various forms of talipes (see IV) represent the majority of these cases. Infants and babies are photographed prior to surgery and both lower limbs are included in anterior and posterior views. Lateral aspects are not taken at this stage owing to difficulties encountered in accurate positioning. Both anterior and posterior aspects are photographed with the limbs dependant; in the former with the patient supported on the edge of the clinical couch and in the latter whilst lying prone. The couch is covered by a white, cotton sheet which hangs down in front to provide a suitable background. Most babies are photographed in this way. A number of cases are filmed at later stages.

Close-up views of digits, as required in cases of polydactyly and syndactyly, are often achieved by supporting the child so that he partially bears his own weight. This brings his foot into close contact with the background, thus eliminating undesirable shadows.

Older children who are able to support themselves, are photographed whilst they stand on a raised platform (the same as is used for full-length photographs). At this stage the lateral aspect is added to provide a more complete coverage, since many of these cases are photographed routinely throughout treatment, which often extends over many years. Both feet are normally included in one picture for the lateral aspect. This is achieved by asking the child to advance one foot in front of the other, by taking a step forward. In this position, with the child facing 90° lateral to the camera, the inside (medial aspect) of one foot and the outer (lateral aspect) of the other may be photographed. To show the reverse aspects of each foot, the patient is asked to turn through 180° to face the opposite direction.

Since many of these records are needed for comparison over long periods, standardization is of particular importance. It is essential, therefore, that the camera viewpoint is identical on each occasion, since variations will result in lack of comparability. The effects of variations in camera angle are discussed by Duguid and Ollerenshaw (1962) in which they also illustrate a chart showing standard positions of the feet, to overcome many of these problems.

In order to streamline the procedure, a simplified approach has been devised and whilst the number has been kept to a minimum those photographs taken are considered by the author to be adequate for most cases. Further views are added when necessary in individual cases. The following represent the basic set for routine records.

(a) Anterior view of both feet slightly apart, with the camera positioned level with the malleoli.
(b) Anterior view as in (a), but with camera 45° to the malleoli (i.e., with the camera looking down on the feet (dorsal aspect).
(c) Posterior view with camera level with the malleoli.
(d) Left and right lateral aspects each to include both feet, one in front of the other, with the camera positioned 45° to the malleoli.

Other records to show the soles of the feet are achieved by placing the patient supine on the clinical couch, with his head farthermost from the camera and with his feet extending beyond the end of the couch. This allows his feet to be placed through elasticated holes cut out of a small sheet and thus provides a clean white background. A similar method using a *black* flannel sheet is recommended by Duguid and Ollerenshaw (1962).

The shape of the sole of the foot may be demonstrated by the method used by Engel and Hansell (1954), in which grease footprints are produced on bromide paper. For this, the patient's soles are greased and then placed in contact with a sheet of bromide paper. On development a black background is produced with areas of contact shown in white, due to inhibition of the development by the grease. Deformities of the lower limbs such as genu valgum (knock-knee), and genu varum (bow-legs) which may be caused by a number of conditions, are adequately demonstrated by anterior and posterior views with the patient standing. Internal and external rotation deformities are often best demonstrated by marking the patellae. This is usually done by the photographer since they are easily located, and they are marked using a fibre-tipped pen. Two anterior views are taken; one with the patient standing as he does normally and the second with both feet pointing directly forward. This is illustrated in Fig. 12.

Other marking methods described by Evatt (1961) include those required for hip deformities in cases of congenital dislocation of the hip, coxa valga and vara, in which the anterior superior iliac spines are located and marked so that the degrees of pelvic tilt may be demonstrated. He also mentions the use of wooden blocks of different thicknesses, placed beneath the affected limb to demonstrate the degree of under growth and pelvic tilt in cases such as osteitis of the lower limbs.

A large number of cases photographed in paediatrics require full-length views to show, in addition, the general state of health and stature. These often eliminate the need for separate views of the lower limbs.

C. Special techniques

1. Transillumination. For many years the technique of transillumination of the head has been used in the study of malformation of the brain, since certain abnormalities allow an infant's head to transmit light. These include conditions where brain tissue is absent and the areas often filled with cerebro-spinal fluid, as in hydrocephalus and hydranencephaly. Gamstorp (1970) mentions the use of a special torch to observe a number of neurological disorders. The torch is pressed up against the child's head and examinations takes place in a darkened room. This simple method, which may give a considerable amount of information, relies upon the accuracy of the clinician's observation and memory, and lacks a permanent visual record. A method using photography was described by Robinson and Brecknell (1965). They used a 200 J electronic flash and gave approximately 15 flashes at intervals to give adequate exposure on HP3 5× 4 film at a wide aperture. This method needs the child to be sedated. Recent work by Pampiglione *et al.* (1972) has resulted in a new technique which combines colour photography with EEG studies. This method does not require the child to be sedated and opens up new possibilities for studying the head in babies with suspected congenital malformation of the brain

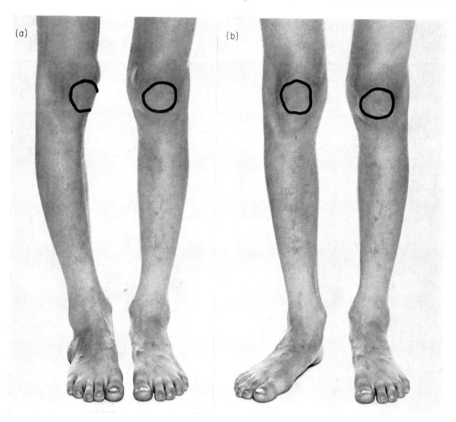

FIG. 12. External torsion of the tibia. (a) Both feet pointing straight forward (patella pointing in). (b) When the patellae are pointing straight, the right foot is turned out. The deformity is clearly shown by taking these two views after marking the patellae with a fibre pen.

and is rapidly becoming an important diagnostic procedure. Many of the abnormalities suitable for transillumination are difficult to diagnose adequately by air ventriculography and other routine procedures.

Photographic method. An electronic flash tube of 3000 watt–seconds is fixed in the base of a box, above which are mounted an opal sheet of glass to disperse light evenly, and a sheet of plate glass on which the child's head is placed. The top of the box is masked to allow a sufficient aperture for the child's head. Further masking is achieved by a black cloth placed round the circumference of the head (see Fig. 13). A 35-mm camera is fixed to a stand and positioned above the child. After focusing, the room lights are switched out and exposures made at apertures f/2·8, f/4, f/5·6 and

TRANSILLUMINATION TECHNIQUE

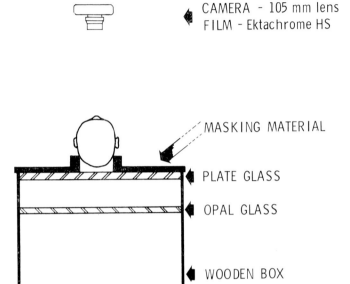

CAMERA - 105 mm lens
FILM - Ektachrome HS

MASKING MATERIAL

PLATE GLASS

OPAL GLASS

WOODEN BOX

ELECTRONIC XENON
DISCHARGE TUBE
(3000 watt/sec), with
reflector

FIG. 13. This diagram shows the equipment for transillumination of the head in babies with suspected congenital malformations of the brain. In combination with EEG studies, this method gives diagnostic information.

f/8 on High Speed Ektachrome colour film. Anterior and both lateral aspects are photographed. It is necessary to take the above range of exposures because of varying degrees of opacity of the skull in different children. Each exposure gives differing amounts of information according to the density produced. A control exposure is always taken on each film by photographing a set of tricolour filters which are mounted in a board and placed over the light source. The control exposure is made with the room lights off at an aperture of f/22.

2. *Retinal photography.* Retinal photography is a specialized technique used for taking pictures of the posterior part of the inside of the eye (fundus oculi). Many of the problems involved and special equipment needed are discussed by Hansell (1957). Retinal photographs are frequently required in paediatrics and can be taken with a portable camera such as the Kowa model RC-2. This type of camera requires little photographic knowledge and yet is capable of producing 35-mm colour slides of very good quality.

Retinal photography of children presents many problems. The child must be kept very still for a period and this is usually achieved by general anaesthesia. There is great expertise and care needed in handling the camera which may be achieved by both photographer and ophthalmologist alike. The variations in photographic controls are virtually nil as the conditions for retinal photography are almost always the same and can be easily standardized. The photographer who regularly takes photographs of eyes will assemble a wide knowledge of ophthalmic conditions, but since specialized medical knowledge is required, this type of photography may be undertaken by the ophthalmologist himself.

3. *Ultraviolet and fluorescence.* Ultraviolet *fluorescence* and *direct* ultraviolet photography techniques are well reported in the literature and include in particular the works of Hansell (1968) and Arnold *et al.* (1971), who discuss the principles involved, equipment needed and a number of applications. Hansell (1961) draws attention to the essential differences between these two entirely separate uses of ultraviolet radiation and mentions a number of applications to medicine.

Ultraviolet *fluorescence* techniques have been given much attention in recent years but comparatively few workers would appear to have investigated the possibilities of *direct* ultraviolet clinical photography. Lunnon (1959) demonstrates the advantages to be gained from *direct* ultraviolet photography of the skin; these being an increased definition in surface detail and enhanced differentiation between areas of varying degrees of pigmentation. A more recent report by Lunnon (1968) described some of the developments in "direct" and "fluorescence" ultraviolet photography applied to medicine, that have taken place in Great Britain in recent years.

Contrary to infrared photography, direct ultraviolet photography is principally concerned with the recording of surface detail and changes in pigmentation, while fluorescence photography portrays the ability of some conditions to emit visible light when the skin or hair is irradiated with ultraviolet radiation. A control photograph should always be taken when using any of the above techniques.

4. *Infrared.* Infrared rays, because of their ability to penetrate human skin, can be used for the photographic study of certain abnormalities which cannot be demonstrated by conventional methods. The first reports of infrared used in medicine were by Haxthausen (1933), who demonstrated its value in dermatology. Much has since been written on the subject; in particular the works of Clark (1946) and more recently Gibson (1968). They both demonstrate many applications, methods and the equipment involved. Additional up-to-date information is given on medical infrared photography (Kodak, 1969) and on applied infrared (Kodak, 1972). Although the technique is relatively simple, it is not used as much as it could be in paediatrics. One area much neglected, is the recording of naevi such as haemangiomas; there is a wealth of information to be gained from such study. A programme of work in this field is, to the author's knowledge, currently taking place by two independent workers. No doubt their results will be published, when complete.

Infrared is particularly useful for showing disorders of the superficial venous system (see Fig. 14) and the underlying states of various skin conditions such as scabs, eczema, lupus erythematosus and tattoos (Lunnon, 1961). It may also be used for studying congenital or operative defects of the iris and for measurement of pupil size in dark adaptation studies (Gibson, 1968). Because infrared produces a visible record of something normally invisible to the eye, a control black and white, conventional photograph should always be taken in addition.

D. *Equipment*

1. *Cameras—still.* At one time it was generally accepted that the $\frac{1}{2}$-plate stand camera was the most suitable format for photographing sick children (Evatt, 1961). Preference for this large format camera was mainly due to the fact that the subject could be photographed at a less reduced scale on the larger negative thus allowing relative freedom of movement of the patient within the negative area, and resulting in an increased depth of field. This did, however, give a comparatively small image which in some cases was little bigger than that possible using a smaller, hand-held, single-lens reflex camera. This fact was confirmed recently when the author checked through a number of old file negatives which were taken on $\frac{1}{2}$-plate film. Apart from the fact that the large camera had always to be fixed to a tripod, a big disadvantage was the time

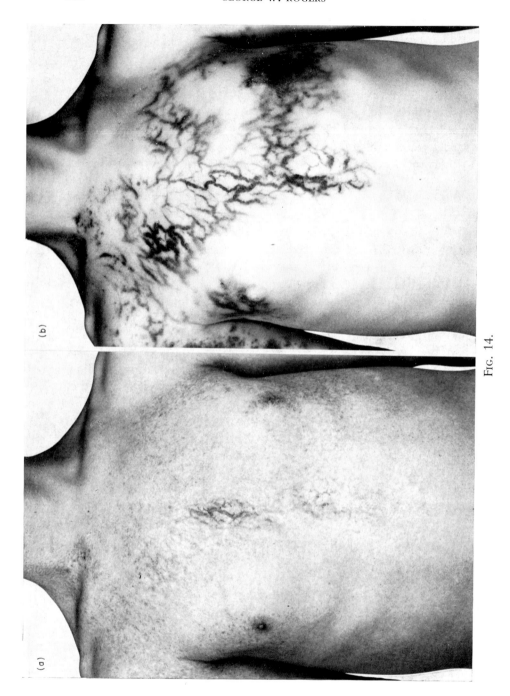

FIG. 14.

taken between initial focusing of the subject and the actual exposure. With the advent of single-lens reflex 35-mm and 6 × 6 cm cameras a new approach has resulted (Rogers, 1969).

(a) *Hand-held, single-lens reflex cameras.* One of the most important advantages of a single-lens reflex camera (35 mm or 6 × 6 cm) is that it can be used hand-held in conjunction with electronic flash, rather than being fixed to a tripod. This freedom of movement enables the photographer to take standard comparative views rather more easily by simply "following" the patient as he moves. The hand-held method however, requires modification of lighting technique (see III.E) to ensure standardized illumination of the subject, independent of camera viewpoint. Photographs to scale can easily be taken while hand-holding the camera. The camera is set to a predetermined scale of reproduction which is either marked on the lens or on the bellows extension bar, the body is simply moved "to and fro" until the image is sharply focused. Used in this way, a very precise degree of accuracy is possible. This method is used mainly for full-face areas and close-up views since the focus change is more obvious at these distances. At greater camera-subject distances, the lens is usually focused by hand because in most cases a scale is required in the picture.

(b) *35-mm single-lens reflex.* A small number of workers use 35-mm cameras for both black-and-white and colour clinical photography. It is the author's opinion (Rogers, 1969) that 35-mm is most appropriately used for taking colour slides (especially since 35-mm projectors are widely available), and that 6 × 6 cm format cameras have definite advantages for routine black-and-white (see p. 183).

Although there are a large number of high quality 35-mm camera systems on the market, few compare favourably with the Leicaflex. No other system of comparable quality offers a *bellow's lens* which is also fitted with automatic diaphragm facility. This requires a double cable release which closes down the lens to the correct aperture immediately before the shutter is released. The system in current use, consists of a Leicaflex SL camera body with a 100-mm Macro-Elmar f/4 lens for bellows use only, giving continuous focusing from infinity to 1 : 1 (same size), and a Summicron-R 50 mm f/2·8 standard lens for general use. The Macro-Elmar lens is used for nearly all clinical photography in colour and is found especially advantageous for theatre work since the surgeon

FIG. 14. Phlebectasia. (a) Control photograph on panchromatic film. (b) Infrared photograph showing the underlying venous structures.

frequently requires general views and close-ups to be taken in rapid succession with the minimum delay. Extension tubes for this purpose have now become obsolete due to the amount of time necessary for changing over tubes in order to alter the magnification ratio. The reproduction ratio may be read directly from a scale marked on the bellows unit and this may be recorded on the request card for future reference. This scale rotates so that the reproduction ratios are given on each of the four sides of the scale corresponding to the lens in use. By depressing a lever on the bellows unit the camera may be rotated from a horizontal position to the vertical. This is extremely useful when taking "half-frame" pictures, which are often requested so that both pre-operative and post-operative results can be shown on the same slide. (See Fig. 20.)

In order to establish correct exposure on location for a given flash unit and film speed combination, the f/number to be used for a given magnification has been marked on the bellows unit for quick reference. The Leicaflex system has stood up to the strain of constant use and produces excellent image quality. One complaint of the system is its excessive weight with the bellows attached, which is found to be especially uncomfortable when held for any length of time. The double cable release provided, in order to retain the automatic diaphragm facility, is easily broken. The author now uses a Japanese double cable release, which is much more flexible, stronger and about half the price! The camera is synchronised at 1/100 s for electronic flash, which eliminates subject or camera movement caused by bright modelling lights at longer shutter speeds (other cameras are often synchronised at 1/60 s or less). The Leicaflex system is comprehensively discussed by Crawley (1965a, b) and the improved version Leicaflex SL is reviewed by Crawley (1968a, b, c, d).

The more recent introduction of the Novaflexar offers a cheaper alternative to the Leicaflex system (Haworth, 1972). The Novaflexar consists of a short mount 105-mm automatic bellows lens with an aperture range of f/4-f/22. When used in combination with the auto-bellows unit, it gives a focusing range of 22·5 cm to infinity and a maximum magnification of 0·75 times. Automatic stopping down of the diaphragm is achieved by pressure on a central trip bar on the bellows: this does away with the need for separate cable releases. It is, however, necessary to open up to full aperture manually after each exposure. Adaptors can be obtained for fitment to a large range of cameras, such as Canon (F, FT, FX), Edixa (-mat) Reflex, Mamiya Sekor, Minolta SR, Miranda, Nikon, Nikkorex, Nikormat, Olympus FTL, Pentacon, Pentax, Practica, Yashica and a number of other makes. It is a very versatile piece of equipment and first trials suggest that it has a number of advantages over the Leicaflex. The quality of image produced by the lens would appear perfectly adequate for most medical applications.

(c) *6 × 6 cm single-lens reflex.* The 6 × 6 cm ($2\frac{1}{4}$ in square) format provides a negative of adequate size which is capable of producing good quality prints, providing *reasonable* care is taken when handling and processing the negatives. Simple blocking out and the occasional retouching is also possible with this size of negative. There are two main reasons for choosing 6 × 6 cm in preference to 35-mm for routine clinical photography in black and white. One is that a far greater amount of precision and care in handling is necessary with 35-mm in order to achieve good quality prints without marks and blemishes. Since the skills of assistants vary, expecially under pressure in a busy department, this precision is not always guaranteed. The second reason, and in the author's experience, a most important one, is that the viewfinder image provided by the 6 × 6 cm camera is of sufficient size to allow accurate positioning of the subject within the negative area. This is extremely important for serial record work and even more so since the camera is hand-held and the subject is often on the move continuously. Another small practical advantage of the 6 × 6 is that roll-film cassettes are changed in far less time than the re-loading of 35-mm cassettes. This has on a few occasions been of importance when photographing in the operating theatre.

A roll of film can be processed and printed in far less time, with greater ease, than can the equivalent number of sheet films. The saving in film cost alone would, in a very short time, pay for the difference in capital outlay between 6 × 6 cm and a "large-format" camera (Rogers, 1969). Roll film costs approximately one-third per exposure compared with 5 × 4 in film.

Exposures can be taken in rapid succession whilst "following" the child as he moves and coupled with the fact that the photographer maintains immediate contact with the patient all the time, the 6 × 6 cm used hand-held is far more convenient than larger-stand cameras. A number of 6 × 6 cm systems are available and most are discussed by Crawley (1965c; 1966a; 1967; 1968e) and Mannheim (1966a, b). Other roll-film systems such as the "ideal format" 6 × 7 cm Asahi Pentax, which gives 10 exposures on 120 and 20 exposures on 220 roll film, have now become available. The Pentax looks just like an enlarged 35-mm single-lens reflex and is perhaps limited by this fact, since it is loaded in the same way and does not have interchangeable magazines. There is no doubt that the 6 × 7 cm format is a big challenge to the 6 × 6 cm, since it is claimed that the former gives more than 40% more useable film area than the latter, at a loss of two exposures on the same 120 film. The recent introduction of the Mamiya R B 67 which is a 6 × 7 cm format having not only interchangeable magazines but also a revolving back offers an even greater challenge to the well established 6 × 6 cm systems. Whilst it is impossible to recommend any particular make of camera as being the "best", especially since

FIG. 15. Complete camera system for full-length clinical pictures to close-ups (1 : 1). 1. Carrying strap; 2. Pistol grip; 3. Close-up lenses; 4. 55-mm extension tube; 5. 21-mm extension tube; 6. Camera with 120-mm lens, lens shade, and 90° pentaprism viewfinder; 7. Cut-film holder; 8. Spare 12-exp. 120 film magazine; 9. Spare films; 10. Lens shade; 11. Ring flash adaptor; 12. Film sheath; 13. 80-mm (standard) lens.

developments take place so rapidly, the author decided to discuss the Hasselblad system with which he is most familiar.

    The above system is comprehensively discussed by Planath (1965), in which he illustrates its advantages for medical photography. The Hasselblad system is conveniently packed into a small carrying case for taking to the wards and other departments and this is illustrated in Fig. 15. The

system in current use comprises a Hasselblad 500C camera body with 90°
pentaprism viewfinder and straight-handled pistol-grip, which does not
require a cable release. This is used in preference to the anatomical grip
which is found to make the wrist ache when holding the camera for any
length of time. Rapid film-winding cranks are available, but the standard
winding knob is found sufficient for most purposes. Magazines capable
of taking as many as 70 exposures are available, but in practice 12-
exposure magazines are found to be more convenient. Two 12-exposure
magazines are used; one in position on the camera, the other loaded ready
for change-over. Two bayonet fitting, quick-release lenses are used. One
is a standard 80-mm Zeiss Planar f/2·8 which stops down to f/22, is
synchronized from 1 s to 1/500 s for electronic flash, and focuses down to
0·9 m (3 ft). This lens is used mainly for para-medical photography and for
those clinical photographs where space and height restrict the use of a
longer focal length lens. The other lens, which is used for *nearly all* clinical
photographs, is a 120-mm Zeiss S-Planar f/5·6 which stops down to f/32
(some later models stop down to f/45). This lens is also synchronised from
1 s to 1/500 s for electronic flash and focusing is from 0·9 m (3 ft) to
infinity. On most occasions this lens is used in combination with a 21-mm
bayonet-fitting extension ring which covers a subject area of approx. 12
to 6 in² allowing a range in practice from an adult full-face (to include the
neck) down to a half-face area of a small child. A 55-mm extension tube
is used for more close-up views, such as intra-oral photography and both
the 55-mm and 21-mm tubes can be used together to give even higher
degrees of magnification. Table I gives the range of subject areas covered
by the above extension tubes along with other practical data.

The above lenses are each fitted with a "quick-focusing" handle for
speed of focusing and a square lens-hood is always used on each lens to
reduce flare, while at the same time providing a convenient platform on
which to rest a portable flash head when on location (see p. 192). A
Hasselblad ring flash can be fitted to either lens but the author uses another
make which is far cheaper. Although the S-Planar 120-mm lens is a special
purpose lens (denoted by the prefix "S") designed to give its optimum
performance at a reproduction scale in the region of 1 : 10, it produces
very good results throughout the range used. This has been achieved at the
expense of a large maximum aperture. In practice the 120-mm lens is a
more convenient focal length than that of the 150-mm Zeiss Sonar,
especially since studio length and space on location are limited.

One disadvantage of the above camera system is that repairs are required
more frequently and are more expensive than is normally the case with

large format cameras. This is to some extent to be expected, since the camera is a somewhat complicated piece of equipment, and because it is more portable, it is subject to damage more frequently. For those with very small budgets, *twin*-lens reflex 6 × 6 cm cameras could be considered, but in the author's view a good quality 35-mm camera would be preferable.

TABLE 1

S-Planar 120 mm lens

Lens distance settings (ft)	Extension tube used (mm)	Subject area covered (in) (approximately)	Exposure increase required in stops (approximately)
3	None	12	—
∞	21	$12\frac{1}{2}$	—
25	21	$11\frac{1}{4}$	$\frac{1}{2}$
15	21	$10\frac{1}{2}$	$\frac{1}{2}$
10	21	10	$\frac{1}{2}$
6	21	$8\frac{1}{2}$	$\frac{1}{2}$
3	21	6	1
∞	55	5	1
3	55	$3\frac{1}{2}$	1

The lens distance settings given in the first column of this table represent those which are most frequently used in practice. Specific areas of the body cannot be usefully related to these settings because of enormous differences in the size of children according to age or progress. The slight gap in the range covered between the two extension tubes can be filled by simply using 2 × 21 mm tubes together. It may be interesting to note that 1 : 1 (same size) reproduction can be achieved by using two 55 mm extension tubes together with the 120 mm lens set on a distance of 5·3 ft.

(d) *Large format (5 × 4 in and half-plate).* Most medical photographic departments appear still to use either 5 × 4 in or half-plate cameras for black-and-white clinical photography. These always need a tripod unless they are of the "press-type". Since the introduction of smaller format cameras, which can be used hand-held, the larger format is no longer suited to paediatric photography. In fact the author would suggest that the 6 × 6 cm (or 6 × 7 cm) single-lens reflex is the obvious choice for adult as well as paediatric clinical photography, and that larger formats would appear to have no advantage over them. Large formats are still needed in the department to cope with certain types of work, such as general photography of buildings and the like. For those who still use half-plate, it is perhaps worth while considering a small compromise by at least reducing down to 5 × 4 in, thereby saving approximately one-third on the cost of each film alone. This saving could be considerable when several thousand photographs are taken in a period of a year, especially when the quality difference is so small as to be hardly detectable. An even greater saving is possible between 6 × 6 cm and 5 × 4 in (see III.D1 (c)).

2. Lenses. When using smaller format cameras, greater demands are placed on the technical performance of the camera and lens, in order to achieve comparative quality to that given by larger formats. Lenses of the best quality available, within the financial limitations, should be used, since present-day emulsions are capable of reproducing the finest detail and separation of tones; limitations are generally due to the optical system. This latter point is worthy of mention because there is little value in having a *perfect* camera lens if prints are made, or transparencies are projected, using inferior optics. Crawley (1966b) mentions this point in his work on the components of image quality, where he also discusses the requirements of the lens, emulsion and developers. Therefore in practice it is far more desirable to have all lenses of comparable quality than to have a good camera lens while economising on "follow-up" lenses. Lenses of longer focal length than normal for the format should be used for clinical photography so as to avoid perspective distortion. Lenses having automatic diaphragms are now considered essential, particularly when the camera is used hand-held.

Zoom lenses would appear to be ideal for clinical photography, especially for operating theatre work, but after testing several, none came up to the standard required for routine work. Even with very expensive zoom-lenses, the author was surprised at the amount of distortion which occurred in his tests. In view of the vast difference in price between zoom lenses and other types, their purchase does not appear to be justified, especially since loss of image quality in terms of sharpness, and definition and coverage, are present even in the most expensive ones.

A special lens has been developed to overcome some of the above problems when used for relative close-up photography. The Medical-Nikkor Auto 200 mm f/5·6 lens achieves this by providing 11 reproduction ratio settings which give a range from 1/15th actual size to 3× magnification in combination with six auxiliary lenses, instead of having a conventional focusing range. This means that optimum performance is achieved at each of these settings. The lens incorporates its own ring-flash around the front element and correct exposure is accomplished by the setting of an automatic programme arrangement. Disadvantages of this type of lens are that the area covered is restricted and also that each change of magnification requires placement of the appropriate auxillary lens, which is then little different to adding extension tubes. However, this lens does give automatic exposure and is extremely useful for intra-oral photography, operating theatre work and other types of photography when the field area is of limited size. Crawley (1966d) discusses a number of its features in one part of his comprehensive coverage of the whole Nikon system.

However, until such time as zoom lenses are perfected and their prices reduced considerably, the short-mount bellows lens with automatic diaphragm is in the author's view the most suitable type for clinical photography. It is to be hoped that leading manufacturers, other than the makers of Leica, will develop an automatic diaphragm for their short-mount lenses to provide a choice; since many of them already have an extensive range of equipment which is only lacking in this one important feature.

E. Lighting

The type of lighting and the methods employed for lighting human medical subjects differ from those required for many other types of photography. The basic requirements of the light source used are summarized as follows:

(a) Sufficient light to allow short exposure times; thus avoiding unsharpness due to subject or camera movement.

(b) Sufficient light to allow small apertures giving maximum depth of field.

(c) Versatile and mobile.

(d) Dependable and safe.

In addition to the above, a modification to lighting technique is necessary in order to ensure standardization of all clinical photographs. This is particularly important since treatment of a large number of conditions, especially paediatric disorders, often extends over a period of many years and comparisons are frequently required to indicate progress. *Accurate* comparisons can only be made when strict standardized methods have been employed, and the following represent the basic requirements of the lighting method used.

(e) Standardization of the position of the light source(s) for easy and accurate repetition.

(f) Simple method for applying in a wide variety of situations.

Electronic flash is now used almost without exception for still photography of patients in black-and-white and colour, and provides a convenient source of light to meet with many of the above requirements. Specific lighting used for particular views is mentioned in section III.B. Other standard lighting procedures for clinical photography are demonstrated by Hansell and Ollerenshaw (1962). Lighting for cinematography is dealt with in section III.L. Bowen (1969) discusses the developments of electronic flash since the 1940's and Hall (1969) published a professional dealers' catalogue covering all portable and studio units available in the U.K.; technical specifications and remarks on each unit being given.

Apart from the following discussion of electronic flash and the mention in section III.L of light sources used in cinematography of patients, it is felt that most other types of lighting used in medical photography are employed in much the same way as in other photographic disciplines and are adequately covered in the literature to make inclusion here superfluous. Aspden (1959) surveys many of the principles and practical techniques of using electronic flash in industry and research, and Edgerton (1965) discusses many aspects of high-speed flash and stroboscopic flash photography. Lighting equipment of all types is discussed by Verbeek (1968) and light sources by Arnold *et al.* (1971). Keeling (1969a, b, c, d, e, f) gives an extensive account of the nature of light, properties of colour, light production and units, and of the many light sources available.

1. Studio electronic flash. A Strobe* electronic flash unit of 3000 watt–seconds total power is used for all clinical photographs taken in the studio. This unit has six outlets of which only four are routinely used. Two background lights each having fluorescent strip modelling lamps are placed *behind* and facing a white paper background. Each lamp is 5 ft in height and 6 in wide. They are placed approximately 4 ft apart and so angled that an area of approximately 6×4 ft is illuminated by the light passing through the paper; this area being found sufficient for most purposes. Two lamps are used for illuminating the subject and on most occasions these are placed on either side of the camera, as close as possible to it. Each has an independent modelling lamp which can be dimmed and for cooling purposes each has an electric fan which is started immediately the modelling lamps are switched on. A small ($7\frac{1}{2}$ in) reflector is used in preference to the more usual 15 in size so that the lamps can be positioned near to the camera. Perspex diffuser discs are fitted to each reflector to disperse the light evenly; at the same time, protecting the patient (see II.E). Each

---

* American authors use the word *strobe* to mean electronic flash, whereas "Strobe" as used above is the name of the manufacturer—Strobe Equipment Ltd., London.

lighting head is situated at the end of a 9-ft-long counterbalanced boom arm. All lamps are on stands fitted with wheels and electric power cables suspended from chains fixed to the ceiling.

By supplying 750 watt–seconds to each background lamp and 375 watt–seconds to each frontal light, a good balance is achieved between background and subject illumination. The resultant background density in the negative gives a good white in the final print, without noticeable flare and yet provides an off-white (slightly grey) background in a correctly exposed colour transparency.

The patient is normally positioned approximately 3 ft away from the background so that flare light reaching the subject, is kept to a minimum. Curtains may be used to mask down the background when taking close-up views. Black-and-white exposures on FP4 vary between $f/32$ for facial and close-up views and $f/16$ for full-lengths ($f/11$ for dark-skinned subjects). Kodachrome II allows an aperture range of $f/16$ to approximately $f/6\cdot3$ (i.e., half-way between $f/5\cdot6$ and $f/8$). Whilst electronic flash heads on boom arms, fitted to stands on wheels, are indispensable when photographing sick children, an improvement would be to have lighting suspended from the ceiling as is common in television and film studios. This would increase the usable floor area considerably, allow the electric cables to be placed out of the reach of most children, and the lamps could be attached to the camera with little loss in mobility. Such a system is currently under consideration for the author's department.

2. Portable electronic flash. Since a large number of photographs are taken on location in the wards, operating theatres and post-mortem room, it is necessary to have portable lighting equipment. Portable electronic flash units provide a convenient source of light, are independent of mains electricity, and give adequate illumination for most needs. Since the introduction of the "Honeywell (U.S.A.) quench-tube" system (Tydings, 1965), a number of "computerized" portable flash units have become available. These give correct exposure automatically for a given film speed by a sensor in the flash head, which reads the amount of light reflected by the subject and then quenches the unit when sufficient light has reached the film. This type of unit is especially useful for ward and theatre photography, since speed is essential and enables attention to be given solely to the subject area in view; correct exposure being guaranteed once the initial setting on the flash has been completed. An added advantage of the automatic flash is that it offers the possibility of using the "differential focus" technique, allowing isolation of the main area of interest by throwing out of focus those areas not required. This is achieved by the use of a wide aperture; the flash being quenched when sufficient light has reached the film. This facility is not easily available with non-automatic units since they generally give out too much light for a wide aperture to be used and to reduce the light sufficiently would require the use of a number of "baffles". Differential focus technique is found to be most advantageous in para-medical work, although on occasions it may prove useful for obtaining certain clinical photographs (see III.I). The first computerized electronic flash unit to be introduced into this country was the Auto-Strobonar 660 made by the American Honeywell Corporation. This was reviewed and tested by Bowler (1966). Since that time numerous units have become available, nearly all of which utilize the same basic principles. Perhaps the best known are the Rollei E34C, reviewed and tested by Maude (1971a) and Hall (1971a), with a claimed guide number of 110 on full-power setting and 73 on half-power for 50 ASA films. The other well known unit is the Mecablitz 202 with a claimed guide number of 130 on full-power and 92 on half-power for 50 ASA films. This unit is reviewed and tested by Maude (1971b) and also by Hall (1971b). Since the duration of the flash may be quite long when using small apertures, care should be taken to avoid using very fast shutter speeds. For instance, the longest flash duration on the Mecablitz 202 when set on full-power is 1/250 s (Hall 1971b).

In order to meet the constant demand for location photography, two portable units are considered essential. The author uses a Mecablitz 202 and a Mecablitz 502 non-automatic. Both units are fitted with "wet-cell" batteries in preference to the dry-cell ones, because the state of charge can be seen at a glance in the former; no indication being given by the latter. Both units are kept on charge throughout the day and switched off each night. By using them alternately they are both kept in a good state of charge. A useful feature of both the Mecablitz 202 and 502 is that each have an extension socket which allows a ring flash to be used (see p. 192).

Another portable unit, the Braun F800, can be used when a little more power is needed. It has a guide number of 150 on full-power for 50 ASA films and is found on test to be almost exactly one stop faster than the Mecablitz 202. Most units that have been tested by the author are given lower guide numbers as a result of these tests than those claimed by many of the manufacturers. Gehret (1967) discusses many of the problems associated with the use of electronic flash and he also gives a practical formulary which is found to be indispensable for evaluating the practical variations between different flash units.

Portable flash is not only found useful for location work but also in the studio for taking close-up pictures such as intra-oral views of the teeth and palate (see III.B2 (e)). A valuable feature of most portable flash heads is that they are a convenient size for resting directly on top of the lens-hood. This position gives adequate illumination of the full area of the subject, and at the same time gives a very clean background by virtue of the fact that the shadow cast by the subject is so small as to be almost unnoticeable (see Fig. 5). When holding automatic flash heads in this position, care should be taken to avoid covering up the sensing device which is easily done by the flash cable or the finger.

3. *Ring illuminants.* A ring-flash provides a convenient source of light for illuminating cavities and certain small lesions. It is in practice used most frequently for intra-oral photography of the teeth and palate in both black-and-white and colour, and occasionally when taking close-up colour transparencies at an operation. Although this type of illuminant is said to produce flat shadowless results, it is found to give in practice more than sufficient contrast for black-and-white work under the conditions used by the author: for colour slides it is an ideal source.

The availability of ring-flash units is limited to only a few which are suitable for professional use. Hasselbland make a "ring light" for use with their cameras and it is possible to use it with several different flash units. However, other ring flashes such as the Multiblitz and Minicam can also be fitted to other flash units while at the same time being cheap in price by comparison. The Minicam which is reviewed fully by Haworth (1969) is designed to fit over a wide range of lens mounts from 48- to 60-mm by using an adaptor supplied with the flash. It can be used in conjunction with a Mecablitz 502 and is conveniently screwed directly on to the inner thread of the lens-hood of the 100-mm Macro-Elmar lens (see III.DI (b)). One complaint of this flash unit is that when unscrewing it from the lens, the internal threads holding the flash together tend to loosen which can result in parts of it falling on to the floor. For this reason it is not an ideal flash for photography in the operating theatre unless it is first glued together! A Multiblitz ringflash adapted to fit the Mecablitz 502 is used connected to the S-Planar 120-mm lens of the Hasselblad by means of a bayonet adaptor ring. The practical convenience of the above two-ring flash units is limited by the fact that the Mecablitz 502 and 202 have different types of sockets for extension head fitment, even though they are both made by the same manufacturer! It is necessary on most of those units used in practice to fit a roll of thick black paper around the inner diameter of the ring flash to stop stray light from the flash passing into the lens. An improved type of ring flash developed by Morgan (1969) and now called the "Texturlite Ringflash" offers a challenge to the accepted type. The Texturlite has four separate flash tubes, each with a modelling light, and all can be switched independently to give several combinations of lighting effect. The overall shape of the unit is square and it is claimed that by using an interchangeable backplate, the flash head may be fitted to the lens mounts of all known 35-mm, 6×6 cm and large format cameras. As mentioned in section III.D2, Nikon produce the Medical-Nikkor Auto lens which incorporates a ring-flash around the front element. This is a particularly useful system, ideal for close-up work, and is to be recommended when one already uses Nikon equipment: otherwise it is an expensive "extra".

4. Bounce flash. The technique of "bouncing" light off the walls or ceiling, is useful when a flat even distribution of light is required without distracting shadows. In practice this technique is most often used for para-medical situations when photographing general areas inside rooms and for the photography of objects that have reflective surfaces, such as surgical instruments. On occasions, photographs of sick children in incubators are taken using the bounce method, to avoid removing or lifting the perspex lid. When photographing children in a room setting or treatment area (such as in the physiotherapy gymnasium) the bounce flash technique is always preferred. Working out the correct exposure requires a degree of experience because the dimensions of the room, colour and darkness of walls and ceiling, and the distance of the flash from the subject (via the ceiling or wall) are factors which have to be calculated. Automatic flash units now eliminate the need for these elaborate calculations and the recent introduction of "umbrella" fitments now offers a more controlled method of bounce lighting. By using umbrellas with modelling lamps incorporated in the lighting head, one is able to see the lighting effect prior to exposure; correct exposure being determined by the use of a flash meter. Umbrella attachments are found cumbersome in small rooms and are not readily accepted by some medical personnel in certain clinical areas.

A number of these types of flash heads are now manufactured for use independently, or in combination with other units; in the latter case, only one head need be connected to the camera with a synchronization lead, as the others can be fired automatically by means of a slave unit attached or fixed to the flash head. The author uses two Courtney Solapak 3 units and each can be set to give 100, 200 or 300 J. They are found to be very dependable, but the method of fixing the bracket which takes the umbrella is *exceedingly poor*. Their use remains limited until present investigations produce a more suitable method of fixing.

Another model, the Courtney Sola 4 has recently appeared on the market (Maude, 1972) and offers a number of additional features to the Solapak 3. These include increased interchangeability of reflectors, higher output (400 J approx.), and half and full power settings which also alter the modelling lights accordingly. The Bowens Monolite 400 flash unit which recently came on the market and is reviewed by Maude (1971c) would appear to be an improvement on others available, and forms only a small part of a very comprehensive studio electronic flash system (Anon, 1965).

F. Film materials

1. Black and white. Orthochromatic films have been used for a number of years in medical photography. This type of film is preferred because of the increased contrast gained in skin detail, and dramatic emphasis of local lesions in skin disorders. Although greater contrast is achieved by using orthochromatic, the range of brightnesses recorded in the final print bears little relation to that observed by the eye. This is because the film is insensitive to red and oversensitive to blue by comparison. Because of this relative distortion, its use is questionable as a clinical recording medium unless it is used in combination with a "control" panchromatic emulsion.

Panchromatic has the advantage that it records tones in a similar manner to the eye. Since the skin of young children, especially neonates, tends to have a very high colouring, the use of panchromatic film is even more desirable for paediatric photography. Evatt (1961) mentions the unnatural bronzed appearance of children's skin when photographed on orthochromatic. This often results in a blotchy and mottled appearance of the skin in the final print. For these reasons which appear to be little realized by many workers, the use of panchromatic film is virtually obligatory for photography of children.

FP4, 120 roll-film is used by the author for all black-and-white clinical photography and also for a wide variety of para-medical work. It is a medium-speed film which gives fine grain negatives of sufficient contrast with good "gradation". Whilst other types and other makes of film are available, the author found in a series of tests that FP4 best suited his needs. Combined with an acutance developer (see III.G), FP4 gives excellent sharpness and definition with good tonal rendition, especially considering its comparatively high emulsion speed. These findings were confirmed by Crawley (1968f) in which he discusses the properties of FP4 and the effects of acutance and fine grain developers on both roll and miniature sizes. A large number of black-and-white 35-mm slides are reproduced from old file negatives, which often include earlier half-plate negatives among them. The slides are produced on Ilford N4E 50 line film and processed in "contrast FF" developer. This results in a slide of adequate contrast with a good tonal range without the need to clear the highlights by rinsing in Farmer's Reducer, as is required by other types of film.

2. *Colour film.* Kodachrome II 35-mm (ASA 25) daylight type film is used for all clinical photography in colour. This type is chosen mainly for the consistency of its colour rendering, although the extra contrast gained by using good quality lenses reduces exposure latitude to very fine limits. Since all clinical photographs are taken using electronic flash of known powers, this limited exposure latitude causes little problem. However, for other types of work, mainly paramedical photography on location, Ektachrome X daylight type is used. This film is faster (ASA 64) than Kodachrome thus allowing smaller apertures to be used, and it also gives almost a full stop in exposure latitude. When an even faster film is needed such as when taking transillumination photographs of the head (see III.C). Ektachrome High Speed is used. The colour rendition given by a colour film is often a matter of preference, as can be seen from the above selection of films. For this reason the author would like to make it clear that the above films are those used by him and he does not suggest that other types and makes are not just as suitable. A list of all reversal and negative colour films which were manufactured for amateur and professional still photography and cinematography in the 30-year period following the introduction of the first Kodachrome film in 1935 was published by Koshofer and Hübner (1965). This list was updated five years later for Florstedt (1970) and has now become a unique collection of work.

Since the vast majority of colour slides produced are clinical subjects, 36 exposure lengths are used to avoid too frequent changes of film cassette. The other types of colour film are stocked in 20 exposure lengths, which is found an economical number for most types of work undertaken. Several rolls of each type are kept in the carrying case for each camera; the rest of the stock being kept in a refrigerator.

G. *Processing*

As mentioned in section III.F, all black-and-white clinical and most paramedical photographs are taken on FP4, 120 roll-film. The number of 12-exposure films processed each day depends upon the amount of work, but is usually between one and four rolls in number. Films are processed in stainless steel spiral tanks. It is found that a single 35-mm, 36 exposure tank, and one each of the 120 size for taking one, two, or four films, provides sufficient combinations for most needs. Acutol FX-14, *acutance type* developer is used at a dilution of 1 : 10, and is found to give excellent image sharpness and definition combined with a good tonal rendition. The advantages of using this developer were confirmed by Crawley (1968f) in his tests on FP4 film with different types of developer which included the well established formulas of I.D.11 and D.76, in addition to Acutol. Apart from the increased quality which it gives, Acutol is found to be a most convenient developer because it is supplied in liquid concentrated form which is simply diluted with water and thrown away after use. This saves the bother of making up stock solutions which have to be replenished, and ensures standardized processing on each occasion.

The manufacturer's recommended development time for FP4 roll film in Acutol is $7\frac{1}{2}$ min at 68°F (20°C) diluted 1 : 10 with 5 s agitation every minute. Due to the rather "flat" lighting used for clinical work, development is extended to gain an increase in contrast. In order to reduce the overall development time, processing is undertaken at 75°F for $5\frac{3}{4}$ min, as opposed to the manufacturer's readjusted time of $4\frac{1}{2}$ min for 75°F. This gives negatives of sufficient contrast for printing on a normal grade of printing paper without any apparent loss of quality. Because acutance developers rely on adjacency effects which give maximum acutance with the *least* agitation as opposed to the fact that the greatest consistency of development is normally achieved by *maximum* agitation, a modified technique is necessary when using an acutance developer. As soon as the films are loaded into the processing solution, they are gently raised up and down for 10 s, by means of a rod passing through the centre of the spirals. This action dislodges any air bubbles that are present. Exactly on the minute, every minute, the tank is inverted while at the same time being rotated one-quarter of a turn and the tank is then returned to the upright position whilst being rotated through a further quarter of a turn. This method is a slight modification of the manufacturer's recommendation and is also very similar to the British Standard on agitation during development. It is only by working in this precise way that consistent results giving the maximum benefits of acutance development is achieved. Crawley (1969b) discusses many of the other factors which affect image quality.

All colour films are routinely sent to laboratories for processing as this is found to be by far the cheapest, most accurate and least time consuming method. However, the thought of patient records going outside the hospital causes some concern. Since a large number of medical institutions routinely send films to outside processing laboratories, it would seem that the setting up of a specialist *medical* processing laboratory would be an economical proposition and at the same time ensure that photographs were handled only in a medical atmosphere.

H. Studio

1. Location. The studio should ideally be situated in the hospital building near to the wards and operating theatres, with easy access to and from the out-patient departments and post-mortem room. It should be possible for stretchers, wheel-chairs and in some cases full-size hospital beds to be easily transported to the studio. This is necessary because on numerous occasions, specialist apparatus and equipment are needed at short notice to assist with the photography of the patient and are available only in the photographic studio.

Many illustration departments are situated in buildings adjacent to the hospital and many are to be found in basement areas. This often results in the patient travelling outside in the open or passing through underground tunnels, not originally intended as a patient thoroughfare, and often as not terminating in a flight of stairs. It would seem more appropriate in some cases if administration offices and other non-clinical departments were moved to the adjacent buildings so that clinical departments could be in their proper place.

Many aspects of the design of the studio in relation to the basic requirements for clinical photography are discussed by Engel (1961), Hansell and Ollerenshaw (1962) and later reports by Harrison (1969), Dove (1970), Broadberry (1971) and Burnard (1971) show many of the special features which have been included in a number of newly designed medical photographic departments.

2. Facilities for children. The photography of sick children requires a number of special studio facilities in order to meet with many of their particular needs. Special safety precautions are necessary (see II.E). The floor should be as clear and as clean as possible and should have a non-slip surface. Simple play items such as dolls, teddy-bears, building bricks and squeaker toys may be used to amuse the child, and assist photography by attracting his attention. The studio can be made more interesting to children by including a number of bright photographs on the wall, and by placing them strategically they attract his attention in the right direction when taking certain views. The studio must be kept warm because many children have to be undressed for photography and some, neonates in particular, need extra heat to help counteract their inability to maintain their own body temperature at a reasonable level. If the general heating system does not provide a consistent heat at the right temperature a small enclosed portable heater is particularly useful for providing local warmth where needed. A hand-basin with hot and cold running water is an essential item for dealing with the frequent nappy change, for rinsing articles taken from the sterilizing solution and for warming such items as cheek retractors or mirrors before placing them in the mouth. Several lighting power points suspended from the ceiling allow cables to hang out of the reach of inquisitive children (see III.E).

3. Studio furniture. A number of special items are found particularly useful for dealing with the variable requirements of children. A clinical couch measuring 35 in high, 59 in long and 21 in wide is used for babies and young children (see III.B) and is normally kept along a side wall; being placed in front of the transilluminated background when needed. Whilst special clinical chairs have been developed to assist with photographing patients (such as the "Westex" postural chair (*Anon*, 1969) a simple rotating stool which may be raised by turning, is found to be adequate for most purposes, and is used to seat many of the older children. A small dental chair is found particularly useful for keeping children in a set position when a number of standard views are required (see p. 163). A standing platform has been developed to provide a base on which the patient stands (see III.B). This consists of a wooden box 12 in high, 42 in long and 14 in wide. A hole at one end of the box takes a pole which has measurements marked on the surface facing the camera. This is shown in Fig. 16. A special table platform capable of being raised and lowered, fixed to a movable stand, is particularly useful for obtaining a number of views (see III.B), especially photographs of the hands and feet.

4. Backgrounds. The suitability of different types of background for use in clinical photography has been the subject of much discussion over the years. Marshall (1957) discusses many of the factors involved and mentions a number of different methods used. The first requirement of a background is to remove unwanted items from the field of view so that a clear record of the subject is achieved. There are many background systems on the market, most of which comprise several rolls of opaque paper in a range of widths and colours to suit individual requirements, supported on brackets fixed to the wall. The roll may be raised or lowered to form a continuous seam-free expanse, by means of a pulley-system.

The majority of clinical photographs are taken in black and white as routine records to be placed in the patient's notes. On occasions colour slides may also be required for teaching purposes. In order to simplify the procedure it is recommended that the background colour remains constant, for both colour and black-and-white photographs. This is essential

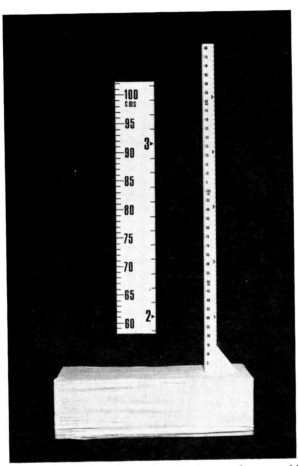

FIG. 16. This shows the full-length standing platform with removable measuring scale now marked in centimetres on the left side and inches and feet on the right (see insert). The measuring scale may be removed and placed beside the patient when he is photographed supine.

when dealing with young children in a busy department, as they easily become impatient if delays occur in order to change the background. The choice is basically limited to black, white, or an intermediary tone (mid-grey or a colour).

(a) Two of the most important disadvantages of a mid-grey tone are that it is virtually impossible to maintain the same level of grey in each print over a period; also the contrast between skin tone and background would generally be insufficient since skin represented in black and white varies between a medium grey and almost black. Mid-grey is therefore unsuitable for comparative records and the obvious choice lies between black or white.

(b) A good contrast is obtained between white-skinned patients and a black background, but not with dark skinned. In order to distinguish the dark skin and hair from the background sidelighting is necessary, and is the common practice where a black background is chosen. Since black material is not readily available on location (for instance on the wards), the alternatives are that the photographer carries a portable background when photographing outside the department, or that a different tone is accepted. In producing a rich black care must be taken (by masking of the negative) to reduce flare at the printing stage.

(c) One of the most usual problems created by white backgrounds is that of flare, caused by excessive reflection from the white surface into the camera lens, thereby reducing subject/background contrast. This problem is largely overcome by correct balance between the light reaching the subject and the light on the background, and reduced to a minimum by masking the background area so that as little as possible is displayed. Good contrast between skin and background is maintained in most cases since skin is generally represented in black-and-white photography as a mid-grey tone. White material is freely available and can be found on almost any location (e.g., wards) in the form of sheets, napkins, gowns, towelling, white coats ad infinitum. Whilst it is not suggested that white backgrounds should be used on all occasions regardless, (black may be used to advantage in some types of work, for instance, dermatology) white is considered more suitable on the vast majority of occasions due to availability, and clean, "clinical appearance". For these reasons, a white background is preferred for all routine record photographs; black being used only on rare occasions where it is essential for some special purpose.

I. Wards

Many photographs have to be taken in the wards due to the many problems peculiar to paediatric work. Apart from the need for portable equipment, a number of other special points arise.

With all requests for photography in the ward it is important to contact the ward sister or staff nurse by internal telephone. They are often able to suggest the best time to coincide with treatments, feeding, bathing and with other ward routines such as doctor's rounds. This procedure will avoid much inconvenience and misunderstanding caused by making arrangements with junior nurses and ward receptionists who are not in a position of authority. A nurse is generally present, to assist by removing clothing, moving the patient and holding him still in a particular position when necessary. As a general rule the photographer should not handle the patient, and he should always keep to the ward routine. For instance, it is common practice when photographing infectious cases to put on a clean gown and face mask before entering the patient's cubicle. The camera case is left outside and only essential items of equipment taken inside the cubicle. On no account should equipment be allowed to touch items in the room and after taking the photographs the gown is removed and hands washed before leaving the room. Any further precautions are usually indicated by the ward sister when the photographer first arrives.

To obtain full-length views of patients it is often necessary to stand on a stool, chair or even the bedside trolley. Since it is rarely possible to stand sufficiently high above the patient, full-length views are best taken from one side rather than from the end of the bed, thus avoiding a distortion of perspective. A standard lens may be needed because the space available is often limited. One flash head positioned above the camera, resting on the lens-hood, gives even illumination of the patient and casts an unobtrusive shadow (see Fig. 5).

A large percentage of those photographs taken in the ward are of children who have to be nursed in an incubator. It is sometimes possible for the child to be taken out for *brief* periods in order to take photographs, but this is done only with sister's permission. Some types of incubator have hinges along the length of one side allowing the lid to be held fully open. Others have a hinged door in the side of the lid which when opened, provides a sufficiently large aperture to allow photographs to be taken. In these cases a white napkin or towel placed behind the patient, serves as a backcloth and prevents reflection from the walls of the perspex lid. As a last resort bounce flash has been used on the rare occasion to achieve an essential picture of a very sick child (see p. 193). This technique makes it possible to obtain an acceptable record of the child *in situ* by photographing *through* the perspex lid and thus avoids the risk of endangering the patient.

J. Operating theatre

Most problems connected with photographing in the operating theatre are common to both adult and paediatric work. They are adequately covered by other workers including reports by Fletcher (1969) who discusses the availability of automatic theatre cameras, Greppin (1950) on safety aspects of photographing in the operating theatre, and Duguid (1971) on the use of "membrane mirrors" which enable photographs to be taken from a room situated outside the operating theatre. This new type of mirror was reported by Sansom (1965) shortly after its introduction (see p. 168). Other reports include those by Irvine (1964) on the problems associated with still photography in the operating theatre, Eriksson *et al.* (1971) on the dangers of using high intensity lamps for photographing procedures and Heiss (1961), who demonstrates a new spotlight for surgical cinematography. There is little need therefore to explain the basic techniques of theatre photography but one or two additional points should be mentioned. Generally, the operating field is proportionately smaller in paediatric than in adult surgery, and consequently the operating team crowds closely round the patient. In order to maintain a "safe" distance from the operating site it is necessary to use lenses of longer focal length than is normal for the format in use. The most suitable focal lengths for this purpose are in the range 90 mm—110 mm for 35-mm cameras and 120 mm—150 mm for 6 × 6 cm cameras. Longer focal lengths than these result in very long working distances which are not only inconvenient, but also require more powerful portable flash units than normally used. Sufficient height above the operating area is gained by using a tubular steel step-ladder. This has wheels which retract when weight is applied, so that it becomes stable and cannot move when in use. It also has side hand rails which are found to be most reassuring when leaning over the operating area! It is kept in the operating theatre suite for this purpose. On no account should a method of support be used which is in any way precarious. Since close-ups and general views are often required in rapid succession, a single lens reflex with short mount bellows lens such as the Leicaflex described in section III.D, offers a number of advantages over other types of equipment.

K. Gross specimens

Photography of specimens, a subject in its own right, is fully covered in the literature. Martinsen (1952) gives a review of methods used in the early 1950s in which he includes more than eighty references to other work. Many of the basic methods he mentions have changed little in the intervening years and Salthouse (1955), Marshall (1957) and Martinsen (1968) give further information. Martin (1953) discusses the care of specimens required for photography. However, a number of extra points are summarised as follows:

Infection: Special care is necessary when handling specimens which are fresh or partly fixed. They should *always* be handled using gloves and instruments, and treated as though capable of causing infection. Martin (1961b) discusses the precautions necessary when handling specimens, and the application of antiseptic solutions.

Scales: Millimetre or centimetre scales should always be included in the picture area to give an indication of size. These can easily be made in the department by photographing an accurate drawing or actual measure, and printing by contact or projection on to photographic paper, which after mounting on to card can be trimmed to size. When using a trans-illuminated background, the scale can be reproduced directly on to a glass plate (old 3 × 3 lantern slide) or lithographic film and sandwiched between glass.

Hand-held method: Since many specimens are photographed on location (generally in the post-mortem room) they are conveniently taken with the camera hand-held. The specimen is placed on an almost colourless matt surface (formica board) and photographed from above. A portable electronic flash-head is placed directly on top of the camera lens-hood. This position gives even illumination of the specimen, with the background devoid of shadow except for an unobtrusive thin, black line (shadow) which surrounds the specimen. Burgess (1975) demonstrates the use and advantages of this simple method as compared with other established techniques which require more elaborate set-ups. Whilst it is realized that this simple approach has a number of limitations, in particular the problem of specular reflections, it is suggested that the technique is suitable in a large number of cases.

L. *Cinematography*

A large number of medical conditions give rise to abnormal movements which can only be, or are best, demonstrated by cinematography. The basic technique, special equipment involved and many of the particular requirements of medical cinematography are discussed by Cardew (1961). Some of the problems associated with the cinematography of children are reported by Gessell (1946) and Stone (1952). Evatt (1961) mentions a number of conditions which are conducive to cine-recording in paediatric work. These include behavioural habits such as teeth-grinding, tongue chewing, eye-rubbing and head banging. He also mentions the use of film to record limitation of movement due to burns contractures, and abdominal peristalsis (see pyloric stenosis, section IV) among others.

Neurological disorders, with associated abnormal eye and body movements and orthopaedic gaits, represent the greatest proportion of those cases filmed at The Hospital for Sick Children. When making full-length teaching films to demonstrate new medical and surgical procedures, advance notice is required so that proper plans can be made. However, on most occasions a short length of film is all that is needed for *routine* cases. This is often taken at very short notice; either because the child is an out-patient about to go home (many have long journeys) or because a child is exhibiting an abnormal movement such as a fit which, if not filmed immediately, may not be repeated for some time, if at all. Many of these cases are filmed on the ward and require the use of portable equipment. Most hospital wards and operating theatres have special 13 A "safety" points, so lighting cables need a special type of plug. These plugs usually have a small cut-out section in the earth pin which allows a small bar to pass through it when the current is switched on, and thus prevents the plug being pulled out of the wall-socket by accident. To overcome delays in setting up equipment for filming on the ward, arrangements are being made to adapt one of the cubicles on one of the wards. By fitting it with overhead lighting controlled by a rheostat so that light intensity can be increased gradually, the patient may become accustomed to the brightness and yet still remain in his usual ward surroundings. This need has arisen as a result of increased interest in the observation of certain neurological disorders in which spasmodic movements occur, and which must be filmed with the least delay.

Most other cases are filmed in the photographic studio, and a large proportion require the gait to be recorded. The standard procedure for filming gait is to position the child approximately 18 in in front of a white background and to film him as he walks to and fro from one side of the room to the other. He is then filmed as he walks directly towards the camera and away from it. For this, an intermediary point of focus is chosen as a compromise since it is very difficult in practice to achieve continuous focusing to include the nearest and furthest points in sharp focus. Children who display abnormal body movements are often filmed from above whilst they lie on the floor. The same method of cushioning as for full-length still photography is used (see III.B) and a full-size sheet is spread out to provide a continuous white background. Eye movements are usually filmed with the patient seated and a clinician is often present in order to induce certain effects. A small squeaker toy or a stick which has a small brightly coloured ball at one end, is used to attract the child's attention in the right direction during filming.

The use of bounced lighting, achieved by having a number of lights fixed to a grid system on the ceiling (such as is used at St Mary's Hospital, London, (Burnard, 1969) is preferred because of the even light spread which it gives without shadows being cast on the background. This type of lighting is now under consideration at The Hospital for Sick Children to replace the present system which utilizes a mixture of tungsten lighting units; these include a 500 W spotlamp, two portable stands each taking three 500 W bulbs, and two quartz-iodine "cine-lamps". Most light sources suitable for cinematography are discussed by Keeling (1969e), (see III.E).

Kodachrome II type A 16-mm cine film is used for routine cases and these short lengths of film are tape-spliced together in large rolls for easy filing. Retrieval of films from the roll and editing are made easy by using an Acmade "Mineviewer" editing machine, which is electrically driven. This machine also gives a bright picture for viewing, has variable speeds from 1 frame to approximately 75 frames and has a fast rewind. One of the big advantages of using such a machine is that films can be wound easily on to plastic cores for storing purposes, and thus the need for numerous individual film reels is eliminated.

IV. PAEDIATRIC CONDITIONS

A. Introduction

The medical photographer needs to have a general knowledge of a large number of diseases. This knowledge is indispensable when deciding the type of photograph to be taken to illustrate a particular condition *properly*. Much of the basic information of value to those concerned with medical photography is discussed at length in the recent work of Boyd (1971), in which he includes a very useful section on prefixes and suffixes used in medicine.

It is most important that the photographer sees his work in the circumstances in which it is used so that maximum "feedback" is obtained. Unfortunately, he is rarely encouraged to attend clinical meetings and lectures where the deficiencies, or qualities, of the work can easily be seen; after all, this is the point of his work—to produce photographs which demonstrate a condition most accurately. A useful compromise, practised by a small number of departments is to view, within the illustration unit, the finished work before it is sent out, and the work is then discussed between the members of staff. This practice, of course, lacks the most important ingredient—discussion and comment from the clinician himself. Slides must show the condition adequately, and good photographic quality will help towards this end. Distortion, however produced, must be avoided since the clinician is not always fully aware of its presence.

The patient and the equipment used for paediatric photography have already been discussed, but many of the points made are of little value, unless considered in relation to the conditions which give rise to the need for photographs. An attempt has been made to include as many conditions as possible, so that this section may provide a reasonably comprehensive source for reference. Many of the conditions mentioned are fairly common and many may be seen in general hospitals. Others are rare, but have been included either because they present special problems to the photographer, or because they are "classic" paediatric conditions.

The unusual procedure of placing each condition in alphabetical order, rather than classification by group or system, was purposely chosen to provide a quick reference. Much of the reason for this lies in the fact that the name of the condition is usually known, but the non-expert does not always know under which system of the body to look for a particular disorder. The minimum photographic views required for each condition have been included.

While an attempt has been made to note conditions of main interest to the medical photographer, it has not been possible to make this list fully comprehensive. For those who need more detailed information about paediatric disorders, a selected bibliography has been included after the reference list at the end of the chapter.

B. Conditions

Achondroplasia. This condition which affects equally both males and females is caused by an abnormality in cartilage growth. A specific type of dwarfism occurs; patients have a relatively large head with the trunk of normal size in combination with short extremities, with limbs and their epiphysial junctions enlarged and prominent. The buttock is prominent and lumbar lordosis often present. Intelligence is normal. (See Fig. 6.)

Recommended minimum views are:

Full-length with measuring scale AP, left lateral and PA.

Acrocephalosyndactyly (see *Apert's Syndrome*).

Adrenogenital Syndrome (*Adrenal Hyperplasia*). A disorder of the adrenal glands resulting in pseudohermaphroditism. This condition is more common in girls than in boys; and in the former, the clitoris becomes enlarged resembling a penis, which requires surgery in severe cases. Growth of masculine hair on the face, trunk and arms may occur and the breast may remain undeveloped. In boys there may be prodigious muscular development, growth of thick pubic hair and enlargement of the penis, although the testes may remain small.

Rapid growth may take place in earlier years in both girls and boys but stunted stature is fairly common as an end result.

Recommended minimum views are:

Full length AP with scale, and close up of genitalia with legs parted, and a second view with the clitoris held back in the case of females and the penis held back to show underdeveloped testes in the male.

Albinism. A congenital condition caused by the absence of the melanin group of pigments of the skin, affecting the whole body. The skin is milky white, the hair is bleached, pupils appear pink (due to red retinal reflex becoming visible) and *nystagmus* may often be present

Recommended minimum views are:

Full-length with measuring scale, AP and PA: and if appropriate, both laterals. A close-up view of the eyes and cine film to show eye movements may also be necessary.

Alopecia (Baldness). Alopecia may be due to a number of causes such as congenital defect, trauma (due to burns, x-rays, etc.) or disease. Complete absence (alopecia universalis) or poor growth of hair may affect the scalp, eyebrows and eyelashes. Photographs of affected areas are taken.

Apert's Syndrome (Acrocephalosyndactyly). A congenital deformity resulting in a characteristic facial appearance which closely resembles *oxycephaly* and in addition there is severe *syndactyly* (webbing) of fingers and toes. Other features include hypoplasia of the maxillae, relatively prominent mandible, and anterior open bite (upper and lower incisors do not meet together). Mental retardation may be present. (See Fig. 6.)

Recommended minimum views are:

Face same views as for oxycephaly.

In addition both hands (palmar and dorsal surface) and AP teeth in occlusion (with lips retracted).

Asthma. True spasmodic asthma is an allergic condition. Common substances to which the child may be allergic are house dust from house mites, animals, feathers and pollens (especially grass).

Children with this condition tend to be nervous and highly-strung and for this reason should be given special consideration to avoid distress (see II). Allergies such as eczema, urticaria and hay-fever are often associated with the asthmatic child, who appears underweight, thin and with obvious chest underdevelopment.

Recommended minimum views are:

Full-length with measuring scale, AP and left lateral taken at yearly
intervals.

Asymmetry (see *Facial asymmetry*).

Ataxia-telangiectasia. An inherited, degenerative disease resulting in
mental retardation. Main features include telangiectasia (a group of dilated
blood capillaries) in the temporal region, bridge of the nose, ears, eyes and
other parts of the body. Both *nystagmus* and choreo-athetoid movements
are usually present and may be recorded on cine film.

Recommended minimum views are:

Full face AP, close-up of both eyes, and cine film of both eye and body
movements.

Bat ears (see *Ear deformities*).

Battered child Syndrome (Silverman's Syndrome). Occasionally photographs of children may be required to show injuries caused by trauma.
These injuries may be the result of the child being assaulted, and in many
cases are discovered by accident following an examination required for
some unrelated reason. X-ray studies usually show multiple traumatic
bone lesions in various stages of healing, which indicate that the child has
been assaulted on a number of occasions. Nearly all children suffering
from this condition are under three years of age and the majority are less
than one year (Chapple and Moore, 1964).

If legal action is involved, black and white photographic records will
be required as evidence. For this reason panchromatic film is used and
extra care is taken to ensure that the photographs are a true representation
of the condition. Any attempt to distort the appearance (by increasing
contrast by the use of an orthochromatic film or filters) is avoided so that
the evidence may not be challenged for its accuracy; especially since the
photographer may be required to substantiate these in court. Colour slides
are also taken to show subtle changes in colour that may not be differentiated in black and white.

Photographs of the whole body should be taken from the front, back
and both sides (to show the distribution of lesions), and close-up views of
each area involved, including areas which show obvious signs of fracture.

Burns. Burns occur frequently in children of all ages, particularly the
young and are often the result of a household accident. Most severe cases
are nursed initially in a separate heated cubicle with the patient lying
naked on a specially designed foam mattress. Children often have their
limbs tied to restrict their movement and to prevent them from touching
raw areas. Extensive areas of the body may be affected and this may cause

problems when taking full-length views due to the limited cubicle space (see III.I). Special precautions are taken to avoid the risks of infection and it is usual to wear a face mask before entering the cubicle. In the author's experience a few friendly words to the child on entering are extremely beneficial. These often reduce some of his fears of being hurt and at the same time remove his feeling of isolation produced by the strange clinical atmosphere. An immediate friendship is often established in this way and results in a greater amount of co-operation with the photographer throughout the many photographic sessions that follow this first visit.

In some cases it may be necessary to turn the child in order to obtain further photographs, but this is done only when it is essential. The excessive heat in some cubicles is liable to cause condensation of the camera lens and it is therefore, worthwhile to check the lens before taking photographs. In most cases a record is needed to show the extent of injury and sometimes to show the method of treatment such as skin-grafting procedures. Colour transparencies are usually taken from which colour prints are made for insertion in the patient's notes. The patient is photographed at frequent intervals in the early stages of healing to show progress and at longer intervals thereafter.

Cleft lip. A congenital fissure of the upper lip which may in severe cases extend to the floor of the nose. Often called "hare lip" due to its resemblance to the appearance of a hare. It is more frequent in males than females and may be either unilateral (more often the left side) or bilateral. Cleft lip may occur alone but is more often associated with a *cleft palate*. The lip is repaired at about the third month and sometimes requires further plastic surgery in the early teens for nasal correction. (See Fig. 10.)

Recommended minimum views are:
Full face AP, left and right laterals and "infra-nasal" views.

Cleft palate. A congenital defect of the roof of the mouth due to failure of fusion of the palatal processes. The opening in the soft palate may extend beyond into the hard palate exposing one or both nasal cavities. The condition may be unilateral or bilateral. Although a cleft palate may occur alone (as in *Pierre-Robins Syndrome*) it is more usually associated with a *cleft lip*. Cleft lip and cleft palate cases form a high proportion of cases which are sent to photography for routine follow-up studies. (See Fig. 17.)

Recommended views are:
Full face AP, left and right laterals and palate.

Club-foot (see *Talipes*).

Coeliac Disease. A chronic condition of early childhood caused by the failure of carbohydrate and fat metabolism due to an intolerance to the protein in wheat and rye flour. This gives rise to an enlarged abdomen, with general wasting. Loss of fat is seen in the buttock and a "pinched" face with sallow complexion is common if the disease is allowed to progress.

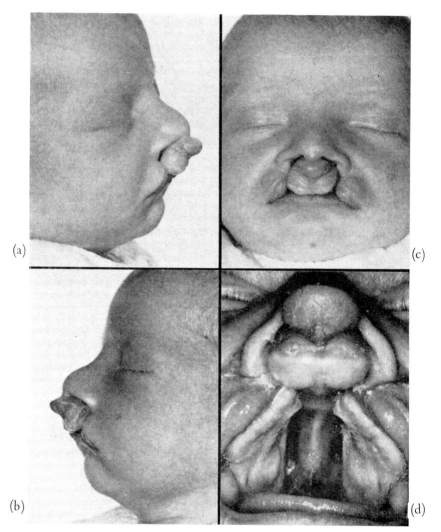

(a)

(c)

(b)

(d)

Fig. 17. The four standard views for cleft palate cases. (a) Right lateral; (b) Left lateral; (c) Anterior; (d) Palate.

Recommended minimum views are:
Full-length with measuring scale AP, left lateral and PA; and AP full-face (face in colour to show complexion).

Congenital dislocation of the hip (C.D.H.). C.D.H. is due to poor development of the acetabulum and in older children results in the thigh being held in partial flexion, widening of the perineum and asymmetries of the buttock, groin and ankle creases. Lordosis in later stages of the condition and a waddle gait are often present.

Recommended minimum views are:

Early stages: Full-length prone and supine.

Later stages: Full-length AP, PA and left lateral and cine film of gait.

Craniofacial Dysostosis (see *Crouzon's Disease*).

Craniostenosis. This deformity of the skull results in a narrowing of the top of the head. *Exophthalmos* and *strabismus* may also be present.

Recommended minimum views are:

Full head AP, both laterals and PA.

Cretinism. This is a congenital condition caused by lack of thyroid secretion and is successfully treated in most cases by regular doses of thyroid extract. The condition is typified by a "pig-like" appearance of the face, with heavy eyelids, squat nose, thick lips, enlarged and protruding tongue. Patients are short in height, with thickened limbs, broad stumpy fingers and frequently have a protruding abdomen with an umbilical hernia. (See Fig. 6.)

Recommended minimum views are:

Full-length with measuring scale AP and left lateral; AP full-face, and hands (dorsal aspect).

Crouzon's Disease (*Craniofacial Dysostosis*). A congenital deformity of the head consisting of a skull indistinguishable from *oxycephaly*, with marked bilateral *exophthalmos*. Other features include hypoplastic maxillae with *prognathism*, a beaked nose and anterior open bite (upper and lower incisors do not approximate). *Hypertelorism* may be present. (See Fig. 6.)

Recommended minimum views are:

Full-face AP (with measuring scale) and both laterals.

Cushing's Syndrome. This condition in children is typified by obesity, abnormal distribution of hair, atrophy of the genital organs, stunted growth and a facial appearance which is commonly described as "moon-face".

Recommended minimum views are:

Full-length AP and left lateral with measuring scale and AP full-face.

Cystic Fibrosis (*Fibrocystic disease of the pancreas*). A relatively common condition which may affect more than one child in a family. It is thought to be caused by an abnormally viscid mucus. There is pancreatic fibrosis which results in a failure to produce external pancreatic secretion. This gives rise to the typical distended abdomen. Bronchiolar obstruction results in over filling of the lungs, areas of collapse and bronchial infection.

Recommended minimum views are:

Full-length with measuring scale, AP and left lateral (repeated at six-monthly intervals).

Cystic Hygroma. This is a soft fluctuant tumour of the lymph glands which usually appears in the neck but may also develop in the axilla or groin. Photographic views vary according to the site of the tumour.

Down's Syndrome (see *Mongolism*).

Dupuytren's Contracture. Bending of one or more fingers due to contracture of the palmar fascia of the hand.

Recommended views are:

Palmar and dorsal aspects of both hands and palmar view with fingers clenched, extended and lateral extended.

Dwarfism. Arrest of growth which may be due to endocrine, genetic or renal disorders. Some of the conditions in which dwarfism is associated are discussed elsewhere. See: *Cretinism, Turner's Syndrome, Achondroplasia, Renal Rickets, Coeliac Disease* and *Cystic Fibrosis.*

Ear deformities. There are many malformations of the ear which may be congenital or acquired, that require corrective surgery. Photographs are generally taken before surgery to record the condition and afterwards to demonstrate the result. Deformities include conditions such as protruding ("bat") ears, "lop-ears", accessory auricles and absent ears. Most of the deformities require AP, both laterals and PA views, although on some occasions a single close-up view may be all that is required. Deformities may be unilateral or bilateral. (See p. 169.)

Encephalocele. An encephalocele is a congenital protrusion of the meninges through a gap in the cranium, and consists of a sac filled with cerebro-spinal fluid and brain tissue. The sac varies in size from small to very large (it can even be larger than the head itself) and it may appear on the back of the head (occipital encephalocele) or anteriorly, where it may protrude into the naso- or oro-pharynx. Small ones are photographed to show posterior and lateral aspects; usually only lateral views are possible with large masses owing to difficulties encountered in moving the patient. Both anterior and lateral aspects are photographed in cases of nasal-encephaloceles. (See also *Hypertelorism.*)

Epicanthus. This is a congenital condition in which folds of skin are present over each inner canthus of the eye. The fold extends vertically downward between the upper and lower lids and results in an oriental appearance similar to that seen in Mongolian races.

Recommended minimum view is:

Anterior close up to include both eyes.

Epispadias. Epispadias is an abnormal development of the lower urinary tract and anterior abdominal wall affecting the penis and terminal urethra. Although the condition affects both males and females, it is more common in the former. In the male the urethra opens on the dorsum of the penis (opposite to *Hypospadias*) and the penis is short, broad and has upward chordee (ventral curvature of the penis). In the female the clitoris is split into two elements, each lying lateral to and a little behind the urethral meatus. In both sexes the rectum may be placed further forward than normal and umbilical or inguinal herniae are common.

An anterior close-up view of the lower trunk with the legs held apart is normally taken to show the deformity and a lateral view is included when necessary. The penis may have to be held (by gloved hands) in order to demonstrate the abnormal opening, and with females the surrounding skin may have to be held apart.

Erb's Palsy. Paralysis of the upper arm due to injury at birth. Usually only one arm is affected, which hangs limply from the shoulder, rotated inwards with the palm of the hand directed backwards and outwards.

A view of the arm and shoulder taken from the back and from the front will adequately demonstrate the position of the arm and palm of the hand.

Exomphalos (Congenital umbilical hernia). This is a congenital condition in which the internal mid-gut protrudes through the abdomen into a hernial sac. Extreme care regarding cleanliness should be taken since infection is easily caused. Dressings should only be removed by trained personnel.

Recommended minimum views are:

An AP and lateral view of the abdomen.

Facial Asymmetry. The face is never completely symmetrical since one side always differs in shape and size from the other. This fact is rarely noticed, but when this difference becomes obvious, the condition is given the name "facial asymmetry", and may be of congenital origin or acquired. Occasionally defects such as mandibular displacements and centre line anomalies give rise to a similar appearance which is then given the name "apparent asymmetry".

Recommended minimum views are:

Full-face AP both laterals, and superior view of head. (See also Fig. 8.)

Fibrocystic Disease of the Pancreas (see *Cystic Fibrosis*).

Gargoylism (*Hunter-Hurler Syndrome*). Gargoylism is a rare bone disease which produces characteristic features. These include a large head,

H

coarse facial features, squat nose (with almost constant nasal discharge) and a large protruding tongue. Flexion contractures of the knee and elbow are present along with lumbar-kyphosis and a distended abdomen due to an enlarged liver and spleen (also present in Morquio's disease). Patients are severely retarded mentally. Martin (1961c) describes the condition and demonstrates many of the photographic views required. (See Fig. 6.)

Recommended minimum views are:

Full-length AP and left lateral (often taken with the child in a sitting position) and full-face AP.

Gaucher's Disease. A disease in which fat is deposited in the reticulo-endothelial cells (Gaucher cells) resulting in a progressive enlargement of the spleen (and liver). More than one child in a family may be affected.

Recommended minimum views are:

Full-length AP with liver and spleen marked by the doctor in ink (usually a fibre-tipped pen is used) and left lateral.

Gynaecomastia. Excessive growth of one or both male breasts necessitating surgical removal in severe cases.

Recommended minimum views are:

AP and a left and right lateral of both breasts.

Haemangiomata. Haemangiomas are well-defined areas of discolouration of the skin due to an increase in blood vessels. They are mainly congenital in origin and can be divided into the following groups:

(a) *Naevus flammeus* or *Port wine stain.* This may appear on any part of the body but is frequently noticed on the face and neck. It consists of *flat* patches of discolouration which may be red or purple. It may be quite extensive. If they are above the eyes they may signify the presence of the *Sturge-Weber Syndrome* or intracranial *Angiomatosis.* Another syndrome associated with Port wine stains is the *Klippel-Trenaunay Syndrome* with overgrowth of bone.

(b) *Cavernous haemangioma* (*Strawberry mark*). These marks are *raised*, bright red and vary greatly in size. The speckling appearance has given rise to the term "strawberry mark". Most disappear without treatment within 5-6 years. Sometimes they extend into the subcutaneous tissue.

(c) *Spider naevi.* These are bright red vascular structures surrounded by a network of dilated capillaries. They arise after birth and may disappear without treatment. They may be associated with liver disease.

Photographs of haemangiomata (and other naevi) represent an important (and frequent) aspect of paediatric photography, especially as they give valuable information on the changing features of these lesions.

Photographs of local areas are taken in colour and where surgical treatment is involved, black-and-white routine views are also taken. When the face is involved to any extent, both left and right laterals are taken in addition to an anterior so that comparisons may be made throughout the period of treatment.

Hare lip (see *Cleft lip* and *Cleft palate*).

Hermaphrodite (see *Intersex*).

Hernia (see *Exomphalos* and *Umbilical hernia*).

Hirschsprung's Disease. A condition commonly seen in males in which there is massive distension of the abdomen caused by severe dilatation of the large bowel. Peristalsis may be demonstrated on cine film by gentle tapping of the abdomen.

Recommended minimum views are:

Left lateral of the abdomen and AP full-length.

Hunter's Syndrome (see *Gargoylism*).

Hurler's Syndrome (see *Gargoylism*).

Hydrocephalus ("*Water on the brain*"). Hydrocephalus is a condition in which there is an abnormal collection of cerebro-spinal fluid in the skull, resulting in progressive enlargement of the head and bulging of the fontanelles. Down-turning of the eyes producing the "setting sun" sign is typical of this condition and *nystagmus* is often present. The disease may be due to congenital malformation or may be acquired after birth as a result of chronic inflamatory diseases of the meninges (see *Spina Bifida*). Transillumination of the skull in conjunction with E.E.G. studies is rapidly becoming a useful diagnostic technique (see III.C).

Recommended minimum views are:

Full head, AP, both right and left laterals and PA views.

Hypertelorism. This is a congenital deformity resulting in a typical facial appearance. Major features include a broad nasal bridge with increased interpupillary distance. Patients are usually mentally normal. Many cases are associated with frontal encephalocele. (See Fig. 6.)

Recommended minimum views:

Full face AP (with measuring scale for follow-up studies) and both laterals.

Hyperthyroidism. Over-secretion of thyroxine due to an enlarged thyroid gland (goitre) resulting in *exophthalmos* (abnormal protrusion of the eyeballs). Patients are often thin. Tremor of the hands is sometimes present and this may be recorded on cine film. Since these patients are generally emotional and nervous, special care should be taken to avoid stress. The condition is more commonly found in adults.

Recommended minimum views are:

AP and left lateral of face and neck to show goitre, full-length AP and left lateral and cine film demonstrating tremor.

Hypospadias. Hypospadias is a malformation in which the external urinary meatus opens at some point on the ventral surface of the penis.

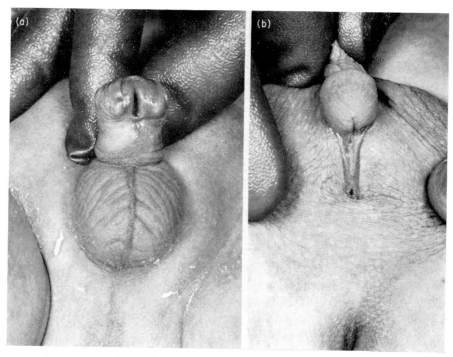

FIG. 18. Hypospadias; (a) Glandular (commonest type); (b) Perineal (rarest type). Gloves should always be used when handling the genitalia.

Downward chordee (dorsal curvature of the penis) is often associated with this congenital abnormality. The condition is normally divided into four different types according to the site of the opening; these being glandular, penile, penoscrotal and perineal. Photographs are taken with the penis held up (with gloved hands) to demonstrate the abnormal opening. The most common is the glandular opening; the rarest, perineal. These are shown in Fig. 18. A lateral view of the penis as it normally rests may serve to illustrate the degree of chordee.

Hypothyroidism (juvenile). Juvenile hypothyroidism is an acquired condition, similar in appearance to cretinism (*Congenital Hypothyroidism*) caused by atrophy of the thyroid gland. Severe cases may develop into myxoedema.

Recommended minimum views are:

Same as for cretinism.

Imperforate anus. A congenital condition in which the rectum has no external opening. In the majority of cases there is in fact a small opening

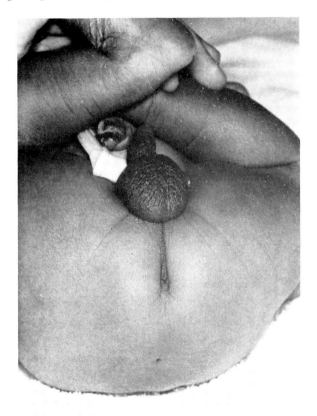

FIG. 19. Imperforate anus. The child's legs are held apart and up on the chest so that a clear view of the perineum may be obtained.

of some kind, either on the surface of the perineum, or vulva, or internally. This condition is corrected by surgery.

Recommended minimum views are:

Close-up of the perineum (the area between the anus and external genitals) with the legs apart and held up towards the chest. (See Fig. 19.)

Intersex (see *Adrenogenital Syndrome* and *Turner's Syndrome*). The term intersex is applied to patients whose sex characteristics are incompletely differentiated. Nixon and O'Donnell (1961) divides these cases into five clinical types:

(*a*) Female intersex.
(*b*) Male intersex.
(*c*) True hermaphroditism.
(*d*) Sex chromosome variations.
(*e*) Local genital defect.

(See also III.B3. Lower trunk.)

Keloid scars. Keloid scars are raised tumour-like growths of skin resulting from trauma. The cause is unknown but surgical incisions, insect bites or vaccinations may produce keloids in susceptible people. Keloids are more likely to occur in dark-skinned races than in those with fair complexions. Close-up views are taken to show the extent of the lesion by including an anatomical landmark in the picture.

Lipodystrophy. A condition in which there is a loss of subcutaneous fat in the upper part of the body, affecting the face and trunk and occasionally the arms.

Recommended minimum views are:

Full-length with measuring scale, AP, left lateral, PA and AP, full face. (See Fig. 6.)

Malocclusion. This is an abnormality in which the teeth do not bite together (occlude) in a normal way, and in some cases results from facial deformity. There are many causes. Photography of this condition is rather specialized and adequate coverage is given elsewhere (Rogers, 1971).

Recommended minimum views are:

Full-face AP and front view of teeth in occlusion with lips retracted.

Mandibular and Maxillary Protrusion (see *Prognathism*).

Mandibulofacial Dysostosis (see *Treacher–Collin's Syndrome*).

Meningocele (see *Spina Bifida*).

Microcephaly. This name is given to those patients who have an abnormally small head and cerebral hemispheres, and where the eyes are usually set close together. Mental retardation is usually present. (See Fig. 6.)

Recommended minimum view is:

Full-face AP.

Micrognathia (see *Pierre Robin's Syndrome*).

Mongolism (*Down's Syndrome*). A condition of congenital mental deficiency caused by an abnormal chromosome pattern which tends to be present in children born of parents who are approaching the end of their reproductive life. The typical appearance of a mongol includes such features as a small skull, broad flat bridge of nose, exaggerated epicanthic folds, protruding tongue, squat hands with short fingers, and eyes which slope upwards from the inner canthus. The condition is so named due to the resemblance to features present in the Mongolian race. (See Fig. 6.)

Recommended minimum views are:

A full-length with measuring scale AP, and a full-face AP and dorsal view of both hands.

Morquio's Disease. This is a rare, inherited disease of the bones which may affect several members of the family. Typical appearances are dwarfism, dorso-lumbar kyphosis, genu-valgum (knock-knee) and the sternum pinched forwards. The face appears normal.

Recommended minimum views are:

Full-length with measuring scale AP and left lateral.

Myelomeningocele (see *Spina Bifida*).

Naevi (see also *Skin*). Moynahan (1963) mentions the confusion about the use of the word *naevus* in the dermatological literature and he also states that most British authors use the word for many benign tumours of the skin, both of ectodermal and mesodermal origin. Further information can be obtained from a study of the literature, references to which are contained in the bibliography section at the end of this chapter.

Naevi are very common and a large number of cases are routinely photographed. Photographs are often taken in colour and the position and size of the lesion is shown by including an anatomical landmark in the picture. Black-and-white photographs are taken in addition to colour when surgical treatment is involved. The affected parts can vary in size from a small pigmented naevus or mole to extensive areas involving most of the body, such as is common in *Neurofibromatosis*. (See also *Haemangio-mata* and *Tuberous Sclerosis*).

Nephroblastoma (see *Wilm's Tumour*).

Neuroblastoma. This is a highly malignant tumour which generally causes death within six months. The patient should be handled as little as possible during photography and extreme care should be taken with the handling of specimens taken from patients suffering from this condition (see III.K).

A full-length AP with scale to show the general condition and an AP full-face to show secondary deposits in the orbits are usually taken. (See Fig. 6.)

Neurofibromatosis (*Von Recklinghausen's Disease*). A rare disease of skin pigmentation and of multiple benign tumours. Brown patches of pigmentation, varying in size, appear on the limbs, face and trunk along with painless pigmented fibromata distributed along the course of the peripheral nerves. The condition affects both children and adults.

Recommended minimum views are:

Full-length appropriate to the areas involved, with selected close up views.

Niemann-Pick Disease (associated with Tay Sach's Disease). An incurable condition found chiefly in Jewish children, in which the liver and spleen become grossly enlarged. Mental degeneration, spastic paralysis blindness and fits are often present. The condition is usually recorded on cine film.

Nystagmus. An involuntary, rapid movement of the eyeball often present in diseases involving the nervous system (see *Ataxia-Telangiectasia*). The condition is recorded on cine film.

Obesity. Obese (fat) children are normally treated by a strictly controlled diet, since this condition is usually caused by simply over-eating (Sheldon, 1962). They are photographed before, in the middle of, and on completion of treatment. The photographs show clearly the progress made, and copies are given to the parents by the doctor to encourage them to continue with the diet.

Recommended minimum views are:

Full-length with measuring scale, AP, left lateral, PA and an AP full-face. (Silhouettes of the lateral views are very useful as a demonstration of this condition.)

Osteogenesis Imperfecta. A congenital condition of unknown cause in which the bones are extremely fragile and liable to fracture. The long bones become bent and give rise to a striking feature where the thighs and legs bend to form a circle with the feet together. The teeth are generally soft and yellow in colour due to lack of calcification of the enamel. Growth is arrested and often the patient is unable to walk or stand. Extreme care is required when handling infants with this condition (due to the liability to fracture), and they are usually photographed on the ward.

Recommended minimum views are:

Full-length AP (child lying down), left lateral (older children in sitting position) and full head AP and left lateral.

Oxycephaly. A deformity of the head resulting in a narrow, tall skull and an abnormally high, protruding forehead which towers upwards and forwards over the brows. The eyes protrude (exophthalmos), due to the shallow orbits which are spaced widely apart (*Hypertelorism*). This condition is present in *Crouzon's Disease* and is also associated with *Apert's Syndrome*. (See Fig. 6.)

Recommended minimum views are:

Full face AP (with measuring scale for follow-up studies of interpupillary distance), and both profiles of head.

Pierre Robin's Syndrome (*Micronathia*). This is a congenital condition in which there is a *cleft palate* in association with an abnormally small mandible. The appearance is often improved by plastic surgery undertaken over a period of several years.

Recommended minimum views are:

Full-face, AP, left and right laterals, and view of palate.

Polydactyly. A condition in which more than the normal number of fingers or toes are present. (See also *Syndactyly*).

Recommended minimum views are:

Hands—palmar and dorsal aspects.

Feet—plantar and dorsal aspects.

Port wine stain (see *Haemangiomata*).

Precocious Puberty (see *Sexual Precocity*).

Progeria (*Hutchinson-Gilford Syndrome*). This is a rare condition in which the patient shows many of the characteristics of old age due to premature senility. (See Fig. 6.)

Recommended minimum views are:

Full-length with measuring scale, AP, left lateral and PA, full-face AP and left lateral.

Prognathism. Abnormal protrusion of the jaws which may be mandibular (of the lower jaw), maxillary (of the upper jaw) or affecting both. Prognathism may be present in a number of conditions, some of which are mentioned elsewhere in this section. (See Fig. 6.)

Recommended minimum views are:

Full-face AP, both laterals and anterior and lateral aspects of teeth in occlusion.

Pseudo-Hermaphroditism (see *Adrenogenital Syndrome*).

Ptosis. Ptosis, the drooping of the upper eyelids may be congenital or acquired. It can be caused by injury to the 3rd cranial nerve. An anterior (front) view of both eyes open is generally all that is required. (See Fig. 6.)

Pyloric Stenosis (*congenital*). This condition appears mainly in the first three months of life and is caused by an obstruction to the passage of food from the stomach, causing it to contract. These contractions (peristaltic waves) may then be filmed.

H*

Recommended minimum views are:

Full-length AP and a close-up of abdomen showing contraction by still photography and cine film when needed.

Renal Rickets (Vitamin-resistant Rickets: "Renal Dwarf"). A chronic kidney disease associated with delayed growth and marked rickets. A large degree of "knock-knee' 'and dwarfism typify the condition.

Recommended minimum views are:

Full-length with measuring scale AP and PA. (See also *Rickets*.)

Rickets (vitamin D deficiency). Due to lack of vitamin D, cartilage formation is abnormal and calcium is not deposited in the newly formed bone, resulting in the condition of Rickets. This deficiency leads to softening and irregular growth of the bones, causing bowing of the long bones ("bow legs") and enlargement of the epiphyses. The condition is treated by exposure to sunlight, ultraviolet radiation and an increase in vitamin D.

Recommended minimum views are:

Full-length with measuring scale AP, and PA. (See Fig. 20.) (See also *Renal Rickets*.)

Scoliosis. In this condition there is an abnormal curvature of the spine which may be due to *kyphosis*, posterior curvature of the spine (hump back); or *lordosis*, i.e., forward curvature of the lumbar spine.

Recommended minimum views are:

Full-length with measuring scale—AP, both laterals and PA; each view to be taken with the patient standing erect and also bending with an attempt to touch the toes (without bending the knees).

Sexual Precocity. The term *precocious puberty* is applied to conditions of premature sex development in which spermatogenesis in males and ovulation in females is present. Cases of premature sex development without corresponding spermatogenesis or ovulation are more common than precocious puberty and are referred to as *sexual precocity*. Common appearances are axillary hair, and enlarged genitalia in males, and in girls, enlargement of the breasts and increased pubic hair. Both male and female may show advanced bone growth.

Recommended minimum views are:

Full-length AP with measuring scale, close-up of genitalia, and in females anterior and both lateral aspects of upper trunk (see III.A3).

Silverman's Syndrome (see *Battered child Syndrome*).

Skin. The dermatological problems encountered in a paediatric photographic department are often of an unusual or advanced kind, especially those having systemic implications. The commoner skin diseases are either dealt with outside the children's hospital or are not referred for photography. There is a considerable amount of relevant literature to this specialized field. Many aspects of the photography of the diseased skin are discussed by Dent (1941), Fasal (1951), Gibson (1960), Hansell and Ollerenshaw (1962), Lunnon (1961; 1970), Moynahan and Engel (1962)

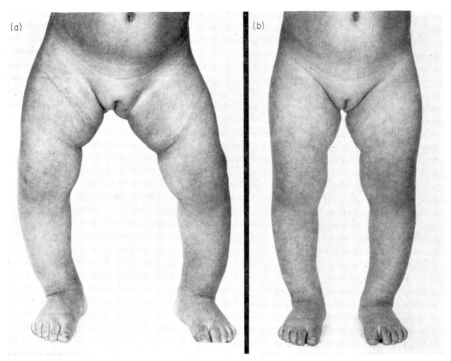

(a) (b)

FIG. 20. Rickets. (a) Pre-operative; (b) six weeks after treatment. "Before" and "after" photographs may be reproduced on the same 35-mm slide so that direct comparisons can be made. This obviates the need for two projectors.

and Salthouse (1958); and other more specialized applications reported by Bowes (1950), Gibson (1945), Lunnon (1959) and Sarkany and Phillips (1965).

When photographing skin conditions it is important to show the distribution of the lesion(s), their size, shape, contour, colour, consistency and any other physical sign which can be accurately recorded. Most conditions are best demonstrated by colour photography since *colour* is the most important of all the visual diagnostic signs (Lunnon, 1961).

Infrared, ultraviolet and fluorescence techniques used in combination with black-and-white control photographs may also prove useful in the recording of certain skin disorders. Filters and orthochromatic emulsions may also be used.

Standard views cannot easily be formulated for each condition owing to the fact that lesions may appear on any part of the body. Standardization mainly consists of close-up views of selected local areas and general views to show distribution. Normal lighting procedures (see III.E) are adequate for most general views, although a small single light source may be used to give a strong shadow for certain close-ups. A black background is recommended by a number of workers.

Spider Naevi (see *Haemangiomata*).

Spina Bifida. Spina Bifiida is a congenital deformity of the spine. In its simplest form (*Spina Bifida Occulta*) the deformity is hidden below the intact skin and its presence is usually indicated by a scar, dimple or a hairy patch on the back. A more serious form (*Meningocele*) is when a swelling which is filled with cerebro-spinal fluid protrudes through a congenital opening commonly situated in the lumbo-sacral region. In *Myelomeningocele* the spinal cord and nerve roots pass out into the swelling. *Hydrocephalus* is often a complication of this condition. The tumour is soft and covered by a very thin, almost transparent membrane, which gives little protection against infection. Photographs are usually taken on the ward whilst the child is in an incubator and only trained medical personnel handle the child.

Recommended minimum views are:

Close-up of tumour, posterior trunk and left lateral aspects. (See Fig. 11.)

Sprengel's shoulder deformity. A congenital elevation of the scapula which usually affects only one side of the shoulder.

Recommended minimum views are:

Head, neck and upper trunk, AP and PA.

Squint (see *Strabismus*).

Still's Disease. A form of rheumatoid arthritis in children, associated with enlargement of the lymph glands. Swelling of the joints of the knees, wrists, elbows, fingers and ankles are the main features together with an enlarged spleen. Special care must be taken when photographing children suffering from this condition, since movement of the joints can cause the child severe pain. Some children also develop partial blindness.

Recommended minimum views are:

Full-length with scale (with spleen marked in fibre pen) AP, left lateral and close-up of affected joints.

Strabismus (*squint*). A condition in which one eye deviates by a fixed amount from its normal direction. The condition may be divergent (eye turns outwards) or convergent (eye turns in towards the nose).

Standard views are:

Both eyes are photographed together in the nine positions of gaze. (See Fig. 9.)

Strawberry mark (see *Haemangiomata*).

Syndactyly. This condition consists of webbing of the fingers or toes (which may also include fusion of the bones). Syndactyly most frequently involves the third and fourth fingers and second and third toes. The condition is part of *Apert's Syndrome*. (See also *Polydactyly*.)

Recommended minimum views are:

Both hands, palmar and dorsal aspects and both feet, plantar and dorsal aspects.

Talipes (*Club-foot*). A condition which may be congenital or acquired and is caused by contraction of muscles or tendons of the foot. There are four types: *Talipes Equinus*—walks on toes only. *Talipes Calcaneous*— only the heel touches the ground when standing. *Talipes Varus*—walks on outer edge of foot. *Talipes Valgus*—walks on inner edge of foot. (*N.B.* It is fairly common for this condition to be a combination of *two* types eg: *Talipes Equino-Varus*, i.e., walks with toes and outer edge of foot touching the ground.)

Recommended minimum views are:

Lower limbs AP, left and right laterals and PA. (Babies AP and PA only.) With older children also cine film of gait.

Torticollis (*Wry neck*). Wry neck is a fairly common condition in which contraction of one or more of the cervical muscles (one side only) results in an abnormal position of the head. Asymmetrical development of the face may sometimes occur.

Recommended minimum views are:

Face, neck and shoulders AP looking straight ahead, to the left and to the right.

Treacher-Collins Syndrome (*Mandibulofacial Dysostosis*). An hereditary condition causing severe facial deformities including a symmetrical deformity of the mandible and ears. Appearance may be improved by long-term plastic surgery. (See Fig. 6.)

Recommended minimum views are:

Full face AP and both laterals to include ears.

Tuberous Sclerosis (*Epiloia*). This is an inherited neurological condition which may result in severe mental retardation. The typical skin lesion, adenoma sebaceum, appears symmetrically on the cheeks and alongside the nose. *Café-au-lait* spots may also appear on the trunk and extremities. Adenoma sebaceum also exhibits small tuberosities at the base of the great toe nail and thumb. (See Fig. 6.)

Recommended minimum views are:

Full face AP and close-ups of pigmented areas on trunk and extremities (all in colour).

Turner's Syndrome (*Gonadal Aplasia*). This is a rare chromosomal abnormality of unknown cause resulting in a characteristic appearance. External genitalia remain infantile and generally appear female although most children are found to be male by nuclear sex determination. Main features include considerable stunting of height, webbing of neck, cubitus valgus and a typical facial appearance. (See Fig. 6.)

Recommended minimum views are:

Full-length with measuring scale AP and left lateral; face and neck AP and PA.

Umbilical Hernia. A condition in which there is a weakness of the abdominal wall in the region of the umbilicus. Most of the hernias close within 1-3 years; otherwise surgical correction is required. The hernia bulges when the baby cries (see also *Exomphalos*).

Recommended minimum views are:

Left lateral of umbilical area and an AP.

Von Recklinghausen's Disease (see *Neurofibromatosis*).

Wilm's Tumour (*Nephroblastoma*). A highly malignant congenital tumour of the kidney. Usually surgically removed within the first five years of life. Special care should be exercised in handling (see III.K).

REFERENCES

Anon (1965). *Br. J. Photogr.* **112**, 970-992.
Anon (1969). *Br. J. Photogr.* **116**, 1105.
Adams, C. P. (1968). "Dental Photography." John Wright, Bristol.
Armstrong, K. F. (1964). "Aids to Anatomy and Physiology for Nurses. Baillière, Tindall and Cassell, London.
Arnold, C. R., Rolls, P. J. and Stewart, J. C. (1971a). *In* Spencer, D. A. (ed.), "Applied Photography", pp. 257-282. Focal Press, London and New York.
Arnold, C. R., Rolls, P. J. and Stewart, J. C. (1971b). *In* Spencer, D. A. (ed.), "Applied Photography", pp. 109-142. Focal Press, London and New York.
Aspden, R. L. (1959). "Electronic Flash Photography." Temple Press, London.
Bowen, K. S. (1969). *The Photographer* **4**, 172-175.
Bowes, K. (1950). *Photogr. J.* **90B**, 63.

BOWLER, S. W. (1966). *Br. J. Photogr.* **113**, 246-249.

BOYD, C. (1971). "An Introduction to the Study of Disease." Lea and Febiger, Philadelphia, U.S.A.

BROADBERRY, P. (1971). *Br. J. Photogr.* **118**, 862-863.

BURGESS, C. A. (1975). *Med. biol. Illust.* **25**, 159-166

BURNARD, J. H. (1969). *Br. J. Photog.* **116**, 1137.

BURNARD, J. H. (1971). *Br. J. Photogr.* **118**, 148-156.

CALLENDER, R. M. (1966). *Photogr. J.* **106**, 327-332.

CARDEW, P. N. (1961). *In* LINSSEN, E. F. (ed.), "Medical Photography in Practice", pp. 83-123. Fountain Press, London.

CHAPPLE, C. C. and MOORE, J. R. (1964). *In* NELSON, W. E. (ed.), "Textbook of Pediatrics", pp. 1387-1388. Saunders, Philadelphia and London.

CLARK, W. (1946). "Photography by Infra-Red." Wiley, New York.

CRAWLEY, G. (1965a). *Br. J. Photogr.* **112**, 202-212.

CRAWLEY, G. (1965b). *Br. J. Photogr.* **112**, 242.

CRAWLEY, G. (1965c). *Br. J. Photogr.* **112**, 1066-1069.

CRAWLEY, G. (1965d). *Br. J. Photogr.* **112**, 125.

CRAWLEY, G. (1966a). *Br. J. Photogr.* **113**, 504-520.

CRAWLEY, G. (1966b). *Br. J. Photogr.* **113**, 442-448.

CRAWLEY, G. (1967a). *Br. J. Photogr.* **114**, 376-379.

CRAWLEY, G. (1967b). *Br. J. Photogr.* **114**, 438-441.

CRAWLEY, G. (1967c). *Br. J. Photogr.* **114**, 462-472.

CRAWLEY, G. (1968a). *Br. J. Photogr.* **115**, 444-457.

CRAWLEY, G. (1968b). *Br. J. Photogr.* **115**, 492-500.

CRAWLEY, G. (1968c). *Br. J. Photogr.* **115**, 534-537.

CRAWLEY, G. (1968d). *Br. J. Photogr.* **115**, 558-570.

CRAWLEY, G. (1968e). *Br. J. Photogr.* **115**, 236-246.

CRAWLEY, G. (1968f). *Br. J. Photogr.* **115**, 822-829.

DENT, R. V. (1941). *J. Lab. clin. Med.* **26**, 1852.

DOVE, P. L. C. (1970). *Br. J. Photogr.* **117**, 1224-1226.

DUGUID, K. (1969). *Ind. comml. Photogr.* **9**, 40-42.

DUGUID, K. P. (1971). *Med. biol. Illust.* **21**, 73-74.

DUGUID, K. P. and OLLERENSHAW, R. (1962). *Med. biol. Illust.* **12**, 241.

DUPERTUIS, C. W. and TANNER, J. M. (1950). *Am. J. phys. Anthrop.* **8**, 27-47.

ECKHOFF, N. L. (1952). *Med. biol. Illust.* **2**, 240-246.

EDGERTON, H. E. (1965). *Photogr. J.* **105**, 237-247.

ENGEL, C. E. (1961). *In* LINSSEN, E. F. (ed.), "Medical Photography in Practice", pp. 19-61. Fountain Press, London.

ENGEL, C. E. and HANSELL, P. (1954). *Med. biol. Illust.* **4**, 66-72.

ERIKSSON, E., BARKMAN, P. E., FRASER, A., SON HOLMDAHL, M. H., MÅNSSON, S. and NILSSON, B. (1971). *Med. biol. Illust.* **21**, 211-214.

EVATT, L. A. (1961). *In* LINSSEN, E. F. (ed.), "Medical Photography in Practice", pp. 193-226. Fountain Press, London.

FASAL, P. (1951). *Med. Radiogr. Photogr.* **24**, 40-61.

FLETCHER, R. T. (1969). *Med. biol. Illust.* **19**, S36-S43.

FLORSTEDT, J. (1970). *Br. J. Photogr.* **117**, 14-20.

GAMSTORP, I. (1970). "Pediatric Neurology." Butterworths, London. Meredith Corporation, U.S.A.

GEHRET, E. CH. (1967). *Br. J. Photogr.* **114**, 204-219.

GESSELL, A. (1946). *Am. Nat.* **80**, 470.

GIBSON, H. L. (1945). *Radiogr. clin. Photogr.* **21**, 42.

GIBSON, H. L. (1960). "The Photography of Patients." Charles C. Thomas. Springfield, U.S.A.

GIBSON, H. L. (1968). *In* ENGEL, C. E. (ed.), "Photography for the Scientist", pp. 299-356. Academic Press, London and New York.

GREPPIN, E. H. (1950). *J. biol. photogr. Ass.* **18**, 182-187.

HALL, J. C. (1969). *Ind. comml. Photogr.* **9**, 86-96.

HALL, J. C. (1971a). *Ind. comml. Photogr.* **11**, 53.

HALL, J. C. (1971b). *Ind. comml. Photogr.* **11**, 75-78.

HANSELL, P. (1957). "A System of Ophthalmic Illustration". Charles C. Thomas, Springfield, U.S.A.

HANSELL, P. (1961). *In* LINSSEN, E. F. (ed.), "Medical Photography in Practice", pp. 175-192. Fountain Press, London.

HANSELL, P. (1968). *In* ENGEL, C. E. (ed.), "Photography for the scientist", pp. 363-382. Academic Press, London and New York.

HANSELL, P. and OLLERENSHAW, R. (1962). "Longmore's Medical Photography." Focal Press, London.

HARRISON, N. K. (1969). *Br. J. Photogr.* **116**, 58-59.

HAWORTH, J. P. (1969). *Br. J. Photogr.* **116**, 615-616.

HAWORTH, J. P. (1972). *Br. J. Photogr.* **119**, 702, 703.

HAXTHAUSEN, H. (1933). *Br. J. Derm.* **45**, 506.

HEISS, W. (1961). *Med. biol. Illust.* **11**, 257-258.

HERTL, M. (1964). *Med. biol. Illust.* **14**, 82-88.

IRVINE, R. F. (1964). *J. biol. photogr. Ass.* **32**, 163-165.

JONES, B. A. (1961). *Br. dent. J.* **111**, 217-218.

KEELING, D. (1969a). *Br. J. Photogr.* **116**, 4.

KEELING, D. (1969b). *Br. J. Photogr.* **116**, 34-35, 62-63, 92-93, 116-117, 138-139, 166-167, 192-193.

KEELING, D. (1969c). *Br. J. Photogr.* **116**, 216-217, 238-239, 259-261, 282-283, 306-307, 328-330, 384-385, 406-408, 434-435, 454-456, 478-480, 500-501.

KEELING, D. (1969d). *Br. J. Photogr.* **116**, 552-554, 577-579, 598-600, 620-622, 643-645.

KEELING, D. (1969e). *Br. J. Photogr.* **116**, 694, 718-721, 730-733, 789-791, 811-813, 835-837, 856-859, 880-882, 905-907, 927-929, 951-953, 976-977, 991-995, 1042-1045, 1071-1072, 1092-1093.

KEELING, D. (1969f). *Br. J. Photogr.* **116**, 1117-1119.

KODAK (1969). "Medical Infrared Photography". 2nd Ed. Eastman Kodak Company publication, U.S.A.

KODAK (1972). "Applied Infrared Photography". 3rd Ed. Eastman Kodak Company publication, U.S.A.

KOSHOFER, G. and HÜBNER, K. (1965). *Br. J. Photogr.* **112**, 780-786.

LUNNON, R. J. (1952). *Med. biol. Illust.* **2**, 205.

LUNNON, R. J. (1959). *Med. biol. Illust.* **9**, 150-154.

LUNNON, R. J. (1961). *Med. biol. Illust.* **11**, 98.

LUNNON, R. J. (1968). *J. biol. photogr. Ass.* **36**, 2.

LUNNON, R. J. (1970). *Br. J. Derm.* **83**, 493.

MANNHEIM, L. A. (1966a). *Br. J. Photogr.* **113**, 845-867.

MANNHEIM, L. A. (1966b). *Br. J. Photogr.* **113**, 913-927.

MARSHALL, R. (1957). *Med. biol. Illust.* **7**, 13-21.

MARTIN, D. (1953). *Med. biol. Illust.* **3**, 216.

MARTIN, D. (1961a). *Med. biol. Illust.* **11**, 76-84.

MARTIN, D. (1961b). *In* LINSSEN, E. F. (ed.), "Medical Photography in Practice", pp. 247-276. Fountain Press, London.

MARTIN, D. (1961c). *Med. biol. Illust.* **11**, 4-12.

MARTINSEN, W. L. M. (1952). *Med. biol. Illust.* **2**, 179-190.

MARTINSEN, W. L. M. (1968). *In* ENGEL, C. E. (ed.), "Photography for the Scientist", pp. 451-480. Academic Press, London and New York.

MASON, E. (1964). *Med. biol. Illust.* **14**, 8-12.

MASON, R. (1960). *Med. biol. Illust.* **10**, 90-97.

MAUDE, N. (1971a). *Br. J. Photogr.* **118**, 751.

MAUDE, N. (1971b). *Br. J. Photogr.* **118**, 598-599.

MAUDE, N. (1971c). *Br. J. Photogr.* **118**, 512-513.

MAUDE, N. (1972). *Br. J. Photogr.* **119**, 496-497.

MORGAN, J. (1969). *Br. J. Photogr.* **116**, 450-451.

MOYNAHAN, E. J. (1963). *In* NORMAN, A. P. (ed.), "Congenital Abnormalities in Infancy", pp. 273-330. Blackwell, Oxford.

MOYNAHAN, E. J. and ENGEL, C. E. (1962). *Med. biol. Illust.* **12**, 72.

NIXON, H. H. and O'DONNELL, B. (1961). "The Essentials of Paediatric Surgery." Heineman, London.

PAMPIGLIONE, G., LUNNON, R. J. and ROGERS, G. W. (1972). "Combined EEG and Transillumination Photography of the Head in Babies with Suspected Congenital Malformations of the Brain." Personal communication to EEG Society. (To be published.)

PAUCHET, V. and DUPRET, S. (1968). "Pocket Atlas of Anatomy." Oxford University Press, London and Tokyo.

PLANATH, F. (1965). *Med. biol. Illust.* **15**, 74-77.

ROBINSON, R. J. and BRECKNELL, C. R. (1965). *Med. biol. Illust.* **15**, 75.

ROGERS, G. W. (1969). *Br. J. Photogr.* **116**, 888-892.
ROGERS, G. W. (1971). *Med. biol. Illust.* **21**, 134-141.
SALTHOUSE, T. N. (1955). *Med. biol. Illust.* **5**, 75.
SALTHOUSE, T. N. (1958). *Med. biol. Illust.* **8**, 150.
SANSOM, L. (1965). *Br. J. Photogr.* **112**, 594-597.
SARKANY, I. and PHILLIPS, R. R. (1965). *Med. biol. Illust.* **15**, No. 2 (supplement), 57-61.
SHELDON, W. (1962). "Diseases of Infancy and Childhood." Churchill Ltd., London.
STONE, L. J. (1952). *Child Dev.* **23**, 227-233.
TURLINGTON, E. R. (1957). *Med. biol. Illust.* **7**, 130.
TYDINGS, K. (1965). *Br. J. Phtogr.* **112**, 813-823.
VERBEEK, L. H. (1968). *In* ENGEL, C. E. (ed.), "Photography for the Scientist", pp. 175-230. Academic Press, London and New York.
WHITLEY, R. (1970). *Med. biol. Illust.* **20**, 249.

SELECTED BIBLIOGRAPHY

Paediatrics

DUNCOMBE, M. and WELLER, B. (1972). "Paediatric Nursing." Baillière, Tindall and Cassell, London.
GELLIS, S. S. and FEINGOLD, M. (1968). "Atlas of Mental Retardation Syndromes." U.S. Department of Health, Education and Welfare.
GOODMAN, R. M. and GORLIN, R. J. (1970). "The Face in Genetic Disorders." Henry Kimpton, London, and C. V. Mosby, St Louis, U.S.A.
KORTING, G. W. (1970). "Diseases of the Skin in Children and Adolescents." CURTH, W. and CURTH, O. H. (translated by). W. B. Saunders Co., Philadelphia-London-Toronto.
LIEBMAN, S. D. and GELLIS, S. S. (eds) (1966). "The Paediatrician's Opthalmology." C. V. Mosby, St Louis, U.S.A.
LIGHTWOOD, R., BRIMBLECOMBE, F. and BARLTROP, D. (1971). "Paterson's Sick Children." 9th Ed. Baillière, Tindall and Cassell, London.
MUSTARDE, J. C. (ed.) (1971). "Plastic Surgery in Infancy and Childhood." Livingstone, Edinburgh and London.
NORMAN, A. P. (ed.) (1963). "Congenital Abnormalities in Infancy." Blackwell, Oxford.
TANNER, J. M. (1962). "Growth and Adolescence." Blackwell, Oxford.
WILLIAMS, D. I. (ed.) (1968). "Paediatric Urology." Butterworth, London.
YOUNG, D. G. and WELLER, B. F. (1971). "Baby Surgery, Nursing Management and Care." Harvey Miller and Medcalf, Aylesbury, England.

Photographic

GIBSON, H. L. (1960). "The Photography of Patients." 2nd Ed. Charles C Thomas, Springfield, U.S.A.

HANSELL, P. and OLLERENSHAW, R. (eds) (1962). "Longmore's Medical Photography." Focal Press, London.

LINSSEN, E. F. (ed.) (1961). "Medical Photography in Practice." Fountain Press, London.

5
Photography in materials science

J. C. RUCKMAN, E. E. LARNER *and* C. J. E. SMITH

I. INTRODUCTION

In the days of the earliest microscopes dating from about 1720, it was only possible to record and compare observations by careful drawing or by sending actual specimens to interested parties. This handicap existed for some 130 years and included the efforts of Sorby and others who were attempting to relate microscopic structure to material properties (Fig. 1).

It was not until the early nineteenth century that the work of Daguerre, Fox Talbot and others showed that permanent accurate records of images could be obtained by utilizing the sensitivity of certain chemicals to light. At first this took the form of an immediately visible change where the light had fallen. Later on the presence of a "latent" image was demonstrated which could be chemically developed and which permitted greater contrast and control. Excess of the sensitive chemical was removed by "fixing". In all this preliminary work the silver halides outstripped all other light-sensitive materials and since then a great amount of work has contributed to the process as we know it today.

The earliest efforts at photomicrography were of necessity made with both microscope and emulsions still in the developmental stage. It was even necessary to use wet plates. However, results were encouraging and provided permanent records free from the subjective assessment which occurs in making drawings. This is not to say that subjective assessment is undesirable; even in scientific photography the operator is at pains to provide conditions which will reveal some details more than others. However, the accuracy and repeatability are far greater than drawings can produce, to say nothing of the saving in time.

Around 1830, Lister, experimenting empirically with lenses, found ways of overcoming some of the aberrations by combining them into compensating systems and, by 1880, oil immersion lenses were in use, and the microscope was approaching its theoretical limit of resolution. Fortunately the development of dry photographic emulsions and chemical development of the latent image had by this time—1890—reached a point which could do full justice to instrumental development. From this point microscope design turned towards more rigid construction and more powerful light sources—both very necessary for successful photomicrography, less so for visual observation only. Ultraviolet and infrared illumination, colour and cine photomicrography were soon added and in the case of ultraviolet and infrared this necessitated new optical systems owing to the inability of glass lenses to fully transmit wavelengths outside

---

FIG. 1. A popular type of microscope from 1800–1830, when microscopes were taken seriously only by a minority. Probably made by William Carey around 1827. These microscopes frequently had polished jewels as objectives and were capable of about ×200 magnification. The cost of microscopes in the mid-nineteenth century was around £40 for the best obtainable down to £3 for a "students" compound microscope. Some had very long tubes to obtain greater magnification and looked more like a telescope than a microscope.

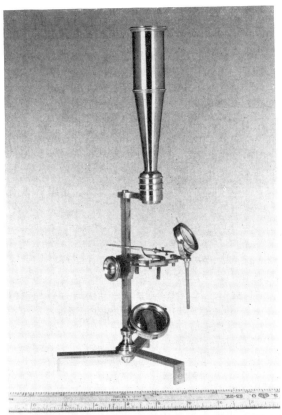

Fig. 1.

the visible spectrum. Photographic emulsions were also modified to bring their maximum sensitivity into the wavelength range being used.

Further developments which took place early in the twentieth century were the quantitative uses of polarized light, phase contrast, fluorescence and interference microscopy. These have now become so well established that purpose-built instruments are now available which are specifically designed for these methods.

While these advances were being made in visible and near-visible microscopy, it was discovered by Becquerell in 1896 that if a sensitive photographic emulsion was left near to or in contact with uranium-bearing ores in complete darkness, an image or fog was produced on development which was of the same nature as that produced by light. We recognize in this the first demonstration of autoradiography in which invisible radiation affects a photographic emulsion and no lenses are present. In fact the emulsions available at that time were much more sensitive to shorter wave radiation than to visible radiation. Today we have available emulsions which are sensitive to almost any form of radiation including infrared, ultraviolet, electrons, neutrons, α-particles and x-rays. Many of these forms of radiation have been used to generate images, either by lens-like focusing or other means which will be described later. These images, which are recorded on photographic emulsion, contain within them a large amount of data concerning the material they have passed through or been reflected from. This is the basis of all electron and optical microscopes, so much so that the camera and photographic plate have become an integral part of these instruments.

In transmission electron microscopy especially, photography has played an essential part because an electron image can only be made visible by impinging on a fluorescent screen. This visible image is often of very low intensity so that detail becomes difficult to see, added to which the inherent grain of the screen is a further limiting factor. Consequently, a lot of information will remain undetected until a photograph has been taken which does not rely on the screen for its image. Other instruments which have adopted photography as their means of recording are the Scanning Electron Microscope, Electron probe microanalyser and x-ray diffraction camera. These we will discuss in turn as the details of recording the image differs in each case. Finally, we have radiography which utilizes x-rays after projection through the specimen on to the emulsion, and autoradiography where the specimen itself becomes the source of radiation as previously mentioned.

The principle of the kaleidoscope and cinematograph, of utilizing rapidly changing sequential images with a finite gap between each image has been known for a long time. It was certainly used in toys in the form of separate drawings on rotating mechanisms early in the nineteenth century. However, it was not until long lengths of celluloid film were available (around 1890) that the principle was really developed, and Edison devised mechanisms for accepting and projecting the images of real life movements. Applied rather belatedly to microscopy, it is capable of either contracting or expanding the time scale in sequential changes according to the relative speeds of accepting and projecting the images. Although it is a permanent record of dynamic events, it is not equal to a "still" for fine detail.

Recently, video-tape has found an increasing use for recording dynamic experiments, but it is not yet able to provide the resolutions possible with photographic emulsions.

In the sections which follow we have attempted to describe the general principles of image formation in each instrument with special reference to factors which influence their photographic recording. In later sections, commencing with the "The study of crystal defects", we have considered the use of these techniques in materials research. Within the scope of this work it is obviously impossible to cover the whole field of materials science; instead we have concentrated on those aspects in which we feel that electron optical and x-ray diffraction techniques have made their greatest impact.

II. OPTICAL MICROGRAPHY (THE OPTICAL MICROSCOPE AS A CAMERA)

We propose in the present chapter to discuss briefly those aspects of microscopy which especially concern an image intended for photography, assuming at the same time that the reader is already familiar with the usual visual use of the microscope and its optical geometry. It is only too true that any minor errors in method or adjustment which would be quite acceptable in visual work will be rendered more evident, and placed on record for all to see when photographed. This is because the eye has its own ability to adjust and becomes part of the optical system when viewing the visual image, whereas in photography a real image on a screen is being observed, correct adjustment of which is then independent of the observing eye (see Fig. 2). Other factors, such as colour assessment and appreciation of depth, are not so easily conveyed through a photograph as when examined visually. Slight movements of specimen or instrument which may be acceptable in a visual examination can ruin a photograph, but exceptions must be made here for cinemicrography which is of course purposely used to capture change and movement.

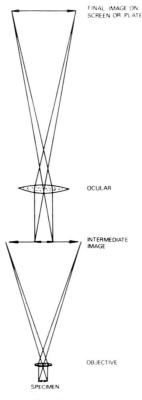

FIG. 2. Diagram to illustrate the formation of a real image in the optical microscope.

A successful photomicrograph will require careful consideration of the following factors:

1. Method of illumination (vertical, dark field, etc.).
2. Instrumental adjustments (focus, stability).
3. Emulsion characteristics.
4. Specimen presentation.

These factors we will now discuss separately with special reference to a photographic record as distinct from a visual examination.

A. Methods of illumination

The method by which the specimen is illuminated deserves as much care as the choice of lenses used to form the image. However, there is considerably more scope for experiment in this field and time will be well spent exploring how much and what type of information the various systems will reveal. The two basic methods are the use of transmitted light for transparent materials, and a reflective mode for opaque materials. Particulate samples can be studied by both methods. The optical principles involved in these two methods are really the same, but their practical achievement requires physically different arrangements in the instrument. Within these two basic methods we have a number of possible modes which are described briefly here, and Fig. 3 illustrates schematically how they relate to each other from an optical point of view.

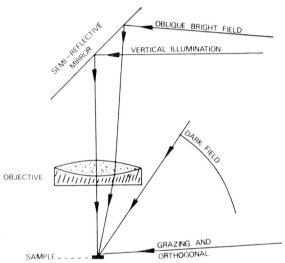

FIG. 3. Schematic diagram to show the various types of illumination for opaque materials. The illumination may be supplied directionally or as a cone in dark field and grazing incidence.

1. *Axial illumination.* This is the most frequently used method for materials studies, the reflective mode being illustrated in Fig. 4. Light of controllable convergence falls on a semi-reflecting mirror set at 45° to the beam so that it both transmits and reflects. The reflected portion is collected by the objective lens which thereby functions as part of the illuminating system, focusing the light on the specimen. The reflected light from the specimen then passes back through the objective and is this time transmitted by the semi-reflecting mirror, up the microscope tube to form an image near the focal plane of the eye piece.

In the transmitted mode, it is of course, no longer possible to utilize the objective lens as a condenser so that a specially constructed condenser must be positioned behind the specimen, and equipped with an iris diaphragm. This lens will need to have a numerical aperture matching or somewhat higher than that of the objective in use, which for oil immersion objectives may call for an oil interface for the condenser as well.

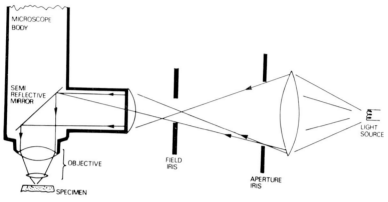

Fig. 4. An optical system for axially incident illumination.

2. Oblique bright field. This is a modification of the above method in which the light is caused to fall on the specimen at a small angle to the vertical and lying within the cone subtended by the objective. This can be accomplished in several ways, either by displacing the illuminating source slightly, or by slightly altering the slope of the semi-reflecting mirror, or by masking one side of the condenser aperture. The effect is to give a slight relief effect due to the short shadows which are formed. This in turn gives added contrast to boundaries of slightly differing height such as is obtained in polishing with soft laps, or vibratory polishing.

3. Dark field illumination. This method has several variations but the essential feature is that light reaches the specimen from outside the angle subtended by the objective. At its simplest this can be achieved by focusing a light obliquely on to the specimen, in which case relatively long shadows will be formed. However, a better way is to arrange for the illuminating rays to reach the specimen in a cone which is outside the objective grasp. Special deflecting mirror condensers known as catoptric condensers are available to fit objective lenses to achieve this. In some of these condensers it is possible to alter the angle of the cone quite easily.

The image formed under dark field conditions is very different from a bright field image. With surfaces giving a high degree of scatter (textiles, pigments, etc.) it has the appearance that the specimen is self-luminous, colours being visible to advantage (in contrast to axial illumination). At the same time highly polished surfaces will appear black. Very small features (specks of dust, scratch marks) are greatly accentuated sometimes to an embarrassing extent. Detection, as distinct from resolution, of particles may be as low as a tenth of the wavelength of the light used.

There are a variety of methods for achieving dark field conditions and the reader is referred for further details to the books quoted in the bibliography.

4. Polarized light. Polarized light is a type of illumination usually applied in conjunction with normal illumination. When light passes through certain materials, conveniently in the form of plates about $\frac{1}{4}$ in thick, the plane of vibration of the electric component becomes restricted to one direction; it is then said to be polarized. If a second piece of material is placed in this polarized beam, light will be passed or obstructed according to its relative orientation to the first piece. By arranging the "polarizer" and "analyser" as they are called, to be at 90° no appreciable light will pass through the pair of plates. If now a third piece of a different material—the specimen—is introduced between the polarizer and analyser, it may itself rotate the plane of vibration and light will now pass through all three pieces. The material is then said to be optically active, and this property is associated with asymmetry in the crystal planes and molecular structures of the material. Most microscopes have built-in facilities for applying polarized light, and in any case they are very simple to add for qualitative work.

An example of the use of polarized light to reveal grain size is illustrated in Fig. 5. This shows a polished beryllium metal surface, unetched in vertical illumination using polarized light. The grains are visible as different colours but this has no relevance to size so that a black-and-white picture is all that is needed. Nothing was visible without the use of polarized light, except for some very minute pores.

5. Interference contrast. This is a group of methods which develops contrast by application of interference phenomena, with or without polarized light, associated with such names as Zernicke, Heine, Nomarski and others. They are usually bought as accessories which are fixed on as complete units and only require adjustment to meet the lens system in use. Their effectiveness varies greatly according to the type of sample and its detail. Often coarse features remain unaltered yet fine detail becomes enormously enhanced, so that interpretation requires care.

A striking case of Nomarski contrast can be seen in the two photographs (Fig. 6(a) and (b)). These pictures were taken from the polished (not etched) surface of a uranium/molybdenum alloy, the final polishing stage being $\frac{1}{4}$ μ diamond on Selvyt cloth to produce considerable relief effect. The first picture, taken in normal vertical illumination shows only ghost-like images of the structure, whereas the second picture using Nomarski interference contrast has revealed a clear martensitic structure. The method does not always produce such results, and factors such as

Fɪɢ. 5. Optical micrograph: Polished beryllium surface photographed using polarized light. × 100. (By kind permission of Mr J. Dingle, AWRE.)

depth of relief, wavelengths of light used and surface reflectance are all relevant. Because crossed polarizers are used the exposure times are long—in this case 8 min using a tungsten filament lamp and yellow filter.

When "macro" work is undertaken (i.e., work below about × 25), there is the opportunity for ingenuity in rigging up one's own method of illumination on less orthodox lines. We have found a 25 W fluorescent ring lamp a useful accessory, especially if it has moveable masking segments fitted to it. Of course in this range of magnification much rougher specimens can be photographed and the use of shadow to give a 3-dimensional effect becomes an important method of displaying relief features.

(a)

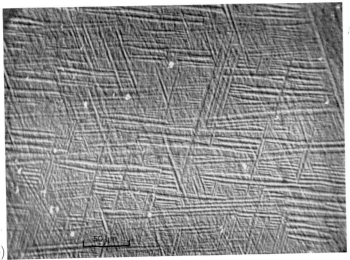

(b)

FIG. 6. (a) Optical micrograph showing polished uranium—2 w/o molybdenum alloy photographed using vertical illumination. × 200. (b) Same surface as in (a) photographed using Nomarski; interference contrast × 200.

B. Instrumental factors

1. Stability. Most modern instruments are built either to accept a camera attachment, or the image is projected on to a screen which can be replaced by a photographic plate. In either case a high priority must be given to mechanical stability, especially for work involving fluorescence, dark field or polarization microscopy which give low levels of illumination and therefore require long exposures. These exposures can be up to 10 min when studying dark materials. The most likely causes of movement are bench vibration, operating the plate slide, stage slip, thermal drift and, with short exposures in particular, operation of the shutter. Bench vibration can be greatly reduced by the use of anti-vibration mats which are manufactured by most microscope makers. Instruments anchored to a concrete floor (such as the older Vickers Projection Microscopes) are less susceptible to vibration trouble, but heavy machinery in the vicinity can still be detrimental to low intensity images requiring long exposures.

Stage slip is only likely to be encountered when heavy samples are placed on the stage of "inverted" type microscopes. Asymmetrical loads are particularly bad as a temporary or permanent slant may be imparted to the stage, making focusing impossible. Despite this, there are many advantages to the "inverted" instrument when most of the work is on bulky opaque specimens which must not be broken up.

Thermal drift in the focus will only be noticeable at high magnifications and long exposures when the depth of focus is less than 1 μ. Turning a radiator on near the instrument, or changing light sources from a few watts to 250 W may account for temporary drift which will disappear after a while.

2. Light sources. Assuming that exposure times should be kept as short as possible, it follows that considerably more powerful light sources will be needed for photomicrograph than for visual work. There are a number of choices available such as xenon and mercury discharge lamps, Quartz-halogen lamps, carbon arc, "Pointolite", zirconium arc and electronic flash. All of these are suitable for black-and-white photomicrography, provided the right filters are used, but only a few are suited to colour work, the xenon lamp and electronic flash being satisfactory without a compensating filter.

An important point, often overlooked, is that the black-and-white rendering of a specimen can be radically changed by altering the spectrum of the illuminating light. Features having adequate contrast in one light may be almost extinguished in a different light. Easily interchangeable light sources are a wise addition for photomicrography but are not always available. Illumination suitable for cinematography must be totally free from a.c. fluctuation of brightness as this is likely to cause a stroboscopic effect in the final pictures. Certain mechanical vibration frequencies will have a similar effect.

Illumination for fluorescence microscopy is almost entirely confined to the mercury vapour lamp which is very rich in ultraviolet radiation.* Two filters are employed, the first one known as the "exciter" passes only the appropriate u.v. wavelengths and is placed before the specimen, the second one or "barrier" filter passes the fluorescing colour and specifically cuts out all ultraviolet light. This one is placed just before the eyepiece. For short-wave ultraviolet fluorescence work special quartz lenses are required owing to the high absorption of ordinary optical glass. Such lenses are also required in ordinary ultraviolet microscopy (i.e., not fluorescent) and focusing must be carried out by using a fluorescent screen or by taking several through-focus pictures.

Fluorescence micrography can be used either to detect natural fluorescence in substances, or to detect features which accept staining by a fluorescent dye. An illustration of the former is readily seen in the uranyl salts, and the latter in fabrics which adsorb the fluorescent dyes put into modern washing powders.

3. *Focusing.* The next point of divergence from visual work is in the assessment of correct—or most effective—focus. The problem is nearly always present when working at magnification over × 500, but in specimens having appreciable topographical depth it can be a problem even in macro-work. Critical focusing can only be undertaken by using a small magnifier—about × 5—for viewing the image. This magnifier is simply a lens mounted in an adjustable tube so that when placed on any flat object the image produced is at the point of nearest distinct vision. The magnifier is placed on a clear glass plate substituting for the photographic plate and the image critically focused with the microscope adjustments. Some workers use a ground-glass screen which, although satisfactory for lower magnification, is not suitable for work above magnification of × 250 owing to the grain of the screen. However, it is very useful for assessing the evenness of illumination and pictorial value of the field in view.

An important feature of examining the real image through clear glass is that its quality can be assessed, and further adjustments made—usually with the iris diaphragm to decrease any diffraction effects or allow sufficiently for depth in the sample. These adjustments will be very critical —of the order of $\frac{1}{4} \mu$ on the focus at × 500 upwards, but unless great care is taken at this point a poor picture will result. Inevitably, with samples having some depth, such as many etched or polished specimens, a certain

* The operator's eyes should be protected when working with ultraviolet radiation.

I

subjective assessment enters into the decision of best focus and quite small variations will alter both perspective *and colour* of smaller features.

Allied to critical focusing is curvature of field which frequently arises in high magnification work. Much of this can be corrected by the use of special flat field projection lenses at the expense of a little peripheral distortion of the image features. At the same time it is well to be quite sure that the lens combination giving rise to excessive curvature is not in error. In any case a little of the picture may have to be sacrificed by trimming the finished print.

4. Filters. Filters are introduced into the light train for a variety of reasons, one having already been mentioned in connection with fluorescent work. Further reasons may be summarized as follows:

   (i) Neutral filters to decrease light intensity while visual examination is made. Usually removed for photography.

  (ii) Yellow-green filters to cut out the blue end of the spectrum for which chromatic lenses are not fully corrected and to which emulsions are excessively sensitive.

 (iii) The use of a filter colour complementary to the colour of some specimen detail in order to increase its contrast.

 (iv) Heat absorption filters when using high-energy lamps (which are normal for photomicrography). A small water cell is also effective.

  (v) Polarization filters and wedges or wave plates.

 (vi) Interference filters. These have a very narrow and low transmission and are effectively monochromatic. The angle to the optical axis controls the wavelengths transmitted. They are made by evaporating, in vacuum, finite thicknesses of materials on to glass.

It frequently happens that the yellow-green filter used under (ii) above also serves adequately for purpose (iii), but it must be emphasized that the combination of light spectrum, filter, sample colour and emulsion sensitivity must be regarded as a single aspect. If a colour is absent in the light source it will be absent in the image regardless of specimen colour, hence giving an undifferentiated picture. (An exception to this is of course fluorescence phenomena.)

Polarization filters, in addition to their use in studying optically active materials, can usefully be employed to reduce high light glare because light reflected under these conditions is somewhat polarized. They are also used in displaying stress patterns in plastics and glasses where stresses can cause a random structure to take up some degree of preferred orientation.

C. The emulsion

Having chosen a light-source and filters for a given sample, further parameters remain to be decided before a correct emulsion can be selected from the commercial range. It may be necessary to consider speed, as with specimens having slight movement or in cinematography. Grain and contrast are not usually a problem as most present-day emulsions will stand enlargements of up to eight times without visible loss of definition. Contrast can to some extent be controlled in the developing process but this will be unnecessary if the filters and exposure times are correct.

For much of the work done on materials studies, it is more convenient to use orthochromatic plates or films, because the kind of feature usually examined, such as grain boundaries, inclusions, cracks, abrasions, etc., do not require a red-sensitive emulsion. This makes dark-room processing much easier, and it is possible to print and develop in the same red light if necessary. However, when the work requires a sensitivity nearer to the human eye, such as in viewing detail in red biological stains, then there is no alternative but to use panchromatic emulsions.

D. The specimen, some general aspects

Although details of specimen preparations will be recorded in each of the illustrations given later on, a few general remarks can usefully be made at this stage.

Translucent specimens can be troublesome in vertical illumination owing to the excessive glare caused by scattered light. This can be completely eliminated by coating the surface with vapour-deposited aluminium in a vacuum coating unit as used in electron microscopy work. Fine detail like grain boundaries, etch pits, etc., are rendered in vigorous contrast, together, unfortunately, with any defects in preparation. Less contrast is produced by coating with carbon or gold/palladium alloy using rather heavier deposits than are used in electron microscopy.

Differences in hardness due to the presence of several phases or crystal orientations can be greatly enhanced by vibratory polishing. The small topographical step which is produced between different hardnesses gives quite effective contrast in slightly oblique light, Nomarski contrast, or by depositing vapour coated aluminium on the surface. A soft lap with abrasive of $\frac{1}{4} \mu$ or less, and a light loading is effective but it often takes several hours to produce an optimum effect. It can be overdone very easily. The method is valuable even at electron microscopy level as is illustrated in Fig. 7.

Replication of a surface by using cellulose acetate film softened in acetone (as in electron microscopy) is helpful in examining topography of surfaces too large to be accommodated on the microscope. Cylindrical surfaces can be "converted" into flat impressions by rolling them over the softened triacetate. Contrast is then developed by aluminizing the

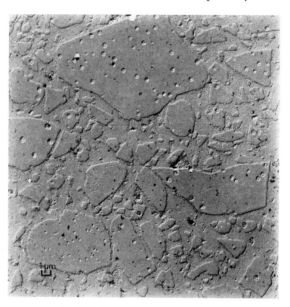

FIG. 7. Cross-section of a dental ceramic after a very light vibratory polish for 2 h under water. The picture is a replica (see Appendices B and C). The small round hollows in the glassy discontinuous phase are gas bubbles, trapped during manufacture on cooling. The examination was required to detect any rounding of the angular particles which would suggest reaction with the continuous phase. × 4000.

replicated surface in a vacuum deposition unit either vertically or at a known angle to produce shadows from which heights may be calculated by measuring the shadow length on the photograph.

We hope to illustrate many of the factors discussed above in the following sections and would add that any artistic streak a scientist may have can often find outlet even in this type of photography.

III. TRANSMISSION ELECTRON MICROSCOPY

A. Introduction

The resolution of any magnifying system is limited by diffraction effects and the spherical aberration of the objective lens which varies as (Numerical Aperture)[3]. Thus the resolution of a microscope whether optical or electron is determined by the wavelength of the radiation used in forming the image. In principle, no microscope can resolve detail smaller than the wavelength of the radiation used and this sets the theoretical limit of the optical microscope at between 3000-5000 Å, (the wavelength of mercury green light = 5000 Å, and in the ultraviolet the wavelength is around 3000 Å). In practice aberrations make the situation worse and the Abbé Formula (which is essentially empirical) gives the limit of resolution as

$\dfrac{\lambda}{2\mu \sin \alpha}$ where λ is the wavelength of the radiation, μ is the refractive index of the medium between the objective lens and the specimen and α is half the angle of the cone of rays subtended on the objective by the specimen. With mercury light and an oil immersion objective having NA (numerical aperture) = $\mu \sin \alpha$ of 0·95 the limit of resolution is 0·2 μm and imperfect alignment can increase this to 0·5-1·0 μm.

Table I shows the wavelengths of radiations covering the spectral range up to 8600 Å.

TABLE I

Type of radiation	Wavelength (Å) 1 Å = 10^{-8} cm
100 keV electrons	0·04
X-rays	0·10-150
Ultraviolet	150-4000
Shortest u.v. radiation used in photomicrography	Approx. 2000
Visible spectrum	4000-7000
Infrared used in photomicrography	7000-8600

Photographic plates are sensitive to all these radiations and theoretically they can all be used in microscopy. Unfortunately, in the case of x-rays no satisfactory lens has yet been found to focus the rays. Electrons, however, are easily deflected by magnetic fields and this principle is used, as shown below, to take advantage of the very small wavelengths of high-energy electrons in the electron microscope.

B. *The transmission electron microscope*

Electron optics are based on the following three basic discoveries:

1. Proof of the existence of electrons, Thomson (1899).
2. Hypothesis of the wave nature of material particles, de Broglie (1924).
3. Lens action of electric and magnetic fields with axial symmetry upon charged particles, Busch (1927).

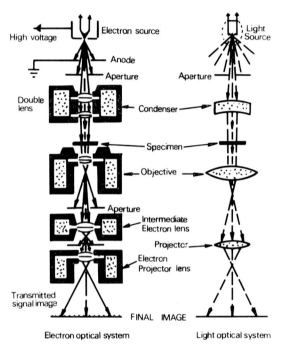

FIG. 8. Schematic comparison of the basic electron optical and light optical microscope systems.

With these discoveries as their starting point Knoll and Ruska (1932) proposed a concept of the transmission electron microscope which was very similar in principle to the light optical system used in the transmission light microscope. During the three decades that ensued the transmission electron microscope made enormous progress but retained its basic similarity to the light microscope as shown in Fig. 8, from which it may be seen that the arrangement of both instruments and the ray paths in these systems are identical. This is because the action of the electromagnetic lens employed almost exclusively in modern electron microscopes is analogous to that of a glass lens. There are, of course, a number of differences between the two instruments. One very obvious difference is the large size of the transmission electron microscope compared with the optical microscope. This is related to the size of the lenses which have to be used to give a strong-enough magnetic field to deflect the high-energy electrons sufficiently so that they can be brought to a focus at a reasonable distance. Conventional 100-kV instruments are generally about 6 ft high and the ultra-high-voltage microscopes now in use can have columns over twice as high. In addition there is usually a larger number of lenses in an electron microscope. Most modern instruments have two condenser lenses and in place of the single projector lens in the optical microscope there are usually at least one and often two intermediate lenses combined with a projector lens. A further difference concerns the control of magnification which, in the case of the optical microscope, is effected by a choice of objective lenses and eyepieces and, in the case of the electron microscope, by varying the power of the intermediate lens. Finally, in order to view the image in an electron microscope, the inter-mediary of a fluorescent screen or photographic plate must be used, whereas the image formed in an optical microscope may be viewed directly through the eyepiece.

A typical layout of an electron microscope column is shown in Fig. 9. It consists initially of a source of electrons which, in a conventional electron microscope, is a tungsten filament heated to a temperature of around $2600°K$, and the electrons thus emitted are accelerated through voltages of typically 100 kV. The beam is thus essentially monochromatic and the wavelength, λ, is determined by the accelerating voltage according to the formula $\lambda = \sqrt{\dfrac{150}{V}}$ where V is the accelerating voltage. At voltages above about 50 kV a correction must be made to V to allow for relativistic effects. At 100 kV the relativistic correction is only about 10% and $\lambda = 0.037$ Å but at 1000 kV the correction approaches 100%.

The beam of electrons is focused and collimated by one, or more usually, two condenser lenses and apertures to a spot a few microns in diameter on the specimen; the circularity of the spot being controlled by a stigmator situated inside the condenser lens. The electrons transmitted through the specimen, both the unscattered and a proportion of the scattered electrons, pass through the objective lens and the intermediate lenses and are projected on to the fluorescent screen by the projector lens where they form an enlarged image of the object. An aperture inside the objective lens is used to exclude some of the scattered electrons and increase the image contrast, which arises from differential scattering by different parts of the specimen. The fluorescent screen can be hinged back to allow the electrons to fall on a photographic plate.

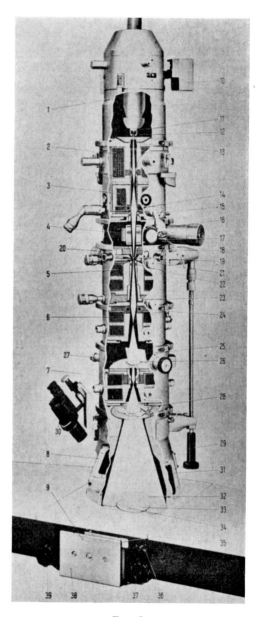

FIG. 9

Electrons are easily stopped by matter and this makes it necessary not only to evacuate all the air from the electron microscope column but also to make the specimen thin enough for the electrons to penetrate through. With electron microscopes operating at 100 kV it is impossible to obtain useful images from objects whose thicknesses exceed a few thousand Angstroms, and, as a result special techniques have had to be developed such as electrolytic thinning for metals and ultramicrotome sectioning for biological materials to reduce their thicknesses sufficiently for examination in the electron microscope. In fact transmission electron microscopy only began to make significant contributions to physical metallurgy after methods had been devised for the production of thin foils of metals and alloys by electrolytic polishing (Heidenreich, 1949; Bollmann, 1956). This also led to improvements in electron microscope construction so that resolutions down to 25Å could be obtained routinely, and a few Angstroms under optimum operating conditions.

The necessity of using these rather laborious techniques to produce thin specimens for the 100-kV instruments provided an incentive to the development of higher-voltage instruments which would be capable of examining specimens up to 1 μm thick so that 1000-kV electron microscopes are made commercially by AEI in England and JEOL and Hitachi in Japan. However, quite significant improvements in electron penetration can be obtained in the JEOL 200-kV microscope (illustrated in Fig. 10) as

---

FIG. 9. Typical arrangement of a transmission electron microscope column—Siemens Elmiskop. (Courtesy Siemens Halske.) 1. Electron gun; 2. Condenser 1; 3. Condenser 2; 4. Specimen airlock with beam deflecting system; 5. Objective; 6. Intermediate lens; 7. Projector; 8. Final-image tube; 9. Photographic chamber; 10. Servomotor for cathode displacement; 11. Cathode; 12. Bias shield; 13. Anode; 14. Electromagnetic stigmator in condenser 2; 15. Control for the apertures in condenser 2; 16. Deflecting system; 17. Automatic ventilation and evacuation of the airlock antechamber; 18. Specimen cartridge; 19. Specimen; 20. Anticontamination device; 21. Control for the objective apertures; 22. Electro-magnetic objective stigmator; 23. Intermediate lens selector apertures; 24. Electro-magnetic intermediate lens stigmator; 25. Mirror for intermediate image observation; 26. Intermediate image screen; 27. Drive for the intermediate image screen; 28. Exposure shutter; 29. Control for specimen stage adjustment; 30. Binocular magnifier; 31. Viewing window; 32. Outer field screen; 33. Central field screen; 34. Small field screen; 35. Lever for opening the photographic chamber door; 36. Control for final-image screen; 37. Drive for film and plate transport; 38. Door of the photographic chamber; 39. Airlock drive.

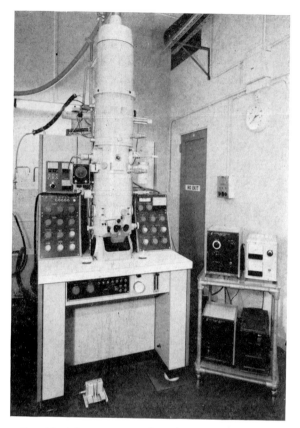

FIG. 10. The JEOL 200-kV electron microscope.

shown by the micrographs of a uranium alloy compared in Fig. 11. Another method of increasing the apparent penetration of electrons through thick objects and hence improving the brightness of their image, without grossly elevating the cost of the microscope installation, will be described in section IV.E, where the latest developments in scanning transmission electron microscopes will be reviewed.

C. Electron diffraction

A facility which greatly increases the analytical values of the transmission electron microscope is its ability to form diffraction patterns of objects placed in the specimen holder. The diffraction pattern from a crystalline specimen is a record of the periodic structure or repeating array of that specimen. If the specimen is a single crystal then the diffraction

FIG. 11. Uranium—6 w/o niobium photographed in the JEM 200A. (a) At 100 kV. (b) At 200 kV.

pattern will consist of a simple array of bright spots as shown in Fig. 12, in which the distance of each spot from the centre spot of the pattern is inversely proportional to the spacing between the planes of atoms giving rise to that spot. If the specimen consists of a large number of small discrete areas, each with the same atomic array but at different orientations to each other, the specimen is termed polycrystalline and its diffraction pattern will consist of a series of concentric rings (Fig. 13). This pattern is really a large number of single crystal diffraction patterns, each rotated by a small amount with respect to each other; the same pattern would be obtained by taking a long time exposure, while a single crystal pattern was continuously rotated.

Once the interplanar spacings for diffraction rings or spots have been determined they can be used to determine:

(a) the crystal lattice to which the specimen belongs,

(b) the lattice parameters,

(c) with the aid of tabulations of the *d*-spacing of elements, alloys and compounds and possibly information as to the chemical composition provided by electron-probe microanalysis, a precise identification of the material giving rise to the diffraction pattern may be obtained.

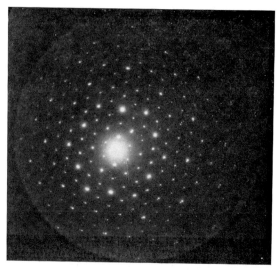

Fig. 12. Electron diffraction pattern from a single crystal of talc.

Fig. 13. Electron diffraction pattern from polycrystalline aluminium.

If the structure of the material under examination is known the electron diffraction pattern can be used to determine:

(a) the orientation in which the specimen is lying with respect to the incident beam, if it is a single crystal, or

(b) the orientation relationship between two or more single crystals if it is polycrystalline, or

(c) the orientation relationship between precipitates, inclusions or twins and the surrounding matrix, or

(d) the crystallographic orientation of defects of all kinds, dislocations, voids and boundaries by correlating the image and the diffraction pattern of the same area of the specimen.

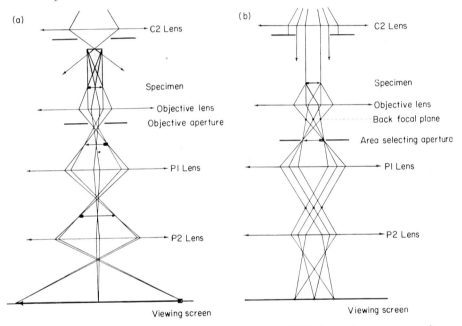

FIG. 14. Ray paths in the electron microscope. (a) Under microscopy conditions. (b) In the diffraction mode.

Let us consider now the formation of the diffraction pattern in the electron microscope. In the normal imaging mode the two projector lenses (P_1 and P_2) are focused to transfer the first image formed by the objective lens on to the viewing screen at high magnification as shown in Fig. 14(a). In order to view the diffraction pattern (Fig. 14(b)) the P_1 lens is weakened, increasing its focal length so that it is focused on the back focal plane of the objective lens rather than the first image plane. The diffraction pattern is then first focused in the object plane of P_2 and finally on the viewing screen.

Diffraction patterns are recorded in the usual way on photographic plate or film placed below the viewing screen which is raised to allow exposure to take place. In order that the central spot should not completely fog the central area of the plate a beam stop is usually placed in position before each exposure of a diffraction pattern. However, determination of the correct exposure to record the pattern satisfactorily is often more difficult than for the normal image. Exposure meters are not always satisfactory since they usually record the average intensity over a large area of the screen and the successful exposure of diffraction patterns is often a matter of experimentation and experience. Reducing the illuminating intensity by defocusing the second condenser lens will usually enable a greater control to be exercised over the exposure time.

Printing the diffraction pattern can also give rise to difficulties caused by the considerable intensity variations around the diffraction spots on a plate. Thus the fine structure of a diffraction spot which is often of great interest can frequently be masked by the spot itself. The Log-e-tronic enlarger described in Appendix A will often help to resolve this difficulty.

D. The use of dark field

In transmission electron microscopy dark field is often used as a means of imaging the areas in a specimen contributing to a particular diffraction spot. In this case the objective aperture can either be moved to the spot in question, the diffraction aperture removed, and the strength of the inter-mediate lens increased to give the required magnification or the incident beam can be tilted so that the spot is moved to the centre of the field of view and the magnification then increased. The latter method will result in a higher resolution image being obtained since no off-axis beams are used in its formation.

The bright areas on the dark-field image will correspond to those areas in the specimen which have contributed to the diffraction spot round which the objective aperture was placed.

An example of a dark field image is shown in Fig. 76(b).

E. Practical considerations

In deciding the optimum magnification at which to operate an electron microscope a number of considerations have to be borne in mind. Firstly, the magnification should be as low as is possible in order that the micrograph should include a large field of view. A well focused plate may be enlarged up to 15 times without trouble from the grain of the photographic plate. However, it is necessary to use a certain minimum magnification if random contrast due to statistical variations in the arrival of electrons at the photographic plate (electron noise) are to be insignificant compared with true variations due to fine structure. Haine (1954) concluded that a minimum magnification of approximately × 30,000 is necessary for this to be small compared to a low contrast 10 Å structure. Agar (1957) concluded that the conditions of visibility were at an optimum (for × 10 optical viewer) at an electron optical magnification of 70,000 times for visibility of fine structure in the image on the fluorescent screen.

The image on the fluorescent screen is limited in resolution both by the grain size of the phosphor and by the scattering of light within the phosphor itself. This also causes loss of contrast in the screen image and may render fine details difficult to distinguish. For this reason it is usually only possible to observe fine details within an electron microscope image by exposing a photographic plate to the electron beam, processing the latent image and examining the plate under an optical magnifier or producing an enlarged print.

There are often advantages in employing image intensification, particularly in the study of biological materials which may be damaged by high beam currents. At low beam currents and high magnifications the light output from a fluorescent screen may be too low for easy viewing. There may also be some advantages in examining thicker sections of materials where electron penetration may be difficult but in these cases further difficulties may arise due to the greatly increased electron energy losses in the material and consequential losses of resolution.

When employing image intensifiers it must also be remembered that some loss of resolution will usually be experienced due to the fact that the television monitor may only have 2×10^5 picture elements compared with 5×10^6 for a photographic plate. In the case of the channel plate system the resolution will be determined by the distance between individual channels. Therefore, when using image intensifiers it is usually best to operate the microscope at as high a magnification as possible, particularly when a video-tape recorder is to be used to record the image, except when a photographic plate is subsequently to be exposed in the normal way.

F. Photography in the TEM

As mentioned above a photograph is usually the end result of an electron microscope examination not only because a permanent record is needed of the image observed on the fluorescent screen but also because a photograph is the best method of exploiting the high resolution available in the image.

The density of photographic plate is defined in terms of the ratio of the light incident on the plate I_0 to that transmitted through an exposed area I

$$D = \log \frac{I_0}{I} \tag{1}$$

The characteristics of photographic plates exposed to an electron beam were studied by Digby *et al.* (1953) who demonstrated a linear relationship between the integrated electron charge falling on a photographic plate and its resultant density. They also found very little difference between the behaviour of different emulsions on exposure to the electron beam. They are all very sensitive to electrons. The main criteria should be a fine enough grain to permit $\times 10$ to $\times 15$ enlargement. It also has to be remembered that over- or under-exposed plates lose contrast range.

Exposure meters have proved to be very useful in ensuring correct exposures, whether of the matching patch type, as used in the viewing telescopes of the EM6B and EM6G electron microscopes manufactured by AEI, or electronic as in the EMU3 and EM200 manufactured by Philips, which integrate the electron intensity over the viewing screen and give an automatic indication of exposure. When tank development of large batches of plates or roll film is employed an exposure meter is almost essential to ensure uniform exposures. However, as in all branches of photography, the production of good quality electron micrographs depends as much on the skill and experience of the operator as on the equipment used to obtain them.

IV. ELECTRON PROBE INSTRUMENTS

A. Introduction

In section III we developed some of the basic features of an electron optical system in which the specimen is a passive object inserted into the path of a suitably controlled electron beam, i.e., the transmission electron microscope. The image formed in a transmission electron microscope gives direct information on the geometry of the object but does not itself contain information concerning the chemical composition or atomic species of the imaged volume, although it is possible to draw certain inferences about these latter characteristics from the electron diffraction pattern. However, the bombardment of a material with a primary electron beam causes a small proportion to be reflected from the surface and also excites other (secondary) electron emissions within the irradiated material. In addition it causes x-rays to be emitted which are characteristic of the atomic species being irradiated, as well as a number of other interactions which can be used to provide chemical and physical information about the specimen.

Figure 15 illustrates the more common physical processes that occur

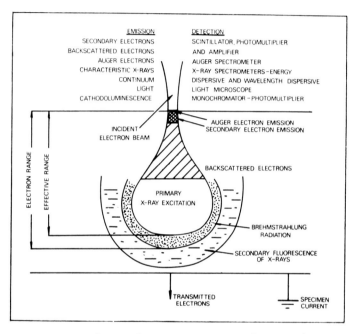

FIG. 15. Electron beam interactions with materials.

when a material is bombarded with a beam of electrons, and in principle all the radiations produced by these interactions can be exploited to provide analytical information about the material. Namely, the characteristic x-rays and Auger electrons emitted can be analysed with regard to the area of origin; back-scattered electrons, absorbed electrons and secondary emitted electrons (i.e., those electrons originally in the solid that are ejected as a result of primary electron collisions, etc.) can be monitored and used in the analysis of surface topography, charge, composition, etc.; specimen fluorescence as a result of photon production in the collision area can be observed; and diffracted electrons can be used to analyse the crystallography of the object.

In principle an instrument could be constructed which would be capable of analysing most, if not all, of these radiations but in practice specialist instruments have been developed with the object of exploiting primarily one mode of operation but with attachments designed to make use of other electron/specimen interactions. Examples of these electron probe instruments are the scanning electron microscope and the electron probe microanalyser.

B. Electron microscopy of surfaces

Although the concept of the scanning electron microscope (SEM) was first proposed by Knoll in 1933 only three years after he and Ruska had suggested the concept of the transmission instrument, progress on the scanning system was very much slower and it was three decades before the first commercial SEM, manufactured by Cambridge Instruments, appeared on the market whereas Siemens and Halske commercialized the first transmission electron microscope in 1939.

Between 1939 and 1965 the only method available for imaging surfaces of materials at high magnifications was the use of surface replicas in conjunction with the transmission electron microscope. The resolution of fine detail by surface replicas was developed to a fine art during this period; however, they have severe limitations, particularly with respect to the degree of surface roughness which they can successfully replicate, and their preparation requires considerable skill and the expenditure of a certain amount of time. The advent of the SEM has removed the need to use replica techniques in the large majority of surface examinations although they still have applications where high resolutions are required or where inclusions or precipitates are to be extracted from a material for detailed analysis. (The extraction replica technique will be discussed later in section VIII.B and the use of replicas for high resolution surface studies in section XI.B).

The scanning electron microscope consists mainly of the upper electron optical system of Fig. 8, comprising a condenser lens arrangement and an objective. In a conventional probe arrangement the objective lens serves the purpose of focusing the electron beam on to an area of the specimen, rather than the direct imaging of the specimen detail as in an image-forming system. Consequently the specimen is positioned at the focal length of the objective lens. Comparing Fig. 8 with Fig. 16, in which the construction of a typical SEM is schematically illustrated, it can be seen that the image-forming lenses of the TEM have been replaced by an electron detector which, in the example shown, is situated to one side of the specimen where it can trap the electrons emitted from the specimen or back-scattered from its surface. In the transmission mode of operation the detector would be positioned below the specimen which, in this case, would be a thin foil.

The signal from the detector, which in most SEMs is a scintillator-photomultiplier combination, is amplified and used to modulate the

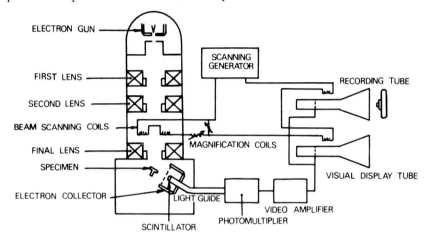

FIG. 16. Schematic diagram of the construction of a scanning electron micro-scope.

brightness of the spot on the surface of a cathode ray tube. The brightness of the spot is thus proportional to the number of electrons received by the electron collector and the detector, and in the case of a solid sample, this depends on the inclination of the surface to the primary electron beam, and on the ease with which the electrons emitted by the specimen are able to reach the collector.

The image of the specimen surface is built up on the screen of the cathode ray tube by causing the electron beam in the column of the SEM to scan a raster (as in a television set) in synchronism with the electron beam in the CRT. As the beam scans the specimen surface the brightness of the spot on the CRT screen varies in accordance with the above factors and a picture is built up on the long persistence screen of the CRT of the variations in tilt of the specimen surface, i.e., it reveals topographical detail.

The view of the specimen, observed on the cathode ray tube, is that which would be obtained by an observer looking along the primary electron beam from the direction of the objective lens. To collect electrons efficiently, the specimen is usually tilted towards the collector at an angle of around 45° so that an oblique view is obtained of features on the specimen surface. Since the human eye is accustomed to observing objects at an angle and to making automatic corrections for foreshortening, this is not a big disadvantage.

The ease with which familiar objects can be recognized when viewed in the SEM may be seen in Fig. 17 which shows a photograph of the image

FIG. 17. A brass screw photographed in the SEM.

of a brass screw; and an unusual view of a familiar object (sticking plaster) is shown in Fig. 18.

The magnification of the image depends on the ratio of the size of the picture on the cathode ray tube (which is kept constant) to the size of the raster scanned on the specimen. The latter area can be varied by varying the current in the scanning coils and in this way the magnification may usually be varied from 20 times up to 100,000 times, corresponding to scanned areas of 5 mm square and 1 μm square respectively on the specimen. The resolution, which depends on the electron probe diameter at the surface of the specimen, and scattering of electrons in the specimen can be better than 100 Å. Compared with this the maximum useful magnification obtainable with the light microscope is 1000 times and the best resolution 0·25 μm. However, the most useful feature of the SEM is its very great depth of focus, which is more than 300 times that of an optical microscope, and means that pictures of very rough surfaces can be obtained.

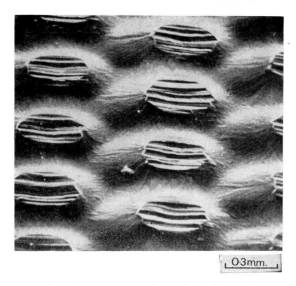

FIG. 18. An array of suction cups on Johnson's sticking-plaster, photographed in the SEM.

This latter feature of the SEM is demonstrated in Fig. 19 which shows the surface of a gold–palladium alloy wire photographed at the same magnification in the optical microscope and in the SEM. Although only a fraction of surface is in focus in the optical micrograph the scanning electron microscope image is clearly in focus from the centre to the edge

FIG. 19. A gold–palladium wire. (a) Photographed in the optical microscope. (b) Photographed in the SEM.

of the wire. The 3-dimensional appearance of the SEM image is also apparent and it is often an aid to the interpretation of such images if stereo pairs are produced by rotating the specimen a small amount (7-10°) between two photographs of the same field of view. Examination of the two photographs in a stereo-viewer gives a 3-dimensional presentation of the image and clearly reveals depressions and protrusions. It is also possible, by carefully controlling the angle of rotation or tilt, to make quantitative measurements of height and depth above and below a reference plane.

C. The analysis of specimen composition

As was mentioned previously, when a material is bombarded with electrons of a sufficient high energy x-rays are produced whose wavelengths are characteristic of the atomic species from which they originate. It is also possible for atoms which have been excited by the primary electron beam to return to their original energy by the emission of electrons whose kinetic energies are characteristic of the atoms which have emitted them. These electrons are known as Auger electrons after their discoverer. It is possible for either type of radiation to be analysed so as to provide information concerning the composition of the material from which they arise but up to the present only the characteristic x-rays have been exploited to their full potential in commercial instruments, mainly because of the technical difficulties associated with detecting and analysing the Auger electrons; therefore most attention will be directed in this section to methods used in exploiting the former type of radiation.

The traditional method of analysing x-rays makes use of a crystal spectrometer in which the x-rays are diffracted at angles which depend on their wavelength and the spacing of planes in the crystal according to Bragg's law

$$\lambda = 2d \sin\theta. \text{ (See section VI.)} \qquad (2)$$

Where λ is the x-ray wavelength
d is the spacing of the crystal planes
and θ is the diffraction angle.

When the crystal is at the correct angle to diffract the x-rays being emitted by the sample they will pass through the spectrometer to a detector which is usually a proportional counter. The signal from the counter is then amplified and passed to a ratemeter, a chart recorder, or a cathode ray tube.

If the electron probe is kept stationary at a point such as an inclusion or precipitate particle on the surface of the specimen and the spectrometer scanned through a range of angles, the peaks corresponding to the characteristic x-rays emitted by the elements under the probe can be displayed on a chart recorder and measurement of the recorder trace leads to the identification of the elements in the volume excited by the electron beam. Alternatively the spectrometer can be "tuned-in" to a selected element and the electron beam scanned in a raster. The x-ray signal from the proportional counter can then be used to build up a picture of the distribution of the element in the area scanned. This mode of operation is illustrated in Fig. 20 which shows the distribution of copper, gold, silver, tin and indium in a section through a gold–silver–copper alloy wire mounted in a lead–tin–indium solder. It clearly shows the reaction zone built up around the wire during soldering and subsequent annealing at 40°C.

The crystal spectrometer made its first appearance in the field of microanalysis as an integral part of the electron-probe microanalyser (EPMA) which was developed by Castaing and described by him and Guinier in 1949. The first commercial EPMA was manufactured by CAMECA in France and installed at the laboratories of the International Nickel Company in 1958. The original Castaing probe did not possess the electron beam scanning capability which was later developed by Cosslett and Duncomb in 1956 and incorporated into the Cambridge Instruments Microscan in 1959.

Most modern EPMAs have two or more spectrometers enabling several elements to be monitored simultaneously as well as an optical microscope to aid in aligning the instrument and for positioning the specimen under the electron beam. They are also generally equipped with electron imaging facilities which usually make use of the specimen current mode described later.

One of the most important features of microanalysers is their high detection sensitivity which in favourable cases can be less than 10^{-16} g of material. This is achieved by the use of high beam currents (usually of the order of 10^{-8} A compared to 10^{-10}–10^{-12} A in the SEM) at the cost of some loss of resolution compared with the SEM. Moreover, since the transmission power of x-rays into materials is generally larger than that of electrons, the size of the x-ray emission area is far larger than the diameter of the electron probe; the former is usually 1–3 μm and is seldom below 0·3 μm. There is very little point therefore in attempting to reduce the electron probe diameter below 0·3 μm. In the case of the SEM, however, where the prime purpose is the imaging of rough surfaces at high resolution, the reverse is the case, and beam diameters of around 100 Å are used with the consequent sacrifice of high beam currents.

The two instruments however are not completely incompatible and one organisation at least (JEOL) manufactures a combined instrument (the

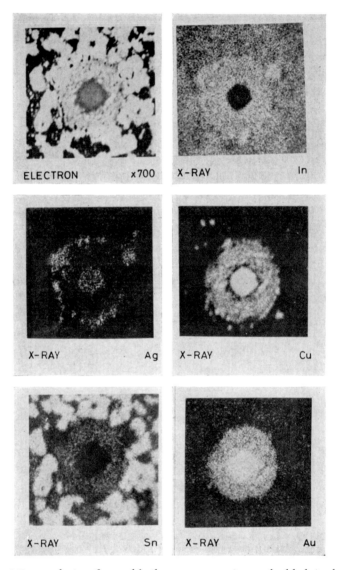

FIG. 20. Microanalysis of a gold–silver–copper wire embedded in lead-tin-indium solder showing a reaction zone between the wire and the solder.

JXA 50A) which can be used either as an SEM or an EPMA. This instrument has an extremely flexible beam current control and is equipped with facilities such as x-ray spectrometers and optical viewing for microanalysis as well as secondary electron detection for electron microscopy. The Cambridge Instrument Company, on the other hand, has marketed a crystal spectrometer which can be attached to their SEM.

It has to be recognized, however, that it is not usually practical to carry out high quality, quantitative microanalysis on rough specimens using a crystal spectrometer because of the very critical positioning of the specimen relative to the spectrometer. It is mainly for this reason that the development of energy dispersive x-ray analysis has been so widely welcomed by scanning electron microscopists. This method can be applied to all kinds of detectors such as the scintillation counter, the gas flow proportional counter and the lithium-drifted silicon semiconductor detector, where the output signal intensity is proportional to the energy of incident quanta. The semiconductor detector which has been mainly used for the detection of γ-rays, has now been improved in resolution and made available for the detection of soft x-rays. Since the output signal from this detector is proportional to the energy of the incident x-ray quanta, measurement of this signal by a pulse height analyser gives a measure of the energy of the x-ray quanta and can be used to identify the elements from which the x-rays originate.

As compared with the wavelength dispersive method, the energy dispersive method can give much higher x-ray intensities because there is no analysing crystal causing a loss of x-ray intensity due to its low reflection efficiency. Therefore the energy dispersive spectrometer can be effectively employed when the total x-rays generated are weak in intensity, which makes it particularly well suited to the analysis of x-rays in a SEM where the beam currents are low.

However the method has a number of disadvantages compared with the wavelength dispersive method.

(a) The resolution of spectra is poor.
(b) The limit of detectability for light elements is poor and sodium is the lowest element in the periodic table which can usefully be detected. Most wavelength dispersive spectrometers are capable of detecting all elements down to boron.
(c) The detection sensitivity is poor because of the low peak to background ratios.

Points (a) and (c) are illustrated in Fig. 21 where a spectrum obtained from a Be-Al-Si alloy using a energy dispersive detector on the Stereoscan is compared with the spectrum from the same sample obtained using a crystal spectrometer on the CAMECA microanalyser.

In spite of these disadvantages, however, the semiconductor detector has found very wide acceptance among electron microscopists because of

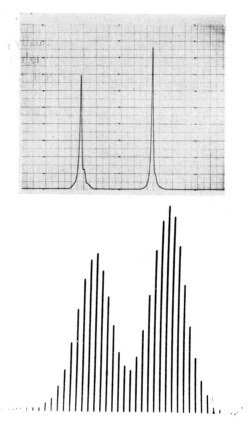

FIG. 21. Neighbouring peaks of aluminium and silicon x-rays from a beryllium-aluminium-silicon alloy obtained by scanning a wavelength dispersive spectrometer (upper figure) and by the energy dispersive detector (lower figure).

its unique ability to analyse inclusions, etc., on rough surfaces, the speed at which data can be collected, and the ease with which the resulting spectra can be interpreted.

D. *The analysis of microstructure*

The analysis of microstructure, by which is meant the morphology of phases and defects in a material, has largely come into the province of the optical microscope and, where high resolutions are necessary, the transmission electron microscope, although, as will be demonstrated in section VI, the electron emission microscope has made a considerable contribution to these studies. Electron probe instruments can also make useful contributions to such work because of their ability to provide information which cannot be observed in the optical microscope and because of the ease of specimen preparation compared with the transmission electron microscope.

It is known that the yield of secondary electrons emitted from a specimen varies depending on the composition. However, since this difference is not large and is screened by molecules adsorbed on the specimen surface, most secondary electron pictures do not show high contrast from heterogeneities of specimen composition. The efficiency with which primary electrons are back-scattered from a material on the other hand is extremely dependent on the atomic numbers of the elements constituting the material, and by varying the voltage on the electron collector it is possible to reject the low energy secondary electrons and accept only the higher energy back-scattered electrons. In this way a scanning image can be built up of the distribution of elements in a section of material. It must be emphasized, however, that the detection of back-scattered electrons is very sensitive to the surface topography of the specimen and when atomic number contrast alone is required it is important to ensure that specimens are flat and well polished.

Absorbed electrons may also be used to display atomic number contrast since the higher the proportion of electrons back-scattered the lower will be the number of absorbed electrons. An illustration of this reversal of atomic number contrast between back-scattered and absorbed electron images is shown in Fig. 22 for the case of the Be-Al-Si alloy mentioned above.

The imaging of defects, such as dislocations in the SEM, has recently been demonstrated by scientists at Cambridge, England and in Japan (Clarke and Howie, 1971; Stern et al., 1972) although the quality of such images is poor relative to those obtainable in the TEM it is, nevertheless, a useful technique since it permits the determination of the defect content of the surface region in bulk specimens without the need to prepare thin foils for the TEM.

E. New developments

A third type of electron probe instrument, the scanning transmission electron microscope (STEM), at present under development, shows great promise for microstructural investigations. Its principle is based on that of the SEM in that the electron column serves purely as a probe-forming system, and imaging is by means of an electron detector placed below the specimen which is a thin foil as in the conventional TEM. It has the

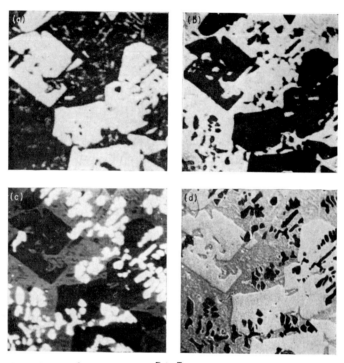

FIG. 22. Atomic number contrast in the scanning electron microscope from a beryllium-aluminium-silicon alloy. (a) Back-scattered electron image—dark areas are beryllium-rich. (b) Specimen-current image—light areas are beryllium-rich. (c) X-ray image of aluminium distribution. (d) X-ray image of silicon distribution.

advantage over the latter instrument, however, of being able to image thicker sections of material because of the high collection efficiency of the detector compared to the electron lenses and fluorescent screen of the conventional TEM.

Scanning coils and detectors have been fitted to TEMs and transmission stages to SEMs but the true STEM system described by Crewe (1970) offers much greater scope for the fitting of accessories for scanning electron diffraction, x-ray analysis, Auger electron analysis, electron energy analysis and signal processing. The ultimate aim is the development of an instrument incorporating all the modes of image formation and specimen analysis at present shared by the TEM, SEM and EPMA and a few more besides, so that materials scientists are able to extract the maximum amount of information from their specimens without the need to transfer them from one instrument to another with all the resulting problems of relocating areas.

V. THE ELECTRON EMISSION MICROSCOPE

Like the scanning electron microscope, the electron emission microscope has been developed specifically for the examination of the surface of materials. A specimen is placed in the instrument, and is stimulated so that secondary electrons are emitted. These are accelerated away from the specimen surface by applying a negative potential to the specimen. The electrons are then focused by a series of electromagnetic lenses so as to produce a highly magnified image of the specimen.

There are several ways in which a material may be made to emit electrons and some of these are listed below.

1. Thermal emission.
2. Photo-emission.
3. Secondary emission.
4. Ionic bombardment.
5. Field emission.

Of these we shall only consider 1, 2 and 4 in the present section. Secondary emission has already been discussed in the section on scanning electron microscopy. Field emission electron microscopy and its companion field ion microscopy are two techniques which are important but do not fall within the scope of this book.

The first emission electron microscope employing ionic bombardment as the means of producing emission was built by Mollenstädt and was described by him in 1963. Resolutions of ~ 1000 Å were obtainable and facilities were available to heat the specimen. One disadvantage of this technique, however, is that small differences in emission which arise from variations in crystallographic orientation are difficult to detect. More recently emphasis has been placed on photo-emission (Schweizer and Form, 1970; Dannohl et al., 1971; Desforges and Fourdeux, 1972; Wegmann, 1972) and thermionic emission techniques (Kinsman and Aaronson, 1971).

A schematic diagram of a commercially available photo-emission electron microscope is reproduced in Fig. 23. Ultraviolet light is focused on the specimen surface by means of a highly polished anode which is situated a short distance away from the sample. A small heater is also provided so that the instrument may be used in the thermionic mode. The emitted electrons are brought to focus on a fluorescent screen at the base of the microscope by three electromagnetic lenses.

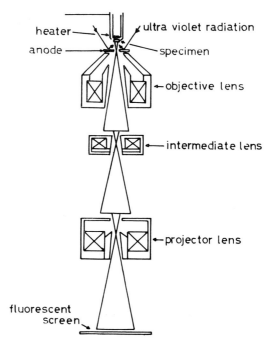

FIG. 23. Schematic diagram showing the construction of an emission electron microscope.

When the instrument is used in the photo-emission mode, resolutions of ~ 200 Å are possible which compares very favourably with the scanning electron microscope. In the thermionic emission mode, the resolution is poorer and may be typically 1000 Å.

Wegmann (1972) has suggested that contrast arises in the photo-emission electron microscope because of differences in electron emissivities of different materials, different inclinations of different surface elements and distortions in the electric field in the vicinity of the specimen surface. The main advantage of the photo-electron microscope over the scanning electron microscope is that there is less distortion of the image and a given phase appears the same in different parts of the specimen.

The main applications of the photo-emission microscope have been in the study of dynamic processes such as phase transformations and grain growth. For a more detailed account of this microscope and its uses the reader should consult the papers by Wegmann listed in the bibliography.

VI. X–RAY DIFFRACTION

The primary aim of crystal structure analysis by x-ray diffraction is to obtain a detailed picture of the arrangement of atoms in a crystal as if one had viewed it through an extremely powerful microscope. This information can then be used to calculate interatomic distances, bond angles and molecular formulae. The structure of a crystal can also be used to "fingerprint" the material and identify it by comparison with known standards.

X-ray diffraction is a very useful tool in establishing phase boundaries in equilibrium diagram studies and for measuring crystallite sizes and strain in crystals from the broadening of the x-ray lines. It is also used by theoretical chemists, concerned with interactions between molecules, to obtain precise molecular dimensions.

In an optical or electron microscope the radiation scattered by the object being viewed can be recombined by the lens system to give a magnified image of the scattering material. X-rays can be scattered by atoms but cannot normally be focused. Consequently an x-ray microscope cannot be used to view atoms. However, it is possible to simulate the recombination of scattered x-rays by a complicated mathematical calculation. Fourier synthesis of the pattern of diffracted radiation is a fundamental step in molecular structure determination by diffraction methods. The resulting picture is known as a Fourier map.

In order to "see" the finest details of crystal structure (with dimensions 10^{-6}-10^{-8} cm) it is necessary to use radiation of wavelength comparable to or smaller than the dimensions of the atoms. This is available in the form of x-rays produced by bombarding a target of intermediate atomic number (e.g., copper, molybdenum, chromium) with fast electrons when about 2% of their energy is converted into x-rays; the balance is converted into heat in the target. The x-radiation consists of a continuous spectrum of "white radiation" and a superimposed line spectrum of high intensity, single-wavelength components—"characteristic radiation". The target and electron source are enclosed in a glass envelope under vacuum to prevent scattering of the electrons by gas atoms and the x-rays are emitted through a beryllium window. A filter is usually placed between the source of x-rays and the specimens, which preferentially absorbs the unwanted components of the x-ray spectrum and results in an essentially monochromatic beam of x-rays arriving at the specimen. In the case of x-rays from a copper target, a thin nickel foil is used as a filter.

The formation of an image of the object being studied is not directly possible when using x-rays, and instead the diffraction pattern produced when scattered x-rays interfere and reinforce is used to provide indirect evidence of interatomic distances. The diffraction pattern resulting from the interaction of x-rays with the atoms in a crystal is produced in a manner exactly analogous to that produced by the interaction of light with slits of dimensions of the same order as the wavelength of light. This is illustrated in Fig. 24 which shows schematically, in two dimensions,

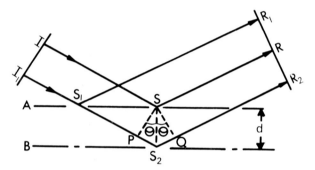

FIG. 24. Schematic representation of the diffraction of x-rays by a crystal.

what happens when x-rays are scattered by planes of atoms in a crystal. If A and B are planes of atoms and II_1 represents one of the crests of the approaching waves the waves scattered by atoms S_1 and S will reinforce each other if the distance ISR equals the distance $I_1S_1R_1$. It will also be true that any other atom lying anywhere in the plane A will reinforce the beam in this direction. Reinforcement takes place when the incident and scattered rays make equal angles with the atomic plane. The planes of atoms can therefore be regarded as mirrors which reflect a portion of the incident radiation at an angle equal to the angle of incidence. For rays such as $S_2 R_2$, scattered by successive crystal planes to reinforce, the difference in path length for rays reflected from successive planes must equal an integral number of wavelengths, i.e., PS_2Q must equal $n\lambda$ or $n\lambda = 2d \sin \theta$ where n is an integer and λ is the wavelength of the x-rays.

This is Bragg's law and is the basis of all diffraction phenomena whether they involve x-rays, electrons or neutrons.

Thus a single crystal in the path of a beam of x-rays can be regarded as acting as a series of semitransparent mirrors. However, any given set of mirrors (or crystal planes) can only reflect (or diffract) x-rays when all the conditions for Bragg's law are satisfied. That is, for radiation of a given wavelength, λ, crystal planes of spacing d will only diffract the x-rays when they are at a certain critical angle, θ, to the incident beam.

If a monochromatic beam of radiation is directed at a single crystal the angle of incidence may not be correct for reflection from any of its planes. To ensure that Bragg's law is satisfied it is necessary to provide a range of values of either λ or θ. The various ways of doing this form the basis of the standard methods of diffraction used in crystal analysis.

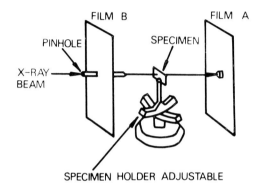

FIG. 25. Schematic arrangement of the Laue camera.

In the Laue method, for example, a single crystal is held stationary in a beam of white radiation, usually from a tungsten target, so that the variable is the range of wavelengths in the beam. In the rotating crystal method, on the other hand, a single crystal is rotated or oscillated in a beam of monochromatic x-rays. The rotation brings different atomic planes in turn into reflecting positions and in this case the angle θ is the variable. Finally, in the powder method, a large number of small crystals are placed in the path of a monochromatic beam of x-rays. A proportion of the crystals will be correctly oriented to reflect from each of the possible reflecting planes. Therefore, in this case also, θ is the variable.

A schematic diagram of the Laue camera is shown in Fig. 25. It consists of a pinhole system which collimates a beam of x-rays into a narrow pencil of rays, a goniometer head, or other device to hold the crystal in a definite orientation, and a flat film in a light-proof envelope placed to receive either the x-rays transmitted through the crystal or those reflected back from its surface. Each reflecting plane in the crystal reflects a portion of the beam, and the diffraction pattern is a series of spots that can be

K

visualized simply as a pattern made by reflection from a number of mirrors inclined at different angles.

Figure 26 shows a Laue transmission photograph of a crystal of apatite. It is quite obvious in this photograph that the spots lie on ellipses that have

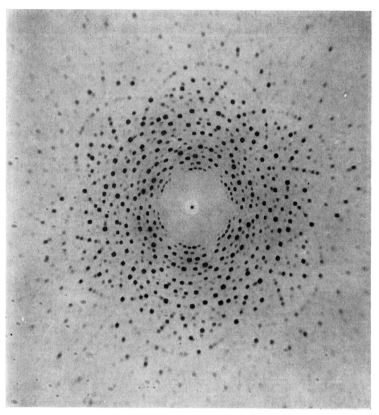

FIG. 26. Laue transmission photograph of a single crystal of Apatite.

one end of their major axes at the centre of the film. All spots on any one ellipse are reflections from planes of a single zone (planes parallel to a single zone axis of a crystal). On a Laue back-reflection pattern of a crystal these zones of spots lie on hyperbolae as shown in Fig. 27 which is a photograph of a back-reflection pattern from a silicon single crystal.

Laue patterns give information about the symmetry of the crystal. For example, it can be seen from Fig. 26 that the apatite crystal has six-fold symmetry about the zone axis perpendicular to the plane of the film. Similarly, the back-reflection Laue photograph of the silicon single crystal displays three-fold symmetry, and in a cubic crystal this means that the [111] direction is in the direction of the x-ray beam and perpendicular to the film.

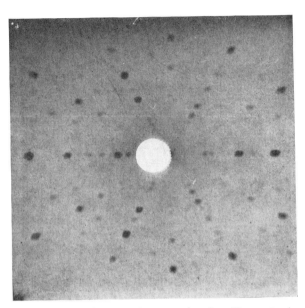

FIG. 27. Laue back-reflection photograph of a silicon single crystal.

The Laue method is also useful for revealing imperfections in crystals caused by deformation. Laue spots from deformed crystals are blurred or elongated in the same way as spots of light reflected by curved mirrors. In the case of a polycrystalline material, where several crystals are illuminated by the x-ray beam the Laue patterns from each crystal are superimposed and this gives a method of determining the grain size in a metal.

The powder method employs a monochromatic beam of radiation falling on a finely powdered specimen or a fine-grained polycrystalline specimen.

A photograph of a Philips powder camera is shown in Fig. 28. It consists of a collimator which directs a fine beam of x-rays on to the specimen, which is in the form of a wire or a powder glued to a fibre, and a strip of film mounted on the inside cylindrical surface of the camera. A tube mounted on the opposite side of the camera from the collimator collects the undiffracted x-ray beam and prevents it from fogging the film.

Diffracted rays leave the specimen along the generators of cones concentric with the primary beam, each cone having a semiapex angle equal to twice the Bragg angle θ. The intersections of these cones of x-rays with the film are revealed after development as arcs concentric around the

FIG. 28. X-ray powder camera manufactured by Philips, Eindhoven.

central spot (as shown in Fig. 29) and the diameter of each arc can be measured (when the film is laid out flat) and directly related to the Bragg angle θ. The "d-spacing" of the set of planes contributing to each arc on the film can then be calculated using the Bragg law, $n\lambda = 2d \sin \theta$. Alternatively a set of scales, supplied by manufacturers of x-ray diffraction equipment for a number of the most commonly used x-ray wavelengths, and calibrated directly in "d-values", may be used to measure the lattice spacings directly from the x-ray film.

The powder method is mainly used in the identification of unknown substances for which purpose the powder diffraction pattern can be regarded as the "finger-print" of an element or compound. Very few substances have identical diffraction patterns and where ambiguity arises the question may usually be resolved by the use of chemical analysis or electron-probe microanalysis to provide additional information. Powder diffraction data on a very large number of substances has been collected and assembled in the JCPDS* powder diffraction file which is reviewed

* Joint Committee on Powder Diffraction Standards.

annually, and unknowns can usually be identified by comparison of their "*d*-spacings" with those listed in the file.

Since the positions of the lines on a powder camera film are very sensitive to changes in interatomic spacings in a crystal, this method is frequently used to measure changes in the unit cell parameters of the crystal structure caused by effects such as radiation damage, and other elements in solid solution. Nowadays, however, the powder camera has largely been

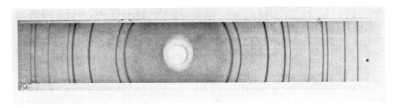

FIG. 29. An x-ray powder photograph of face-centred cubic thorium oxide (ThO$_2$).

superseded for this application by the x-ray diffractometer technique which is based on the same principles but uses a radiation counter to scan through a range of Bragg angles, and the signal from the counter, after amplification, is recorded on an electronic chart recorder. The series of arcs on an x-ray film is then replaced by a series of peaks on the chart recorder. Such peaks can be more accurately defined and measured than the lines on an x-ray film.

A further application of the powder diffraction technique is its use in the measurement of crystal sizes in powders and metals. If the specimen in a powder camera contains crystals smaller than 10^{-4} cm the diffraction lines are broadened and the smaller the crystal size the broader are the lines. After correction for broadening arising in the diffraction equipment, the particle-size broadening, B, should vary with wavelength, λ, and diffraction angle, θ, according to the law

$$B = \frac{K\lambda}{L \cos \theta} \tag{3}$$

where L is the effective size of the crystals and K is a constant. The most convenient method of measuring the width of x-ray lines on a film is by means of a film scanner in which the film is scanned at constant known speed under a light from a source above the film and the light transmitted through the film and a slit is detected by a photo-electric cell. The electrical signal from the detector which is proportional to the brightness of the light transmitted, and therefore, inversely proportional to the degree of blackening on the film, can be recorded on a chart recorder.

Some information as to the sizes of crystals in coarse-grained materials may also be obtained by the degree of "spottiness" of diffraction lines. Fig. 30 shows an example of a diffraction pattern from cordierite which

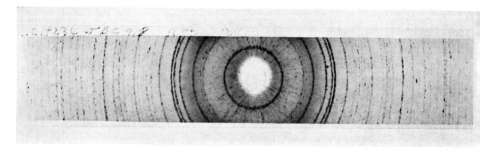

FIG. 30. An x-ray powder photograph of coarse-grained cordierite, a magnesium aluminium silicate.

had a relatively coarse grain size—probably approaching 10^{-2} cm. However the quantitative interpretation of such photographs is very difficult.

Microstresses in materials can also result in diffraction line broadening, but the broadening in this case obeys a different law to broadening from fine crystal size and the two effects can thus be separated.

Finally, preferred orientations in metals or other materials can be recognized by the production of non-uniform arcs or rings in the diffraction pattern. Random orientations produce rings that are uniformly black all round, while the presence of texture is indicated by intense spots at certain points on the rings. The ideal camera for this type of work is the flat-plate camera of the Laue type in which the whole of a diffraction ring is recorded. A series of photographs are taken with the specimen tilted at various angles in the x-ray beam in order to completely specify the texture.

VII. THE STUDY OF CRYSTAL DEFECTS

A. Introduction

Most people are familiar with salt crystals, grains of sand and the crystalline nature of ice, but it is not always realized that many other materials which are in common use are also crystalline. All metals and alloys, ceramics, inorganic salts and many other substances are made up of agglomerates of crystals. By carefully polishing and etching a small sample of a metal and examining it under an optical microscope the crystal structure may be revealed. In Fig. 31 an optical micrograph is shown of a pure iron sample which has been etched in a 2% nitric acid in ethanol solution for 15 s. The crystals making up the sample are clearly visible. In metals the crystals are referred to as grains, and the boundaries separating two grains are known as grain boundaries.

Within a given crystal the atoms or molecules are arranged in a regular 3-dimensional array. In iron, for example, the atoms are situated at the

FIG. 31. Optical micrograph showing grain boundaries in a pure iron specimen.
× 100.

corners and at the centre of a cube, whilst in copper the atoms are located at the cube corners and also at the centres of the cube faces.

Figure 32 illustrates the differences between the two arrangements of atoms.

The hypothetical framework upon which the atoms are arranged is referred to as a lattice, and is built up by repeating throughout space a basic building block known as the unit cell. In the case of iron we have already seen that the simplest unit we could have is a cube with one atom at the centre. In other materials the unit cell may be more complicated, and in α uranium for example, the unit cell is a right-angled parallelapiped. The lengths of the sides of the unit cell and the angles between the faces of the unit cell define the lattice parameters. Given these parameters and the positions of the atoms in the unit cell, we can build up a model of the atomic arrangement in a crystal.

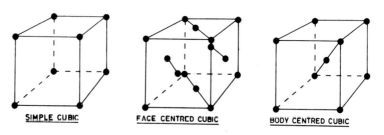

SIMPLE CUBIC   FACE CENTRED CUBIC   BODY CENTRED CUBIC

FIG. 32. Atomic arrangements in three types of cubic lattice.

In the study of defects it is often necessary to refer to a particular direction within the crystal or a specific plane of atoms. To do this we imagine that a unit cell is located at the centre of a set of axes X, Y, Z as illustrated in Fig. 33 (a). Suppose that a plane in the crustal cuts the axes at the points A, B and C as shown in Fig. 33 (b) so that the lengths of the intercepts are r, p and q. The plane is now identified by a set of indices h k l which are given by the ratios,

$$h = a/r, \ k = b/p, \ l = c/q$$

where a, b and c are the lattice parameters of the unit cell. When we are referring to a particular plane within the crystal we identify it by the notation (hkl). In Fig. 33 (c) some of the planes which we shall need to refer to later are illustrated. The faces of the unit cell are (001), (010) and (100) whilst the plane which passes through three corners of the cell is the (111).

A crystal direction may be defined in the way illustrated in Fig. 34. We imagine a line drawn parallel to the direction of interest mn so that it passes through the origin 0 and cuts the surface of the unit cell at a point s. The co-ordinates of the point of intersection are then found. Suppose that in a particular case these co-ordinates are found to be $\frac{1}{2}$, 1, $-\frac{1}{2}$. We multiply each co-ordinate by 2 to remove the fractions to give 1, 2, -1. The direction mn is then written as $[12\bar{1}]$. Some of the important directions which are necessary to our understanding of crystal defects are illustrated in Fig. 34 (c).

Sometimes it is necessary to talk about a set of planes or directions rather than a particular plane or direction and in these cases a different notation is used. $\{hkl\}$ implies the set of planes of this type whilst $\langle uvw \rangle$

is the set of directions. In the cubic system there may be as many as 48 planes or directions which belong to a given type.

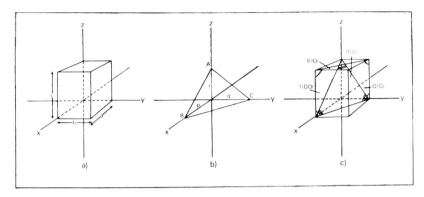

FIG. 33. Technique used for indexing planes in a crystal. (a) Unit cell of dimensions $a \times b \times c$. (b) Plane ABC intersecting the XYZ axes at distances p, q, and r from the origin. (c) Some important crystallographic planes.

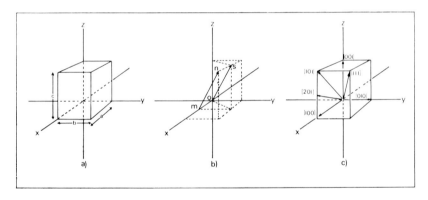

FIG. 34. Technique used for identifying directions in a crystal. (a) Unit cell of dimensions $a \times b \times c$. (b) Line OS is drawn parallel to the direction mn so as to pass through the origin at O and intersect the unit cell at S. (c) Some important crystallographic directions.

B. *The plastic deformation of crystals*

Now that we have considered some of the basic features of the crystalline state, we may next examine how a crystal will behave if it is strained. Most ceramic materials are brittle and under the application of a large tensile stress they will break without undergoing any measurable deform-

K*

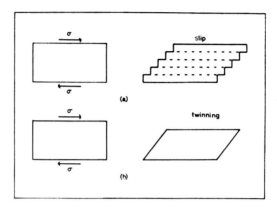

FIG. 35. Schematic diagram showing the differences between slip and twinning processes.

ation. Most metals and alloys on the other hand are relatively ductile, and some plastic deformation will occur before fracture. In the remainder of this section we shall be interested in seeing how we can study the various phenomena which take place during deformation. The use of photography in the study of fracture is dealt with in a later section.

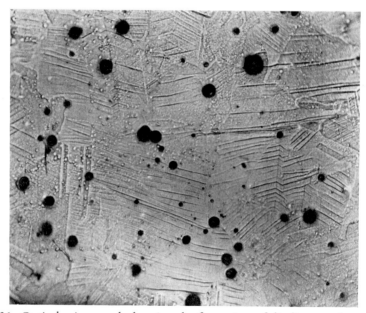

FIG. 36. Optical micrograph showing the formation of slip lines on the surface of a polished and deformed copper specimen. × 500.

Optical microscopy can tell us a lot about the different processes which operate when a metal is strained. By studying the polished surfaces of pure metals it is possible to distinguish two deformation processes, slip and twinning. These two processes have been illustrated schematically in Fig. 35. When a crystal deforms by slip, small regions of the crystal slide over one another. A simple model which demonstrates this is a pack of

FIG. 37. Photo-electron emission micrograph showing the deformation of a copper specimen. (Photographs by courtesy of Balzers.) (a) Fully annealed. (b) Lightly strained. (c) Heavily strained. (d) Strained and annealed.

cards. If this is gently pushed forward from the top, some of the cards will stick together so that at the edge of the pack the surface will appear to be stepped. We can show the formation of slip steps by taking a piece of copper rod and carefully polished it so as to remove all the scratches. If it is now squeezed in a vice and examined under the optical microscope at a high magnification using oblique illumination, it is possible to show up the slip steps. The micrograph shown in Fig. 36 was obtained in this way. The photoemission microscope may also be used to follow the deformation of a metal. The micrographs reproduced in Fig. 37 show the development of slip lines in copper.

In the twinning process part of the crystal moves so that it becomes a mirror image of the undeformed part of the crystal. The diagram in Fig. 38 shows the positions of the atoms before and after twinning in a face centred cubic metal such as copper. To identify a particular twinning system, we first specify the direction in which shear takes place. In the example shown in Fig. 38 the shear direction is parallel to the [111] in the

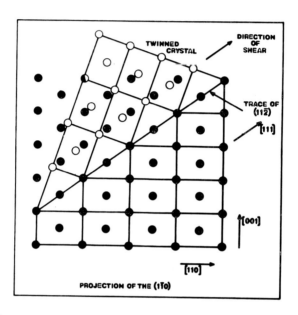

FIG. 38. Schematic diagram illustrating the atomic movements which take place during twinning. Solid circles show the positions of atoms in a face-centred cubic lattice before twinning and open circles show the positions after twinning.

original crystal. In addition to the shear direction we also define the twinning plane, which in this instance is the $(11\bar{2})$ plane.

Many studies have been made of the formation of twins using optical microscopy and by combining this technique with x-ray diffraction it has been possible to identify the twinning planes and shear directions in many metals and non-metals. As in the case of slip, twinning may be induced in metals such as zinc by squeezing a polished specimen in a vice. The twins formed by this process are clearly shown in Fig. 39. Where the twins have interacted with grain boundaries or other twins small cracks have formed and will act as points of weakness during further deformation. The scratch MN visible in Fig. 39 illustrates the amount of surface rumpling which occurs during twinning.

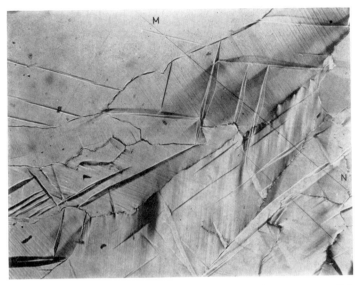

FIG. 39. Optical micrograph showing the formation of twins in a polished and deformed zinc specimen. × 500.

C. *The mechanism of slip*

Although the amount of knowledge on the deformation of metals obtained from optical studies on single crystals is quite extensive, the exact mechanism by which slip occurs cannot be established. Simple ideas would suggest that two neighbouring planes of atoms in a crystal would move over one another. However, if we calculate the stress required to do this we find that this is about 1000 to 10,000 × greater than that measured experimentally. We must therefore look for an alternative mechanism.

In the 1930s the existence of crystal dislocations was postulated. It was suggested that defects might exist within a crystal which could move under the application of a stress. We can illustrate this schematically as shown in Fig. 40. The defect in this instance takes the form of an extra plane of atoms, XX', squeezed into the lattice. When a force is applied the dislocation moves until it reaches the crystal surface, where it forms a step or slip line Y. The stress required for this process is the same as that measured by experiment. The slip lines observed in Fig. 36 are the order of several hundred Angstroms high so that many dislocations must have taken part in the slip process.

If we deform a small block of metal so that part of the top slips over the bottom we introduce a dislocation as shown in Fig. 41. On one face an edge dislocation is formed whilst on the other the dislocation is a screw. Figure 41 shows the atom arrangements for each type of dislocation. In the

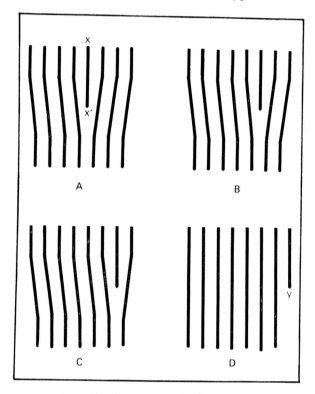

FIG. 40. Movement of a dislocation.

case of the edge dislocation the fault consists of an extra plane of atoms squeezed into the lattice whilst around the core of the screw dislocation the atoms form a spiral. At positions along the line, the dislocation will have both edge and screw components.

In the study of crystal defects, it is necessary to be able to define a quantity which will describe the magnitude and direction of a dislocation. We do this by means of the Burgers circuit. We first compare the atoms arranged in a perfect crystal with those in one containing an edge dislocation, see Fig. 42. Suppose we make a circuit in the perfect lattice about some point 0 so that we start at position (1) then move on to (2) next to (3) and so on until finally we come back to (1). If we now try to make the

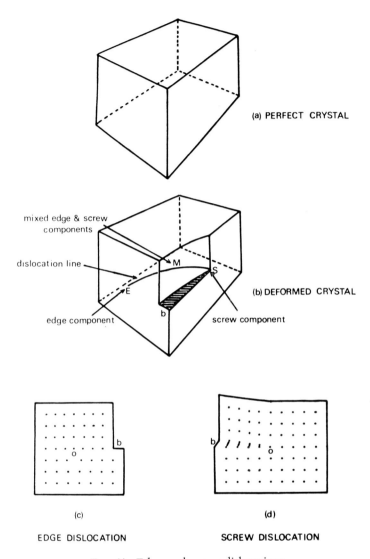

(a) PERFECT CRYSTAL

mixed edge & screw
components

dislocation line

M
S

(b) DEFORMED CRYSTAL

E

b

edge component   screw component

(c)   (d)

EDGE DISLOCATION   SCREW DISLOCATION

FIG. 41. Edge and screw dislocations.

same circuit in a faulted crystal about 0, where this is at the core of the dislocation, we find that it is necessary to make an extra step (9) to (1). The length and direction of this step is known as the Burgers vector of the dislocation and is denoted by **b**. The direction of **b** is perpendicular to the line of the dislocation. We can carry out the same procedure for a perfect screw dislocation but in this case the Burgers vector lies parallel to the line of the dislocation. In general, for a dislocation line the Burgers vector is the same all along it. In materials such as iron, molybdenum and niobium which have the body centred cubic structure the common Burgers vector

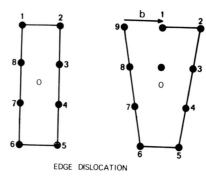

EDGE DISLOCATION

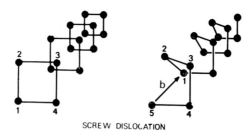

SCREW DISLOCATION

FIG. 42. Burgers circuits for edge and screw dislocations.

is in the $\langle 111 \rangle$ direction and has a magnitude equal to $\sqrt{\dfrac{3}{2}}\, a$. In face-centred cubic metals (aluminium, gold, copper, etc.) the Burgers vector is parallel to the [110] direction and has a magnitude of $\sqrt{\dfrac{1}{2}}\, a$.

After the postulation of dislocations, many attempts were made to observe them directly. In the following paragraphs, we shall consider how this can be done and how crystal dislocations may be photographed.

D. The observation of crystal defects

Of the different techniques which have been developed to study crystal defects the most widely used is transmission electron microscopy. This technique is particularly suitable since it is possible to resolve detail down to 4 Å. Thus under certain conditions individual lattice planes may be observed. Before discussing the uses of this technique, however, we must consider how an image is formed in the electron microscope.

1. *Electron microscopy of perfect crystals.* We can develop several important ideas regarding the interaction of electrons with a crystalline material by making use of the Bragg equation given in section VI.

In Fig. 43 a schematic diagram is given showing the diffraction of an electron beam by a set of crystal planes with interatomic spacing d. In a

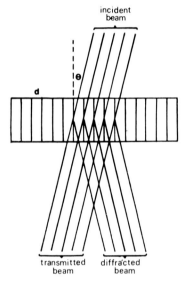

FIG. 43. Schematic diagram showing the diffraction of an electron beam by a set of crystal planes.

material such as iron, the spacing of the {111} planes is 1·655 Å so that for a 100 kV beam of electrons θ will be $\sim\frac{1}{2}°$. In the transmission electron microscope we arrange for the primary electron beam to be more or less perpendicular to the specimen, so that crystal planes which are almost perpendicular to the specimen surface and satisfy the Bragg equation may diffract. On this simple model we would normally only expect to find one set of planes giving rise to diffraction. Tilting the crystal through 1 or 2° would allow a different set to operate. In practice, the very thin nature of the transmission electron microscope specimen results in a relaxation of the Bragg condition so that several diffracted beams may result. This is illustrated in Fig. 44. As mentioned in section III the diffracted beams may be brought to focus to produce a diffraction pattern.

The intensity of the diffracted beams are dependent on how closely the Bragg condition is satisfied. Generally one diffracted beam will be much stronger than the rest and this is known as the operating reflection. In the simple theories of contrast formation in the electron microscope, only the

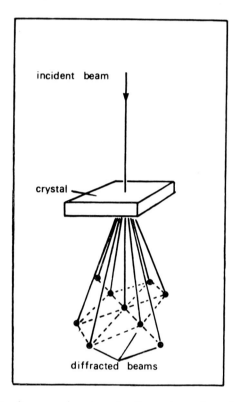

incident beam

crystal

diffracted beams

FIG. 44. Schematic diagram showing the formation of an electron diffraction pattern.

transmitted beam and the operating reflection are taken into account, and the other diffracted beams are neglected. This approximation is reasonable at low operating voltages, but may lead to discrepancies between the predicted and actual images found at high voltages. It is normal to denote the operating reflection by the vector **g**. In practice we can obtain this vector from the diffraction pattern by drawing the line from the centre spot to the operating reflection. In later paragraphs we shall discuss the importance of **g** in photographing crystal defects.

The Kinematical theory of electron diffraction enables us to calculate the relative intensities of the transmitted and diffracted beams. The amplitude of the diffracted beam ϕ_g is given by the equation

$$\phi_g \alpha \int_0^t \exp\left(-2\pi i s z\right) dz \tag{4}$$

where t is the thickness of the foil and $\mathbf{s}$ is a vector which determines how far the crystal planes are tilted from the Bragg angle. The relationship

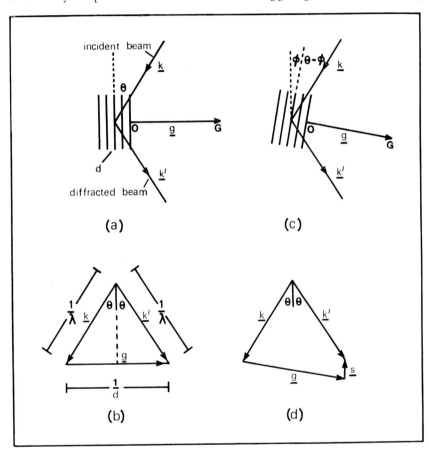

FIG. 45. Relationship between $\mathbf{g}$, $\mathbf{s}$ and the incident and diffracted beams.

between the vectors $\mathbf{s}$, $\mathbf{g}$ and the incident and diffracted beams can be established from Fig. 45. The incident and diffracted beams are parallel to the directions $\mathbf{k}$ and $\mathbf{k}'$ respectively and the Bragg angle is θ. The operating reflection $\mathbf{g}$ is represented by the direction perpendicular to the diffracting planes. If the crystal is orientated exactly at the Bragg angle, we can construct an isosceles triangle as shown in Fig. 45 (b). The sides parallel to **k** and **k′** are equal to $1/\lambda$ and the apex angle is equal to 2θ so that the base is equal to $2.(1/\lambda).\sin\theta$. From the Bragg equation it follows that the base of the triangle is equal to $1/d$ where d is the spacing of the crystal planes. If the crystal is now tilted through an angle ϕ as shown in Fig. 45 (c), we find that it is no longer possible to form the isosceles triangle but instead a quadrilateral is obtained, see Fig. 45 (d). This gives a definition of the quantity **s**. Clearly when $\mathbf{s} = 0$, $\phi = 0$ and the crystal is at the exact Bragg condition.

By multiplying equation 4 by ϕ_g^*, the complex conjugate of ϕ_g we can obtain the following expression for the intensity of the diffracted beam,

$$I_D \propto (\sin\pi st)^2 \,/\, (\pi s)^2 \qquad\qquad (5)$$

Equation 5 predicts that as the thickness of the foil is varied, the intensity of the diffracted and transmitted beams will fluctuate.* Figure 46 is a transmission electron micrograph taken of a tapered thin foil and clearly shows the variation in intensity with thickness. If we were to tilt the foil so as to change **s** we would find that the fringes visible in Fig. 46 would change position. In examining a thin foil therefore it is essential to be able to tilt the specimen so as to obtain the optimum contrast conditions. Most modern electron microscopes used in the study of metals are fitted with stages which allow the sample to be tilted about one or more axes.

2. Electron microscopy of crystals containing dislocations. So far we have only considered the contrast produced by a perfect crystal, and we must now study the effects dislocations and other defects will have on the electron image. Suppose we have a single crystal containing an edge dislocation as depicted in Fig. 40. If we examine the crystal on either side of the dislocation at some distance from the dislocation, we find that the lattice planes are undistorted and in effect we have perfect crystal. We can therefore orientate the crystal slightly away from the Bragg angle, i.e., $\mathbf{s} \neq 0$, so that it gives a bright image. The lattice planes around the dislocation, however, are bent so that the electrons will be scattered out of the transmitted beam, and the image will consist of a bright field containing a dark line. In this way we are able to photograph dislocations in metals and other crystalline materials.

---

* It is assumed that

$$I_D + I_0 = 1$$

where I_0 is the intensity of the transmitted beam.

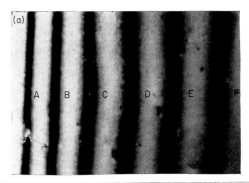

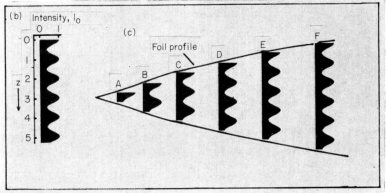

FIG. 46. (a) Transmission electron micrograph showing the formation of fringes at the edge of a tapered foil. (b) Variation in intensity of transmitted beam with depth as predicted by equation 5. (c) Schematic diagram showing the profile of the foil in (a). If the intensity variation with depth curve in (b) is superimposed it is seen that at points such as A, B, C, D, E and F a minimum intensity will be obtained. At points in between these, maximum intensity is achieved.

In practice we find that the image of a single dislocation may assume several different forms depending on the value of $\mathbf{s}$ and on the particular reflection $\mathbf{g}$ which is operating. A few examples of the appearance of a dislocation in the electron microscope are given in Fig. 47. Generally a dislocation is seen as a dark line as shown in Fig. 47 (a) but occasionally we see dotted contrast, Fig. 47 (b) or even two dark lines as illustrated in Fig. 47 (c). The latter may occur when two strong reflections are operating. By tilting the sample into certain orientations we can arrange for the dislocation to become invisible as depicted in Fig. 47 (d). To understand this more fully we must first examine the expression for the intensities of an electron beam in a crystal containing a dislocation. If ϕ_g is the amplitude of the diffracted beam we may write

$$\phi_g \alpha \int_0^t \exp\left(-2\pi i s z\right) . \exp\left(-2\pi i \mathbf{g} . \mathbf{b} \, A\right) dz \tag{6}$$

where A is a $f(z)$ and is dependent on the orientation of the dislocation line. Equation 6 is very similar to equation 4 apart from the extra exponential term $\exp\left(-2\pi i \mathbf{g} . \mathbf{b} \, A\right)$.

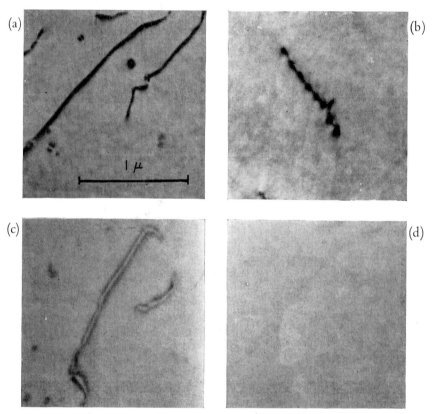

FIG. 47. Examples of dislocation images produced in the transmission electron microscope.

If $\mathbf{g} . \mathbf{b}$ is 0 then this term will be unity and the expression will become identical to equation 4 which is applicable to a perfect crystal. Under these conditions the dislocation will become invisible. In practice, we can make use of this fact to determine the Burgers vector of a particular dislocation. The image of the dislocation is photographed for a number of different operating reflections. We next assume different values for **b** and compute the scalar product **g.b**. When the dislocation is in contrast **g.b** should be + 1, + 2, etc., and when it is invisible **g.b** should be 0. In this way we can eventually arrive at the Burgers vector of the dislocation. This method is known as the **g.b** analysis and has been successfully applied to the determination of Burgers vectors in many materials. However it should be noted here that the Kinematical theory makes several basic assumptions about the interaction of electrons with matter which are not valid in many instances. Strict application of the **g.b** criteria may therefore lead to erroneous results and some care should be taken on interpreting the electron micrographs obtained. More recently methods have been devised for computing the expected images of dislocations for a given Burgers vector for a particular set of **g** and **s** conditions (France and Loretto, 1965; Loretto and France, 1969). This technique makes use of the Dynamical Theory of electron diffraction, and the computer output takes the form of a picture showing the dislocation image. Direct comparison can then be made with the experimentally determined image. These techniques are clearly outside the scope of the present article.

One of the main disadvantages of examining dislocation images using the methods so far described is the lack of resolution which can be achieved This occurs because the intensity of the image is not particularly sensitive to small changes in the strain field around a dislocation when $|s|$ is close to zero. If $|s|$ is very large, a very low intensity image will be produced but the contrast is very large. Cockayne and his co-workers (1971; 1973) have employed this fact to study the images of dislocations in a large number of materials. A particular reflection is selected for study, and the specimen is then tilted so that the diffraction spot corresponding to this reflection is very weak, i.e., $|s| \gg 0$. A dark field image is then formed using this reflection. Very long exposure times are generally required and it is usually necessary to take a series of photographs with the focus slightly changed in each case, this is because it is not always possible to see the dark field image of the dislocation on the viewing screen. This method is known as the weak beam technique and a typical example of the type of image which can be obtained is shown in Fig. 48. Under bright field conditions, the dislocation would probably appear as a single line but in fact, as Fig. 48 shows, the dislocation has dissociated in some parts to produce a pair of dislocations.

In 1956 attempts were made to resolve directly the lattice planes in a crystal and to obtain photographs of the way in which the planes are distorted in the region of a dislocation. Mentor (1966) prepared thin crystals of copper and platinum phthalocyanine and examined them at magnifications of × 77,000 on a Siemens Elmskop 1A electron microscope operated at 80 kV. These materials were chosen since they had lattice spacings similar to the resolving power of the microscope. Images were obtained which consisted of sets of parallel fringes spaced approximately

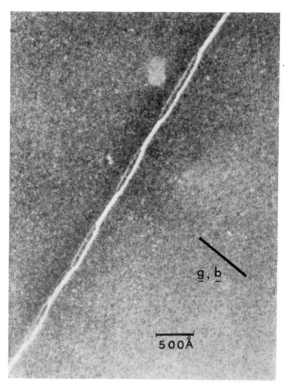

FIG. 48. Weak beam transmission electron micrograph showing a constricted dislocation in silicon. (By courtesy of Dr D. J. H. Cockayne.)

12 Å apart, corresponding to the spacing of the (201) planes. Mentor suggested that the fringes may be thought of as projections of sheets of molecules in the (201) planes. He was able to account for the formation of fringes by showing that a lattice image could only be produced when the main beam was allowed to recombine in the image plane with one or more of the diffracted beams. When a small objective aperture was used which permitted only the main beam to pass no fringes were obtained. Using this technique, Mentor was able to record the distribution of lattice planes around an edge dislocation on a platinum phthalocyanine crystal.

More recently, Parsons *et al.* (1970) have used lattice fringes to study dislocations in aluminium and germanium, GP zones in an aluminium-4% copper alloy and neutron damage in germanium.

Originally it was assumed that there was a one-to-one correspondence between the fringe distribution and the lattice plane distribution but Cockayne *et al.* (1971) have shown that this is not necessarily the case. Simple theory predicts that the number of terminating fringes associated with a dislocation, N, is given by the following expression

$$N = \mathbf{g.b} \tag{7}$$

and is the same for both screw and edge dislocations. Calculations made by Cockayne *et al.* (1971) using the dynamical theory have indicated that by changing the diffracting geometry, the number of terminating fringes associated with a dislocation may be altered. For example it was shown that for an inclined screw dislocation lying in a relatively thick crystal of germanium, the number of terminating lattice fringes was changed from one to three when the diffraction geometry was varied. In both instances $\mathbf{g.b} = 1$ so that only one terminating fringe would have been expected. Cockayne *et al.* (1971) discuss this point further and the reader is referred to their original paper. By making careful observations on germanium crystals, Cockayne *et al.* were able to verify their predictions experimentally and concluded that it is incorrect to assume a one-to-one correspondence between fringes and lattice planes.

An example of the type of photographs obtained using this technique is reproduced in Fig. 49. The arrows indicate the positions of terminating fringes which arise from the presence of a dislocation, and do not necessarily correspond to terminating lattice planes.

One of the main disadvantages of transmission electron microscopy is the need to make very thin samples. Several attempts have therefore been made to observe defects in bulk specimens using the secondary emission and back-scattering modes of the scanning electron microscope. Clarke and Howie (1971) have discussed the possibility of observing dislocations using back-scattered electrons. Their main conclusions were that there was little chance of detecting defects using a conventional tungsten filament gun operated at 20 kV since very long scanning times would be required. Instead either a field emission gun must be employed or the accelerating voltage raised to 80 or 100 kV.

Clarke (1971) has produced a series of micrographs which compare the images obtained in the back-scattered mode with those obtained in transmission. The photographs were obtained by using a conventional transmission microscope fitted with scanning coils and a high energy electron detector. Dislocation networks in aluminium and stacking faults in a copper-8% aluminium were studied. The images produced using back-scattered electrons were found to be inferior to those obtained by scanning transmission. A similar study has been made by Stern *et al.* (1972) using thin molybdenite crystals.

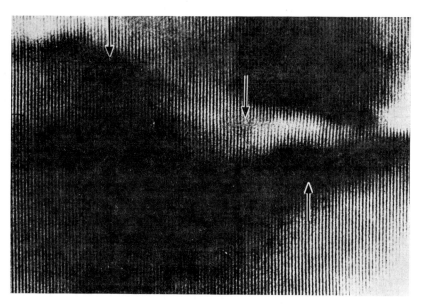

Fig. 49. Transmission electron micrograph showing lattice fringes. (Arrows indicate positions of dislocations.) (By courtesy of Dr D. J. H. Cockayne.)

Other techniques which have been used to observe dislocations include etch pitting, decoration methods and the Lang x-ray diffraction topograph. Further details about these techniques may be obtained from the references given in the bibiography.

E. Dislocation configurations

One of the main aims in the study of defects in crystals is to gain a better understanding of the way in which dislocations and other faults interact with one another, since this will ultimately determine the mechanical properties. To do this we can employ the transmission electron microscope techniques described in section III. Obviously in articles of this nature we can not delve deeply into the theory of dislocation inter-actions but it is possible to give the reader some outline of the problems which face the materials scientist.

1. Dislocation arrangements in deformed materials. As we have already seen, when a piece of metal is deformed slip occurs by the movement of dislocations. Some dislocations are grown into the metal when it solidifies

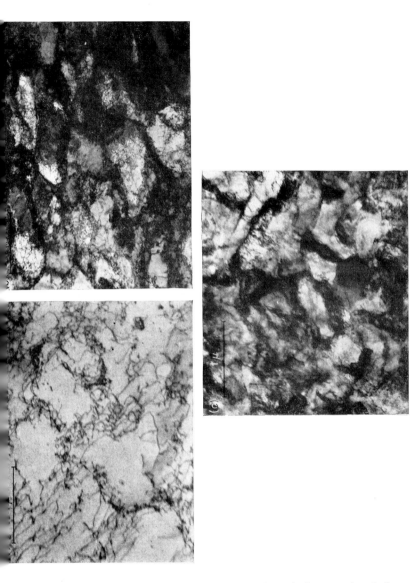

FIG. 50. Transmission electron micrographs showing the effect of deformation on the dislocation arrangements in pure iron. (a) Strain 9% in tension. (b) 70% cold rolled. (c) 90% cold rolled. (C. J. E. Smith and I. L. Dillamore.)

from the melt, but the majority are nucleated during the deformation process. Various mechanisms have been proposed for nucleation, and some of these have been observed directly in the transmission electron microscope. Any advanced book or article on dislocation theory will provide the reader with further details of these processes (see bibliography). If a large enough stress is applied to the metal, dislocations nucleated on neighbouring planes may interact with one another to produce dislocation tangles and networks. The micrographs reproduced in Fig. 50 (a), (b) and (c) show the effects of increasing deformation on the microstructure of a pure metal. These micrographs demonstrate that as the amount of deformation is increased the number of dislocations introduced into the grains rises. There is also a tendency for the dislocations to arrange themselves into a cellular-type structure. An example of this in a nimonic alloy is shown in Fig. 51. Many studies have been made to relate the mechanical

FIG. 51. Transmission electron micrograph showing dislocation cells in a deformed nimonic alloy.

properties obtained for a particular metal with the number of dislocations present. In order to do this, it is necessary to photograph a large number of different areas of the specimen, and to then calculate the density of dislocations present. This is simply the length of dislocation line present per unit volume of the material. Obviously good quality prints are necessary, taken at a magnification where all the dislocations present may be resolved. Some estimate of the thickness of the sample being examined is also necessary, and this can sometimes be done by making measurements from the micrographs.

In some materials such as austenitic stainless steels, the dislocations do not readily form tangles and cells but rather line up at obstacles such as grain boundaries to form pile-ups. An example of this is shown in Fig. 52.

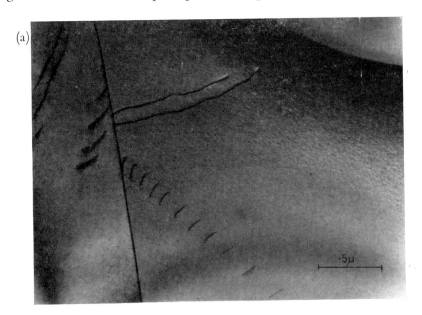

(a)

·5μ

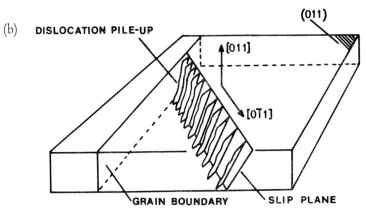

(b) **DISLOCATION PILE-UP**

(011)

[011]

[0T̄1]

GRAIN BOUNDARY   **SLIP PLANE**

FIG. 52 (a) and (b). Dislocation pile-ups in a stainless steel transmission electron micrograph. Schematic diagram showing pile-up and slip plane.

The group of dislocations (a) all lie on the same slip plane, and were probably nucleated by the same source. From the electron diffraction taken of the grain containing these dislocations, we can show that the (011) plane is parallel to the surface of specimen. We can further show that the slip plane intersects the specimen surface along the [0$\bar{1}$1] direction. It is known from other studies that in this particular material slip generally occurs on the {111} planes. This suggests that the slip plane containing the dislocations in group A is probably the (111) plane. The diagrams given in Fig. 52 (b) illustrates this. From the electron micrograph the width of the slip band may be calculated and by carrying out some simple solid geometry we can calculate the thickness of the foil.

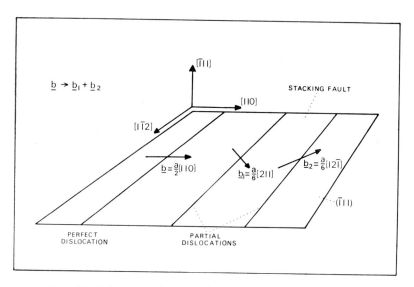

FIG. 53. Schematic diagram showing a partial dislocation.

So far the dislocations we have considered have been of the relatively simple form described in section VII.C. In some face-centred cubic materials and hexagonal close packed metals we find that the dislocations are dissociated into a pair of partial dislocations with a region of stacking fault between them. We can illustrate this schematically in Fig. 53. The dissociation reaction occurs because the formation of the pair of imperfect dislocations represents a decrease in the total energy of the system. If we were to make a Burgers circuit around each partial dislocation and then add the Burgers vectors of each together we find that this is equal to the Burgers vector of the original dislocation. In f.c.c. metals a dislocation with the Burgers vector a/2 [110] may dissociate into two partials of the type a/2 ⟨112⟩. The micrograph in Fig. 54 shows several pairs of partial dislocations together with regions of stacking fault. These appear as alternate dark and light stripes in a similar way to thickness fringes in a wedge-shaped foil. It is not possible to obtain photographs of a dissociated dislocation which show both partial dislocations in contrast as well as the stacking fault and it is necessary to tilt the foil into several different **g** conditions to reveal each feature. The simple Kinematical theory of

FIG. 54. Transmission electron micrograph showing stacking faults in a stainless steel.

electron diffraction assumes that the bright and dark field images of a stacking fault should be complementary but careful studies of stacking faults have shown that this is not the case. To understand why this is we must resort to the dynamical theory which takes into account absorption of electrons from the main beam.

2. *Recovery and recrystallization studies.* It has been known since early times that a metal may be softened after working by heating it to a temperature below the melting point, but it is only in recent years that the softening processes have been understood. Depending on the amount of work the material has received and the temperature at which the specimen is annealed, optical, electron microscopy and x-ray diffraction studies have established that at least three different processes may take place. These are recovery, recrystallization and grain growth.

The recovery process takes place at temperatures lower than those for recrystallization and grain growth and in a metal such as iron, recovery may take place to an appreciable extent at temperatures $\sim 670^\circ$K. With the optical microscope, no change in microstructure can be detected although there may be considerable decreases in hardness and tensile strength and a corresponding increase in ductility. In order to record the changes in structure which occur during recovery it is necessary to employ the transmission electron microscope.

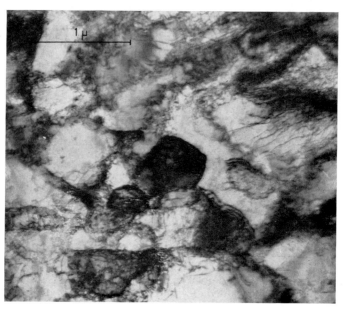

FIG. 55. Transmission electron micrograph showing the formation of sub-grains in iron. (C. J. E. Smith and I. L. Dillamore.)

In the early stage of recovery, some dislocation annihilation and re-arrangement may take place, resulting in the formation of small sub-grains. The misorientation across the sub-grain boundaries is typically 1-2° and they may be resolved into a definite dislocation structure. The electron micrograph reproduced in Fig. 55 shows the early stages in the recovery process and the formation of sub-grains. Occasionally sub-grain bound-aries may be resolved into dislocation networks. The exact form these take depends on the crystal structure of the material (Lytton et al., 1965; Carrington et al., 1960). Examples of networks formed in a duplex stainless steel are shown in Figs 56 and 57. In Fig. 56 the network is in a body-centred cubic grain and consists of dislocations with Burgers vectors parallel to the $\langle 111 \rangle$ and $\langle 100 \rangle$ directions whilst in Fig. 57 the network

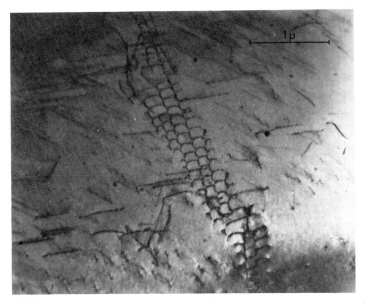

FIG. 56. Transmission electron micrograph showing a dislocation network in a ferrite grain.

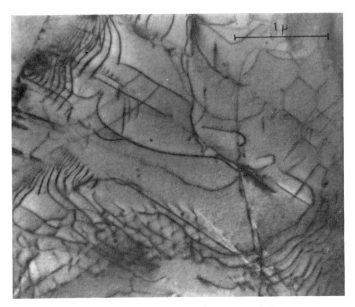

FIG. 57. Transmission electron micrograph showing a dislocation network in an austenite grain.

L

is in a face-centred cubic grain. In this instance all the dislocations have Burgers vectors parallel to $\langle 110 \rangle$ directions. In the latter stages of recovery the sub-grains may grow either by the movement of sub-grain boundaries or by a coalescence mechanism involving the rotation of individual sub-grains. The growth of sub-grains may be seen by comparing the electron micrographs in Figs 58 and 59 with that in Fig. 55. All three micrographs were taken from a 70% cold rolled pure iron specimen aged at 677°K for various times. When the average sub-grain size is compared in each case, it is found that there is an increase in size with increasing time at temperature.

The recrystallization process involves the movement of high angle grain boundaries, and the formation of strain-free grains. A considerable amount of information about recrystallization may be gained by making optical microscope studies of partially recrystallized materials. The sequence of optical micrographs shown in Fig. 60 illustrate the development of a recrystallized structure. During the first stages of recrystallization, new grains nucleate at the grain boundaries and within the old grains. These grow until impingement eventually occurs. Figure 61 is an electron micrograph showing the growth of a strain-free grain into the deformed matrix.

In recent years many studies have been made in order to determine the different nucleation processes which may operate, and to establish the relationships which the new grains have with the old. Classical nucleation ideas proposed that nuclei formed as a result of thermal fluctuations, but with the introduction of electron microscopy several different mechanisms have been identified. One process which has been proposed involves the movement of an existing high-angle boundary, and has been observed in high purity iron (Leslie et al., 1963), aluminium and silver (Bailey and Hirsch, 1962). It is assumed that there is a difference in dislocation density across the boundary and the boundary migrates in the direction of the grain with the higher dislocation density. This process is illustrated schematically in Fig. 62 and by the optical micrograph in Fig. 63.

Another mechanism which has found considerable support is sub-grain growth (Hu, 1962, 1963). This process takes place during the latter stages of recovery and recent electron microscope studies have shown that this may be the first stage in the nucleation of a recrystallized grain. With the increased availability of the high-voltage electron microscope it has been possible to observe directly the nucleation of recrystallized grains (Hutchinson and Ray, 1973). In this technique it is possible to use thicker

FIG. 58. Transmission electron micrograph showing sub-grains in high purity iron. (C. J. E. Smith and I. L. Dillamore.)

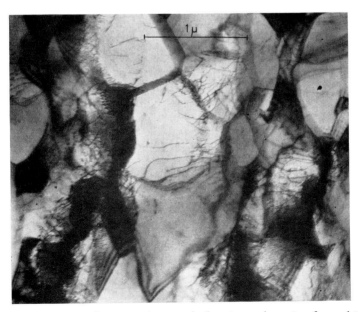

FIG. 59. Transmission electron micrograph showing sub-grains formed in iron rolled 70% and annealed at 727°K for 1 week. (C. J. E. Smith and I. L. Dillamore.)

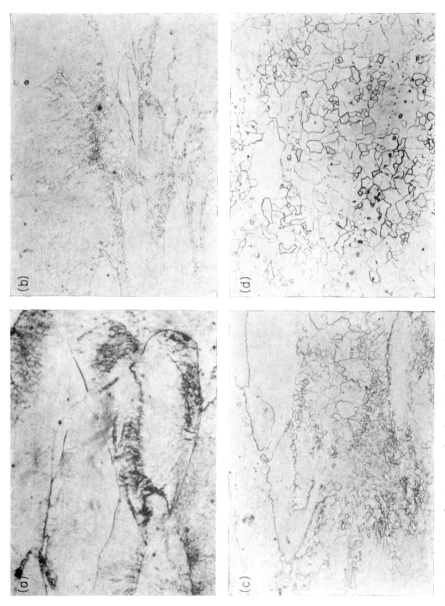

Fig. 60. Optical micrographs showing the nucleation and growth of recrystallized grains in an iron-phosphorus alloy. Cold rolled 70% and annealed at 831°K. (a) 2 min. (b) 32 min. (c) 100 min. (d) 1000 min. (C. J. E. Smith and I. L. Dillamore.)

films so that the processes observed may relate more exactly to bulk samples.

Once recrystallization is complete a third process, grain growth, may take place. The optical micrographs reproduced in Fig. 64 illustrate the grain growth process. This involves the movement of high-angle grain boundaries so that grains which are larger than the average size will grow at the expense of those less than the average size. The kinetics of grain

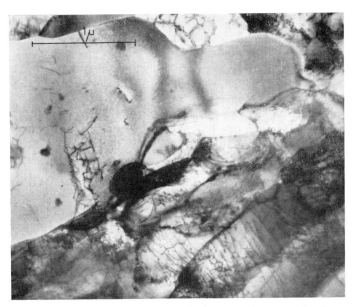

FIG. 61. Transmission electron micrograph showing the growth of a recrystallized grain in iron rolled 70% and annealed at 773°K for 10 min. (C. J. E. Smith and I. L. Dillamore.)

growth were originally determined using optical microscopy by examining a series of specimens which have been annealed for various times at a particular temperature. If we wish to observe the process directly, we can use an optical microscope fitted with a hot stage or an emission electron microscope.

Under some circumstances a breakaway type of grain growth may occur where several grains which are much larger than average grow very rapidly so as to consume all the smaller grains. This process is sometimes referred to as abnormal grain growth or secondary recrystallization. As in the case of normal grain growth the process may be followed optically or with the emission electron microscope.

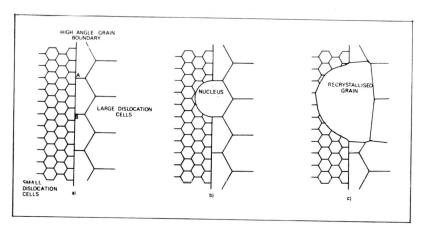

FIG. 62. Schematic diagram illustrating the grain boundary bowing process. Part of the boundary AB (a), bows out into the grain with the higher dislocation density (b). The boundary continues to migrate to form a recrystallized grain (c).

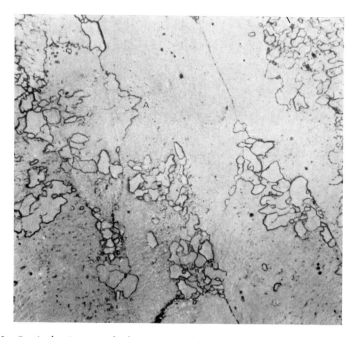

FIG. 63. Optical micrograph showing nucleation of recrystallized grains by the grain boundary bowing process. For example grain A. (C. J. E. Smith and I. L. Dillamore.)

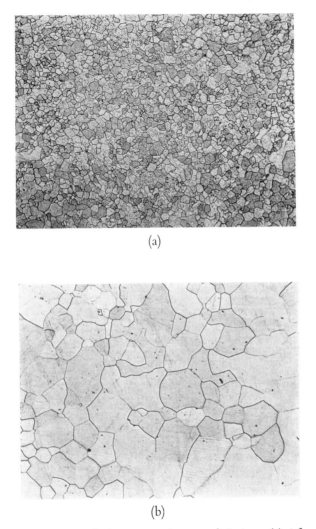

(a)

(b)

FIG. 64. Optical micrograph showing grain growth in iron. (a) After recrystallization. (b) As (a) but annealed for 4 h at 700°C.

3. Irradiation and quenching studies. So far in the discussion of crystal defects we have considered only line defects, namely dislocations. Two important point defects, vacancies and interstitials are also present in metals and alloys and in this section we shall describe how they may form defects which can be photographed in the electron microscope.

A vacancy as the name suggests is simply a site on the crystal lattice which is unoccupied whilst an interstitial is an extra atom squeezed into the lattice. In order to see either of these defects directly we must use a technique such as the field ion microscope which allows the positions of individual atoms to be established. This is a specialized technique and will not be discussed further. A recent review on the subject by Seidman (1973) is recommended.

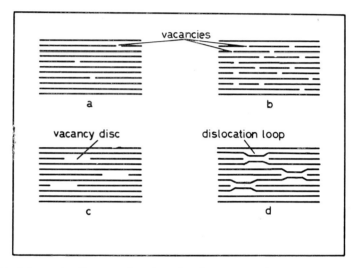

FIG. 65. Schematic diagram showing the formation of a vacancy dislocation loop.

The number of vacancies present in a metal is a function of the temperature. As the melting-point is approached the vacancy concentration increases by several orders of magnitude so that if a metal is rapidly quenched from a temperature close to the melting-point to room temperature, a supersaturation of vacancies will be produced. The situation is shown schematically in Fig. 65. It was suggested that the vacancies would cluster on certain planes in the crystal to form a vacancy disc. The atomic planes surrounding the disc then collapse to form a dislocation loop as shown in Fig. 65. The Burgers vector of the loops in Fig. 65 will be perpendicular to the atomic planes and in face-centred cubic materials would be parallel to the ⟨111⟩ direction.

Early experiments on the quenching behaviour of several metals were carried out by Hirsch et al. in 1958. In specimens of aluminium small dislocation loops of the type shown in Fig. 66 were found. The interesting feature of these loops is that they do not contain a stacking fault as suggested by the model in Fig. 65 (d) and the Burgers vectors of the loops are parallel to ⟨110⟩. It was suggested that the stacking fault was removed from the original loop by the interaction with a partial dislocation. Subsequent experiments by Cotterill and Segall, (1963), Edington

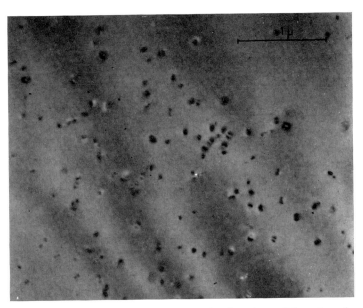

FIG. 66. Transmission electron micrograph showing dislocation loops in aluminium.

and Smallman, (1965) and Westmacott *et al.* (1961) showed that under certain circumstances faulted loops may be produced in aluminium. An example of this is shown in Fig. 67.

Annealing experiments carried out on thin foils within the microscope have shown that during ageing, the faulted dislocation loops in aluminium shrink continuously, returning the fault. Small unfaulted loops also shrink on ageing but at a different rate to the faulted loops. By measuring the difference in shrinkage rate Dobson *et al.* (1967) and Kritzinger *et al.* (1967) were able to determine the stacking fault energies of aluminium and an aluminium magnesium alloy.

Two other defects which form by vacancy clustering in quenched metals are voids and stacking fault tetrahedra. The latter have been found in metals such as silver and gold, Silcox and Hirsch (1959) whilst voids have been studied by Westmacott *et al.* (1968) in aluminium. For a more

L*

detailed description of these defects the reader should consult the references given at the end of the chapter.

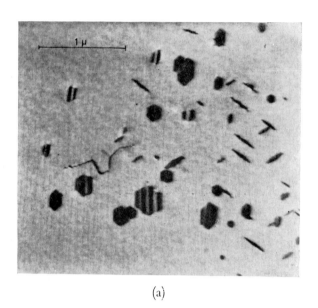

(a)

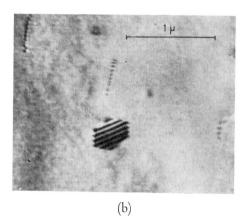

(b)

FIG. 67. Transmission electron micrographs showing faulted dislocation loops in aluminium. (By courtesy of M. H. Loretto.)

During irradiation, atoms are knocked from their sites on the crystal lattice creating vacancy and interstitial pairs. This process is shown schematically in Fig. 68. The interstitial atoms are very mobile and may migrate through the lattice to form an interstitial dislocation loop. The differences between a vacancy and interstitial loop are shown in Fig. 69. The problem of determining the exact nature of a loop has been discussed by Maher and Eyre (1971) and involves carefully photographing the loop under different reflecting conditions.

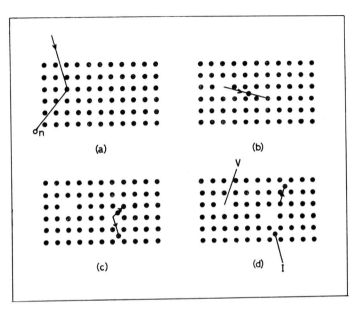

FIG. 68. A neutron, n, knocks an atom from its site (a) causing it to collide with another atom (b). Some of the kinetic energy is transferred to this atom so that it in turn is dislodged (c). Both atoms eventually come to rest in interstitial positions I (d). In this way vacancy, V, and interstitial, I, pairs are produced. Many such collisions occur in practice as a result of one primary collision so producing a great number of V-I pairs. Because the interstitials are effectively squeezed into the lattice, they are extremely mobile and will rapidly migrate through the lattice to form interstitial dislocation loops.

Initially irradiation studies were concerned with damage produced by neutron bombardment in a nuclear reactor. However, the effect of irradiation by ions and electrons have also been examined (Jenkins *et al.* 1973). The electron micrograph reproduced in Fig. 70 shows Frank dislocation loops formed in silicon as a result of irradiation with phosphorus ions.

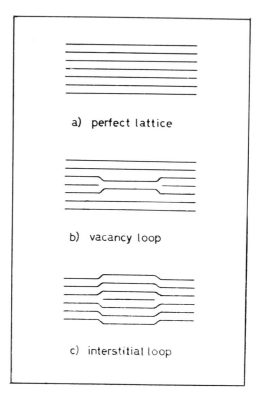

a) perfect lattice

b) vacancy loop

c) interstitial loop

FIG. 69. Schematic diagram showing the differences between vacancy and interstitial loops.

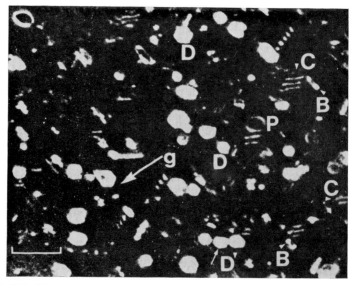

FIG. 70. Weak beam transmission electron micrograph showing loops produced in silicon as result of ion bombardment. (By courtesy of Dr D. J. H. Cockayne.)

VIII. SOLID–STATE PHASE TRANSFORMATIONS

A. Introduction

Interest in solid-state phase changes has been high in recent times. In addition to the numerous technological benefits that result from such transformations, a variety of academic peculiarities have invited enquiry. The most effective way to change the properties (particularly the mechanical properties) of a material is to cause a transformation to occur, e.g., the hardening of steel by a martensitic transformation or the hardening of aluminium alloys by precipitation.

The importance of photography in the investigation of phase transformations arises through its use in recording observations made by means of the light and electron microscopes and its application in x-ray diffraction which is an extremely powerful tool for identifying the phases present in a material and for determining the structure of the phases.

In this section no attempt will be made to discuss solid-liquid interactions and transformations, and attention will be confined to that area of phase transformations where optical and electron metallography in particular have made notable contributions i.e., solid–state transformations. Even to cover the whole of this field would require a book in itself, and therefore the approach must be selective and reflect the author's prejudices which nevertheless may help to provide the reader with an appreciation of the great contribution made by microscopy and diffraction techniques. The various transformations to be considered will involve metals and alloys and the description will be in metallurgical terms, but the principles are general and apply to all solids: for example, age-hardenable ceramics, martensitic reactions in ionic crystals and typical phase changes in crystals of rare gases.

Knowledge and understanding are generally advanced by making distinctions and systematic classifications and the field of solid-state transformations is no exception. As a result there is general agreement as to the nomenclature used in describing the various types of transformation although in many cases there is no clear distinction. For example, massive transformations are considered to be non-crystallographic, yet there are crystallographic aspects to these transformations; an orientation relationship applies to both martensitic and precipitation-type reactions, yet the mechanisms are fundamentally different; some ordering reactions exhibit martensitic characteristics and kinetics typical of a diffusion-controlled reaction. In other words there are a variety of overlapping characteristics amongst transformations which are themselves acknowledged to be different in kind.

In the present discussion solid-state transformations are divided into the following categories: martensitic transformations, precipitation reactions, and eutectoid reactions.

B. *Precipitation from solid solutions*

The discovery of Wilms in 1905 that, given time, aluminium alloys containing a few per cent of copper would harden at room temperature after a quench from a higher temperature excited numerous investigations of precipitation phenomena, particularly those directed towards an

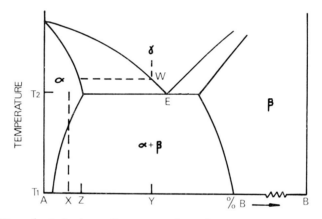

FIG. 71. Hypothetical phase diagram used to discuss eutectoid reactions and precipitation from solid solution.

understanding of "age hardening". Many alloy systems are now known to exhibit age hardening (precipitation hardening) characteristics although Al-base alloys containing Cu (basically "Duralumin") have been most widely studied. A common feature of age hardening systems is that the solute solubility decreases with decreasing temperature. Thus quenching an alloy of composition X (see Fig. 71) from some high temperature T_2 (the solution treatment temperature) to a lower temperature T_1 causes supersaturation of the α phase in component B; hardening upon subsequent ageing is due to the precipitation of a second phase (β) which is richer in solute. (It is frequently necessary to age at some intermediate temperature between T_1—say room temperature—and T_2 to achieve sufficient atomic mobility so that clustering or precipitation will occur.) In early studies the precipitates formed during ageing were called "knots" and a popular explanation of the observed hardening effect was that the precipitates were capable of locking slip planes, thus inhibiting deformation. It is now known that the formation of the precipitate of the equilibrium structure generally corresponds to an over-aged condition beyond that at which peak hardness is developed on isothermal ageing. In fact the peak hardness condition is usually not associated with visible precipitates; by the time precipitates are visible in the optical microscope the over-aged condition is reached. It is usually possible however, to observe precipitates, or at least, the strain fields surrounding them in the transmission electron microscope at the fully-hardened stage.

Some of the earliest attempts to observe precipitation reactions in aluminium–copper alloys were made by Heidenreich in 1949. He prepared his foils by an electropolishing technique and was able to obtain micrographs showing the precipitated phase in the advanced stages of ageing. An alternative approach was adopted in 1953 by Castaing and Laborie, who, after a preliminary electropolish, carried out the final thinning by ionic bombardment. The results were an improvement on those given by Heidenreich and demonstrated the great possibilities of the thin-foil methods. In 1958 Nicholson et al. described a modified electropolishing technique which was used to characterise precipitation processes occurring in alloys of aluminium with copper, silver, zinc and magnesium. Using this technique they were able to follow the formation of zones in supersaturated solid solutions and the transition from zones to intermediate precipitates. They also studied the interaction of moving dislocations and precipitates and gave a more complete explanation of the phenomenon of age-hardening. An example of a thin foil micrograph of an aluminium-4% copper alloy, of the type studied by Nicholson et al. (1958) aged for 13 h at 200°C is shown in Fig. 72. This micrograph shows plate-like particles of the θ' phase, some lying perpendicular and some parallel to the plane of the foil. In this condition the alloy has been over-aged but Nicholson et al. were able to detect effects in electron micrographs and diffraction patterns resulting from the earliest stages of ageing. In this connection it should be mentioned that a particularly powerful technique for studying zone formation and clustering is small-angle x-ray diffraction as used by Guinier in his work on alloys of aluminium with copper, silver and zinc.

Another example of this classical type of ageing reaction is provided by the case of a duplex steel which contains 25 w/o chromium, 5 w/o nickel, $1\frac{1}{2}$ w/o copper, $2\frac{1}{2}$ w/o molybdenum and 0·06 w/o carbon (Smith et al., 1973). Until recently, this material has generally been used in the wrought condition, but work at AWRE has indicated that improvements in mechanical properties are to be obtained by a cold working treatment followed by ageing at 475°C for 4 h.

The effect of this ageing treatment on the microstructure of the alloy was investigated using transmission electron microscopy, scanning electron microscopy and energy dispersive x-ray analysis. Transmission

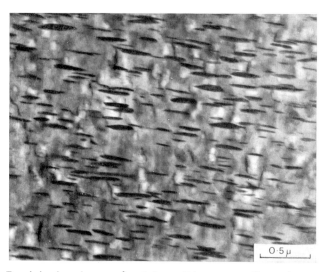

FIG. 72. Precipitation in an aluminium-4% copper alloy observed in the transmission electron microscope.

electron micrographs of material aged at 475°C and 600°C revealed no differences from micrographs of the solution treated material (annealed at 1050°C) shown in Fig. 73; however after 4 h at 700°C two distinct types of precipitate were to be seen—a fine precipitate, designated β-phase, which formed in the ferrite grains of the duplex austenite/ferrite structure, and much coarser particles, approximately 1 μm across, in the ferrite near grain boundaries. These two types of precipitate are illustrated in Fig. 74. More prolonged ageing at 700°C resulted in the formation of a third phase which is shown in Fig. 75.

Electron diffraction was used in attempting to identify the three phases shown in Figs 74 and 75. The coarse particles precipitated in the early stages of ageing at 700°C gave patterns typical of $M_{23}C_6$, a carbide commonly found in steels in which M can consist of any number and combination of Cr, Fe, Mo, Mn, V and W. The second coarse phase was identified as σ-phase, an intermetallic compound which usually contains elements such as Cr, Fe, Mo and Ni. It was not possible to identify the

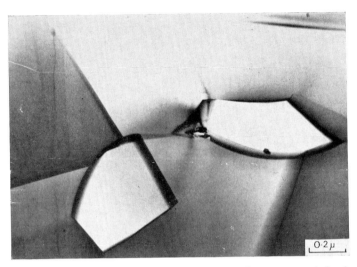

FIG. 73. Transmission electron micrograph of a solution-treated duplex steel.

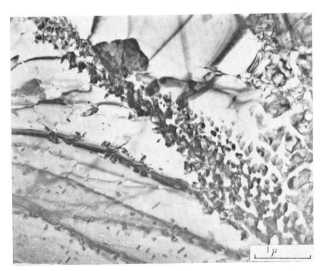

FIG. 74. Precipitation of β-phase and $M_{23}C_6$ in duplex steel—transmission electron micrograph.

β-phase by electron diffraction on thin foils because of the insufficiency of the data provided by the few weak reflections from the fine precipitate.

In order to resolve this problem an extraction replica technique was used in which the particles of β-phase were collected on a carbon film by

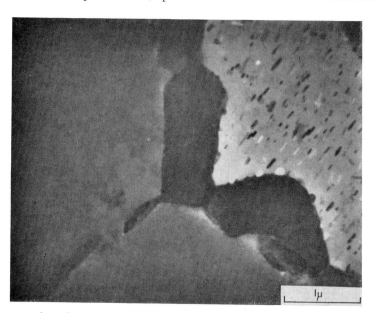

FIG. 75. σ-phase (large particles) and β precipitates in duplex steel—transmission electron micrograph.

dissolving the matrix of the alloy in a hydrofluoric acid solution. Electron diffraction of the replica shown in Fig. 76 (c) gave the pattern in Fig. 76 (d) which could be indexed as a face-centred cubic structure with a lattice parameter of about 3·60 Å which is almost identical to that of copper.

The extraction replica technique was also used to separate the $M_{23}C_6$ and σ phases from their matrix in the alloy to enable them to be analysed using the energy dispersive x-ray technique described in section IV.C. The spectra thus obtained and shown in Fig. 77 revealed that both types of particle consist mainly of Cr and Fe but that the ratios of these two elements are distinctly different in $M_{23}C_6$ and in σ-phase.

A fourth needle-like phase precipitated after prolonged ageing at 650°C and illustrated in Fig. 78 was also extracted from the alloy. Electron diffraction gave its structure as being that of the M_2X phase (hexagonal with a c/a ratio of 1·62) and energy dispersive x-ray analysis showed that the composition of the needles was variable but contained mainly Fe and

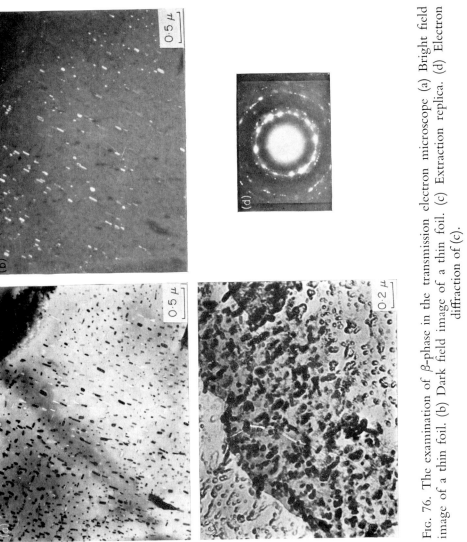

FIG. 76. The examination of β-phase in the transmission electron microscope (a) Bright field image of a thin foil. (b) Dark field image of a thin foil. (c) Extraction replica. (d) Electron diffraction of (c).

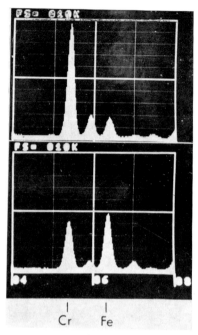

FIG. 77. Energy-dispersive x-ray analysis of particles on an extraction replica. Upper figure—$M_{23}C_6$; lower figure σ-phase.

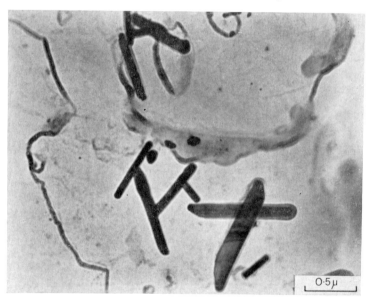

FIG. 78. Transmission electron micrograph of needles of M_2X on an extraction replica.

Cr. The X atoms could be either nitrogen or carbon and the energy dispersive technique is not able to detect either of these elements.

It would appear from these observations that the phase responsible for the increased hardness and strength of this steel after ageing at 475°C is likely to be the β-phase which at that temperature is probably in the form of a pre-precipitation cluster. By the time the particles become visible in the electron microscope at 650-700°C the peak hardness has been passed and they are no longer so effective at pinning dislocations. The other phases formed such as $M_{23}C_6$ and particularly the σ phase are likely to have an adverse effect on the mechanical properties and corrosion resistance of this material, as they do in other steels, and it would therefore be advisable to steer clear of treatments causing these phases to form.

C. Eutectoid decomposition

The formation of pearlite in iron-carbon alloys is the classic metallurgical example of a eutectoid decomposition. Below the eutectoid temperature austenite (an interstitial solid solution of carbon in face-centred-cubic (γ) iron) transforms to a lamellar aggregate of ferrite (body-centred-cubic (α) iron containing a small amount of carbon dissolved interstitially) and Fe_3C, cementite. With reference to Fig. 71 the eutectoid reaction is typified as $\gamma \rightarrow \alpha + \beta$. The name pearlite arises because when the lamellar aggregate is etched, ferrite preferentially dissolves and the Fe_3C platelets standing proud act as a diffraction grating and natural light casts a mother-of-pearl appearance.

The plate-like structure of cementite in the ferrite matrix can be clearly seen in Fig. 79, taken in the Balzers Metioscope.

The process of pearlite formation can be understood by reference to Fig. 71. If an alloy of composition Y is cooled slowly from the γ phase, α of composition Z starts to form at the point W. As a result the composition of the γ-phase is shifted to the right and follows along the line WE as the primary α continues to grow. At the point E instantaneous decomposition of the remaining γ to $\alpha + \beta$ occurs in the form of the lamellar pearlite structure. The spacing between lamellae and their width decreases as the rate of cooling is increased. Also, depending on the rate of cooling through the eutectoid temperature, some degree of supercooling is likely.

As with discontinuous precipitation the formation of pearlite in steels begins almost exclusively at grain boundaries. In inhomogeneous specimens undissolved carbides will act as nuclei. Although the nucleation of pearlite is extremely structure-sensitive the growth rate is not. Pearlite nodules easily cross grain boundaries and are unobstructed by inclusions, precipitates, etc.

According to Hillert (1962) ferrite and cementite can have any orientation relationship with respect to the austenite matrix except certain combinations leading to coherent interfaces that would make co-operative

FIG. 79. Electron emission micrograph of pearlite in a carbon steel. (Courtesy of Balzers.)

growth impossible. Darken and Fisher (1962) suggest, on the other hand that, from observations using the electron microscope and electron diffraction, orientation relationships of cementite and ferrite with respect to austenite do play a role in the formation of pearlite and that stacking faults and other imperfections are also important. There is still some controversy as to whether the ferrite or the carbide phase is the first to form. An elementary view favours a carbide nucleation hypothesis because undissolved carbide particles have been observed (in the transmission electron microscope) to nucleate pearlite. However, there is some evidence for ferrite nucleation.

Eutectoid transformations take place in a large proportion of alloy systems and their study is an important aspect of phase transformations. In some cases, as in steels, it is necessary to avoid the transformation to pearlite in order to obtain the optimum mechanical properties; in other cases, such as uranium alloys, it may be desirable to allow the eutectoid transformation to proceed under controlled conditions. Certain uranium alloys are more resistant to swelling under irradiation in a reactor if they contain a finely dispersed second phase.

Figure 80 shows the pearlitic structure of a uranium-2 w/o molybdenum alloy which was slow-cooled from the high temperature γ phase field to room temperature. During cooling the γ phase decomposed to a α (the orthorhombic phase of uranium) and γ-uranium, containing more than 12 w/o molybdenum. If the same alloy is quenched very rapidly from the γ

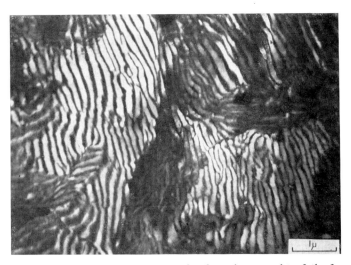

FIG. 80. Transmission electron micrograph of pearlite in a thin foil of uranium-2% molybdenum alloy.

phase field a martensitic α structure is formed and when this is annealed below the eutectoid temperature (565°C) discontinuous decomposition to a lamellar structure of equilibrium $\alpha+\gamma$ (or γ') takes place. During the initial stages of transformation, before any visible precipitation occurs the alloy becomes very hard but softens again as the pearlitic structure develops. According to May (1962) the increase in hardness is caused by the growth of molybdenum-rich zones in the martensitic α structure. May also states that the furnace-cooled alloy is likely to be more resistant to swelling in a reactor than the quenched and annealed alloy because the former consists of α plates in a matrix of isotropic γ which has greater stability than a structure consisting of γ plates in a matrix of anisotropic α.

More recent work by Giraud-Heraud et al. (1970) well illustrates the application of transmission electron microscopy to defining in quantitative terms the morphology of the growth of α/γ pearlite in a uranium-1·5 w/o Mo alloy. Using this technique they observed the growth of lamellae on cooling at different rates through the eutectoid transformation and were able to relate the orientations of the α platelets to the γ matrix. In addition, they studied the effect of cooling rate on the discontinuous pearlitic transformation and showed that the growth rate of the pearlite is rapid when the interfacial energy of the decomposition products is low.

This type of information is invaluable to designers of reactor fuel elements, for example, who have to select suitable alloys of fissile and other materials and predict their behaviour under the conditions of cycling temperature and radiation in an atomic reactor.

D. Martensitic transformations

1. Introduction. Martensitic transformations are of technological and scientific interest; an interest stimulated to a large extent by the responsibility of transformations of this type for the hardening of steels. Although the martensite transformation in steels is the prototype of this class of transformations, considerable insight has been gained by studying the same type of reaction in non-ferrous metals such as copper, titanium and uranium alloys.

2. General features of a martensitic transformation. If a small sample of an iron 0·6% carbon steel is heat-treated at 1000°C for a short time it will become fully austenitic. That is, it is single phase and the atoms are arranged in the face-centred cubic structure. Normally if the sample was allowed to cool to room temperature in the furnace, it would consist of two phases, ferrite and cementite. If instead, we rapidly quench the specimen by plunging it into water we find that a single-phase structure is produced. X-ray diffraction reveals that this structure has the body-centred tetragonal structure. Optical microscopy shows that the phase consists of needles or lathes, and that the surface has become rumpled. In addition we find that there is a marked increase in hardness. Osmond gave the name martensite to this phase in honour of the German scientist Adolf Martens.

Martensitic transformations may be described as nucleation and growth processes in which the barrier to nucleation is very large. They, therefore, only occur after a high degree of undercooling below the equilibrium transformation temperature. The barrier to the growth of martensite is very low and therefore rates approach the velocity of sound. There is always an orientation relation between the martensite and the parent phase which may not always be simple. Nucleation usually occurs in grain interiors and along specific crystallographic planes, which may be fairly high index planes. Many controversies surround the mechanisms of transformation and the rate controlling processes, some of which are beginning to be resolved by electron microscopy.

Initially, a martensitic transformation was characterized as a fast, athermal reaction giving rise to a brittle product but it is now known that these characteristics are not general. Instead, the main features of a martensitic transformation have been found to be crystallographic in nature. Modern metallographic techniques have shown that a martensitic transformation is diffusionless and involves a shear mechanism similar to twinning except that the product has a different crystal structure to the parent phase. Table II below lists some of the more common transformations which have been observed. In uranium alloys for example the

TABLE II

	Parent phase	Product (martensite)
Steels	f.c.c.	b.c.t.
Uranium alloys	b.c.c.	Orthorhombic or monoclinic
Titanium alloys	b.c.c.	Hexagonal close packed

parent phase has the body-centred cubic structure which transforms to give a monoclinic or orthorhombic martensite. We shall consider the transformation in uranium alloys in more detail in a later section.

Experiments with steels showed that the martensitic transformation starts at a particular temperature, Ms, which is dependent only on composition. The transformation continues as the temperature is lowered and is complete when a certain temperature Mf is reached. If the Mf temperature is below room temperature some of the austenite is retained. The rate of cooling from the austenitic region is critical. If the quench rate is not fast enough the austenite decomposes to give the equilibrium phases and martensite is not formed.

3. Martensitic transformations in uranium alloys. At temperatures around 900°C both molybdenum and niobium are highly soluble in the body-centred cubic gamma uranium phase. On quenching the phase may shear to give a monoclinic or orthorhombic martensite. We can get a deeper understanding of the way in which the transformation takes place by studying Fig. 81 (a) which shows the body-centred cubic uranium lattice. The unit cell outlined in Fig. 81 (a) and reproduced in Fig. 81 (b) may be sheared to produce the α'' monoclinic structure or the orthorhombic α' uranium structure. In the example illustrated in Fig. 81 (a), shearing takes

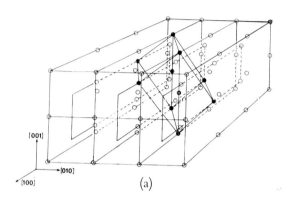

(a)

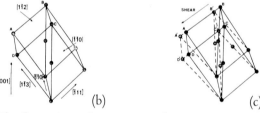

(b)   (c)

FIG. 81. The formation of martensitic α' uranium from α uranium.

place on the $(1\bar{1}2)$ plane and in the $[\bar{1}11]$ direction. The amount of shearing which occurs depends on the alloy content. The diagram in Fig. 82 summarizes the different types of martensites which form in several uranium alloys.

Some information about the martensitic transformation may be gained by examining transformed specimens optically. If the sample is polished flat before transforming we find on examination that the surface is rumpled. Optically this effect is best demonstrated by using oblique illumination or an interference technique such as Nomarski. Figure 6 in section II.A shows a micrograph of a transformed uranium-2% molybdenum specimen obtained using the Nomarski technique.

In order to gain more information about the nature of martensite in uranium alloys and other materials it is necessary to examine the structure in detail. This can only be done successfully using transmission electron

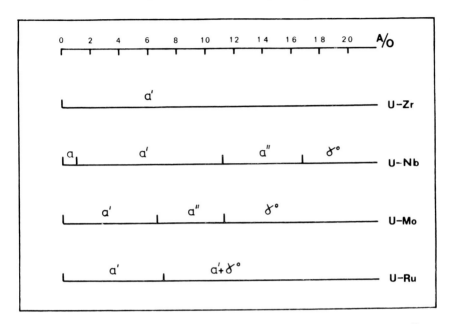

FIG. 82. Summary of the different types of martensite found in uranium alloys.

microscopy. The micrographs reproduced in Fig. 83 show the formation of martensite in U–Mo and U–Nb alloys. Possibly the most striking feature is the occurrence of twinning within the martensite lathes. By combining transmission electron micrographs with electron diffraction data it is possible to determine the nature of the twins. The formation of twins or dislocations during the martensite transformation is predicted in the theories of martensite (Bowles and MacKenzie, 1954; Wechsler *et al.*, 1953). The reader is referred to the bibliography for further details of these theories.

4. *Maraging steels.* One of the main reasons for examining martensitic structures in the transmission electron microscope has been to determine why the martensite phase is harder than the parent material. Several theories have been proposed but all are agreed that the main factors contributing are the production of a supersaturation of substitutional and interstitial elements and strengthening by substructure.

In order to produce a series of harder and tougher steels advantage has

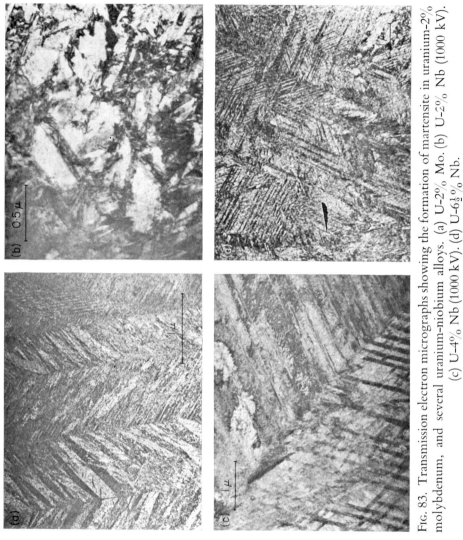

FIG. 83. Transmission electron micrographs showing the formation of martensite in uranium-2% molybdenum, and several uranium-niobium alloys. (a) U-2% Mo. (b) U-2% Nb (1000 kV). (c) U-4% Nb (1000 kV). (d) U-6½% Nb.

been taken of the fact that on ageing certain types of martensite, fine precipitates may form which give a further rise in hardness. These alloys are known as maraging steels and the main alloying addition is nickel. The normal heat treatment involves a solution treatment in the austenite region at 820°C followed by air cooling. This is sufficient to produce a martensitic structure. The electron micrograph in Fig. 84 shows the broad

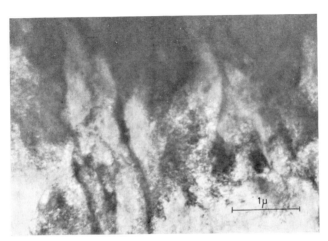

FIG. 84. Transmission electron micrograph showing the martensitic structure in a maraging steel.

lathes of martensite. If the structure is now aged at 480°C for 3 h to pre-cipitate the intermetallic phases such as Ni_3Ti or Ni_3Al a further increase in hardness is achieved.

IX. FRACTOGRAPHY

A. Introduction

To understand the basic mechanical properties of metallic and other materials it is first necessary to formulate clear ideas as to the reasons why materials fail under load and the development of new materials has made great advances as a result of developments in the art and science of fractography. So that a clearer understanding of the various mechanisms of failure of materials has made it possible to design alloys and composite materials which will resist failure under the conditions and environments to which they are exposed.

A second use of fractography is in the study of service failures where the aim is to analyse the fracture microstructure and by comparison with similar materials with known mechanisms of failure to draw conclusions as to the cause of failure and to make recommendations with regard to the treatment of the material or if necessary to suggest a different material which will more effectively stand up to the load and environment concerned.

B. The optical microscope in fractography

The idea of using the optical microscope for examining metal fractures dates back to the eighteenth century when Réaumur classified seven types of iron according to the appearance of their fracture surfaces and speculated as to the relationship between the fracture surface and the quality of the metal. In the nineteenth century Kirdaldy (1891) published what may have been the first definitive results relating the change from fibrous to crystalline fracture to changes in specimen geometry, heat treatment and strain rate. He concludes: "Iron when fractured suddenly presents . . . a crystalline appearance . . . fractured slowly its appearance is . . . fibrous. The appearance may be changed from fibrous to crystalline by altering the shape of the specimen . . . by varying the heat treatment . . . by applying the strain suddenly". He made similar observations on steel where ductile fractures were described as "milky fibrous" and less ductile fractures as "granular". Also granular or crystalline fractures were normal to the tensile axis while fibrous fractures were irregular.

Kirsh in 1889 attempted to describe the conditions leading to cup and cone fractures. He postulated that such fractures originate at the tensile axis in the "necked" region and spread out concentrically under a normal stress creating the base of the cone. The surface or sides of the cone are described as being formed by the maximum shear stress at final separation.

Martens (1889) observed that all fracture surfaces had radial markings which point back to the fracture origin. Also finer grained materials yield sharper radial markings and he distinguished between coarse type shear markings with accompanying fissures and finer markings. Osmond et al. (1904) also produced excellent micrographs of cleavage facets in iron and steel. More detailed descriptions and illustrative photographs were published by Portevin in 1931.

The techniques of optical microscopy were pushed to their limit in the 1940s by Zappfe, (1941, 1945, 1947, 1951) who described the microscopic features of fracture surfaces of a variety of metals. He and his co-workers reported the effects of crystallographic orientation on fracture, the effects of composition and second phases, and were the first to observe striations on fatigue fractures. The fractures examined were limited to relatively flat ones because of the depth-of-field problem.

All the early work on fractography was recorded by laboriously drawing by hand, with the aid of a low-power microscope, the main features of fracture surfaces. However, later workers have been able to employ cameras to great advantage as attachments to optical and electron microscopes, and this more than anything else has turned the art of fractography into a science and has enabled fracture surfaces to be characterized at low

FIG. 85. Fracture surface of maraging steel photographed using a low power optical viewer.

and high magnifications with ease and rapidity. Even today a great deal of useful information may be obtained about the broad classification of a fracture using fairly simple apparatus such as a low-power stereo-microscope by means of which stereo photographs may be obtained by photographing the fracture surface through each eyepiece in turn. Many workers use a photo-copy camera having a lens of 30–100-mm focal length and low-angle oblique illumination to give the required degree of contrast. Highly reflecting fractures need rather diffuse lighting, but with apparatus of this type useful magnifications of up to × 30 or more may be obtained, depending on the flatness of the field and the depth of focus of the microscope or camera.

One important advantage of the optical microscope is its colour differentiation. Figure 85 shows the fracture surface of a maraging steel photographed at low power using a colour film. This component failed under the combined effects of corrosion by a chloride environment and stress and the corroded regions of the fracture may be easily distinguished from the cleaner regions where final failure occurred.

Thus the optical microscope and even the naked eye still play a very important part in the examination of fractures, particularly in the first stages of the classification of a fracture; however, the macrostructure of a fracture does not always determine the microstructure, and cannot invariably be assumed to be a reliable index of the ductility of a material. Even intergranular fractures can differ in their degree of ductility. For this reason it is usually advantageous to study a fracture at high magnifications.

C. Fractography using the transmission electron microscope

The growing diversity of materials and the extended range of service to which they are exposed tends to multiply the cases where macroscopic analysis of the morphology of fractures, mainly based on common materials and employed in classical conditions, can be faulted, either because of an inability to choose between alternatives or because of wrong interpretation.

Until the advent of the electron microscope fracture surfaces could only be studied in detail by laboriously focusing on each small area in turn and taking a series of photographs at different settings of the objective to specimen distance to build up a picture. The much greater depth of focus of the transmission electron microscope (TEM) however, made it possible to photograph quite rough fracture surfaces and obtain useful information. Also, because of its higher resolution, much finer detail can be recorded using the TEM than is possible with the optical microscope.

The main disadvantage of the TEM is that, because of the low penetration power of electrons, it is not possible to view bulk specimens directly and, in the case of surface examinations, it is necessary to prepare a replica which is thin enough to transmit the electrons and also reproduces, as accurately as possible, the topography of the surface.

Most replicating techniques employ a plastic such as cellulose acetate as the primary replicating material. This is softened in acetone and placed on the surface to be replicated and is stripped when dry. The plastic replica is then coated with a thin layer of carbon in an evaporating chamber and the plastic dissolved away leaving behind a positive carbon replica of the original surface. After washing and drying the carbon replica can be examined in the electron microscope. However, in order to improve the contrast a heavy metal such as gold is usually evaporated on to the surface of the carbon film. Since, during evaporation the metal atoms originate from a small volume and travel in straight lines before striking the carbon film the effect is to produce shadows behind bumps and ridges which not only give enhanced contrast and a 3-dimensional effect to the image in the electron microscope but can also be used to measure the heights of particular features from measurements of the widths of shadows.

Occasionally a single stage carbon replication technique is advantageous and in this case the carbon film is deposited directly on to the fracture surface and the metal etched away until the carbon is able to float free and portions can be picked up on electron microscope grids and washed. The disadvantage of this technique is that the fracture surface is destroyed and this could be very undesirable in the case of a service failure. Direct carbon replication is often used, however, when a fracture surface contains particles which may have contributed to failure and an attempt is to be made to identify them using the electron diffraction facilities in the electron microscope or by microanalysis. In this case an etchant is chosen which will only attack the matrix so that the particles are left attached to the carbon film which can then be floated off and picked up in the usual way, on electron microscope grids.

An example of an extraction replica is shown in Fig. 86 (a). The particles were found on the fracture surface of a maraging steel which had failed in service, and were extracted using a solution of bromine in methanol which selectively dissolved the steel through the carbon film and left the particles unattacked. Electron diffraction photographs, an example of which is shown in Fig. 86 (b), showed the crystal structure to correspond closely to that of titanium sulphide (Ti_2S) and analysis of the particles in the electron-probe microanalyser indicated a composition very close to that of Ti_2S.

The magnifications at which it is possible to examine replicas in the transmission electron microscope are generally limited to less than $\times$ 10,000. This is because above these magnifications the granularity of the carbon film or the shadowing material becomes evident. Replicas are also subject to certain artifacts arising during their manufacture which must be recognized if fractographs are not to be incorrectly interpreted. Six of these are listed below and illustrated in Figs 87 to 91.

(a) Failure of the plastic to contact recessed areas of the fracture (Fig.87).
(b) Incomplete removal of plastic from the carbon (Fig. 88).
(c) Tearing and folding of the carbon replica (Fig. 89).
(d) Scraping of the plastic replica during stripping (Fig. 90).

M

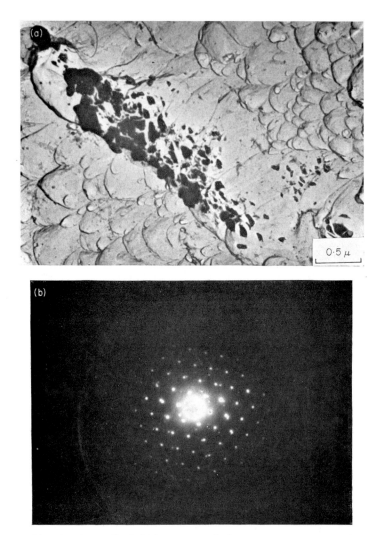

FIG. 86. (a) Titanium disulphide extracted from a maraging steel fracture surface, photographed in the transmission electron microscope. (b) Electron diffraction pattern from inclusion in (a).

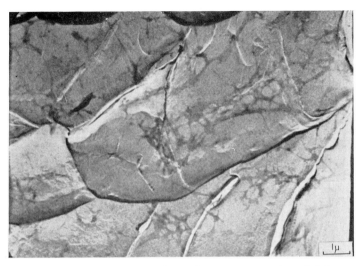

FIG. 87. Replica of the fracture surface of a uranium–10% molybdenum alloy photographed in the transmission electron microscope. The white areas are due to lack of contact of the plastic with the fracture surface.

FIG. 88. Replica of the fracture surface of uranium–10% molybedenum alloy showing incomplete removal of plastic from the carbon replica.

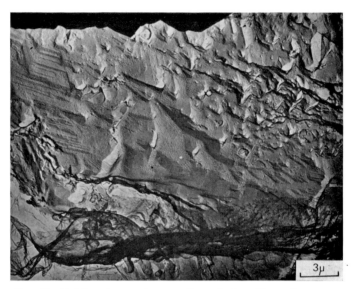

Fig. 89. Folding in a carbon replica of a beryllium fracture.

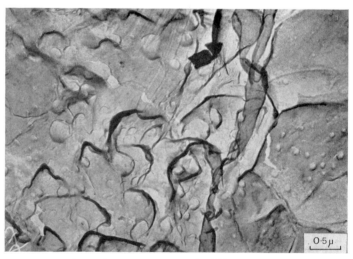

Fig. 90. Scrape marks and acetone vapour bubbles on a replica of the fracture of uranium–10% molybdenum alloy.

(e) Formation of acetone vapour bubbles at the plastic-surface interface
(Fig. 90).

(f) Overheating of the replica during evaporation causing granulation
of the shadowing material (Fig. 91).

A further disadvantage of replicas is their inability to maintain the
proper topographical relationship between different features on the
fracture surface.

FIG. 91. Illustrating granulation of the gold–palladium shadowing material on
a replica of a uranium–10% molybdenum fracture surface.

D. *Fractography using the scanning electron microscope*

The above limitations on the use of the TEM for microfractography
restricted it to relatively few skilled operators who were able to recognize
the presence of artifacts in their replicas as well as the features typical of
different classes of fracture and unambiguously determine the causes of
failure. However, the scanning electron microscope (SEM) has given
greatly increased impetus to fractography by making it possible for
materials scientists to examine fracture surfaces directly without the need
to go through the procedure of laboriously preparing replicas and this
has largely removed the danger of introducing artifacts. A further important advantage is the ability of the instrument to cover a wide range of
magnifications thus making it possible to combine macrofractography
with microfractography in the one examination, and in most cases, to

survey the whole of a fracture surface and follow the development of a crack without the need to relate small pieces of a replica with each other. This facility is shown in Figs 92 and 93. The greatly increased depth of focus of the SEM compared with the light microscope is obviously an important feature when examining rough fracture surfaces, particularly

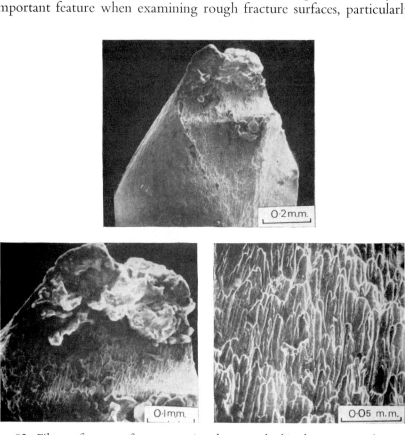

Fig. 92. Fibrous fracture of a copper wire photographed in the scanning electron microscope.

at low magnification; however, it should be noted that the transmission electron microscope still has the edge over the SEM when it is necessary to study very fine detail on a fracture, and in the identification of particles found on fracture surfaces the TEM still has a part to play with its facility for obtaining electron diffraction patterns from extraction replicas. It should also be noted that there are still instances, in the failure of large components of a structure such as a bridge, where it may be necessary to prepare replicas and examine these in the SEM but in this case it is sufficient to take a plastic replica and coat this with a conducting film, such as gold, to prevent it charging up in the electron beam of the instrument.

FIG. 93. Granular fracture of an aluminium alloy photographed in the scanning electron microscope.

E. *The various types of fracture*

All fractures in engineering materials fall into one or more of the general classifications.

A. Transgranular:
   (*a*) by microvoid coalescence,
   (*b*) by cleavage,
   (*c*) by fatigue.
B. Intergranular:
   by grain boundary separation with or without microvoid coalescence.

The majority of common structural alloys fail by transgranular microvoid coalescence or dimple fracture as it is commonly termed. An example of this type of failure, which is invariably seen in ductile materials but is encountered even in the most brittle materials in the regions of final failure, can be seen in Fig. 94. The majority of microvoids are probably

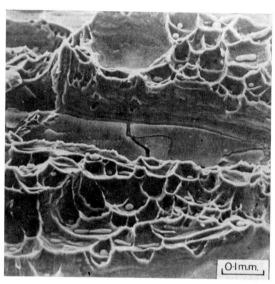

FIG. 94. Ductile fracture of a steel plate, showing the association of dimples with inclusions; photographed in the scanning electron microscope. (By courtesy of Cambridge Scientific Instruments.)

nucleated at grain boundaries, sub-grain boundaries, second phase particles, inclusions, dislocation pile-ups or any other area with a strain discontinuity. They grow under the applied stress until they meet at the well defined edges shown in the photograph and the material separates.

The shape of the dimples gives a guide as to the type of applied stress which caused failure. For example a shear stress will cause the dimples to be elongated in the direction of shear and they will take up a parabolic contour. If the stress is normal to the fracture surface the dimples will be equiaxed. The size of the dimples depends on the dispersion of the nucleating sites and the relative plasticity of the material. In the case of large dimples deformation markings such as serpentine glide, ripples and stretching, are often observed within the dimples.

Cleavage failure is found in brittle materials and usually occurs quite catastrophically as a result of stress concentrations at notches in the form of corrosion pits, inclusions or dislocation pile-ups. Cleavage fractures such as the one shown in Fig. 95 are distinguished as fairly flat areas extending across individual grains in a material and changing direction at grain boundaries. These flat areas or facets are related to crystallographic planes in the grains and neighbouring facets are separated by steps known as "river lines" because of their similarity to a river and its tributaries. The direction along which decohesion occurred is indicated by these lines and

Fig. 95. Brittle cleavage fracture of a carbon-boron steel, photographed in the scanning electron microscope. (By courtesy of Cambridge Scientific Instruments.)

the points of origin are determined by following the "rivers" back to their sources. The rivers join together as the crack advances because step formation requires energy, and the steps increase in height. Faults in the crystal lattice such as twins can cause part of a crack to deviate from its main path causing the formation of "tongues" such as those in Fig. 96.

Another common type of failure observed in materials is intergranular fracture—also known as "rock-candy" fracture. An example of this is shown in Fig. 97. Intergranular fracture can either occur in a completely brittle manner without any sign of deformation or by microvoid coalescence at grain boundaries, in which case a significant amount of deformations may occur before failure. Susceptibility of a material to intergranular failure can arise from a number of causes, but the most usual are the

M*

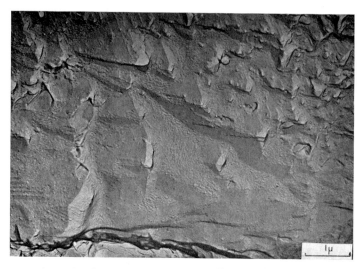

FIG. 96. Replica of a cleavage fracture in beryllium, showing "tongues" on the fracture surface, photographed in the transmission electron microscope.

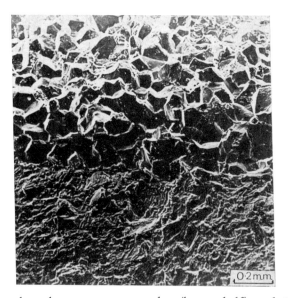

FIG. 97. Boundary between transgranular (lower half) and intergranular (upper half) fracture in steel, photographed in the scanning electron microscope. (By courtesy of Cambridge Scientific Instruments.)

presence of a grain boundary phase, such as carbides in a steel, or segregation of impurity elements such as hydrogen to the grain boundary.

A common cause of intergranular failure is stress corrosion attack in which the effects of stress and a corrosive environment are combined to give rise to failure in a material which would normally be immune to the effects of either applied separately. Figure 98 shows a rather interesting stress corrosion fracture which occurred in a maraging steel structure

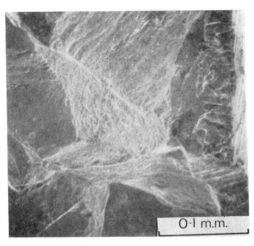

FIG. 98. Scanning electron micrograph of intergranular stress corrosion fracture in maraging steel.

stressed to a level which it would normally have been able to support with ease. However, the presence of a chloride environment caused failure of the steel at a stress well below its yield stress. The evidence for this latter statement was provided by an exhaustive study of the structure of the steel and the crack morphology using transmission electron microscopy, scanning electron microscopy, electron probe microanalysis, and optical microscopy.

Figure 98 shows that the initial mode of cracking was intergranular and examination of the numerous subsidiary cracks using the optical microscope and scanning electron microscope showed these also to be intergranular. The scanning electron microscope revealed a thin sheet of apparently non-metallic material contained within these cracks (Fig. 99) and surface pits were also found containing a similar material. This material, which had a characteristic fan-shaped morphology, was also found on the fracture surface, (Fig. 100) and a sample which was extracted

using a replica technique (Fig. 101) and examined in the transmission
electron microscope using electron diffraction indicated it to be amorphous. Analysis of the material in the electron-probe microanalyser gave
iron, silicon and chlorine as the main constituents with aluminium,
titanium and magnesium present in minor amounts. The material in the

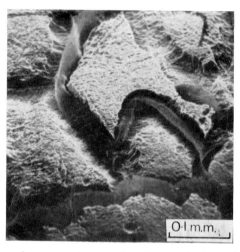

FIG. 99. Scanning electron micrograph of corrosion product in cracks in
maraging steel.

FIG. 100. Corrosion product "fans" on the fracture surface of maraging steel—
scanning electron micrograph.

pits was also found to contain chlorine as shown by the scanning x-ray microanalysis picture in Fig. 102.

Sections of the steel were polished and etched and examined in the optical microscope. This indicated the possible presence of a fine precipitate at the grain boundaries. This was confirmed when an extraction

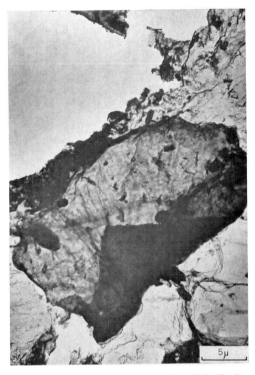

FIG. 101. Extraction replica of a corrosion product "fan" photographed in the transmission electron microscope.

replica was prepared and examined in the transmission electron microscope as shown in Fig. 103. Analysis by electron diffraction and in the electron-probe microanalyser identified the precipitate as a complex oxide of the spinel type containing iron and silicon as its main constituents.

Consideration of this evidence together with information concerning the manufacture of the steel led to the conclusion that inhomogeneity of the composition of the steel—in particular, the presence of a grain boundary phase—rendered the steel susceptible to grain boundary attack

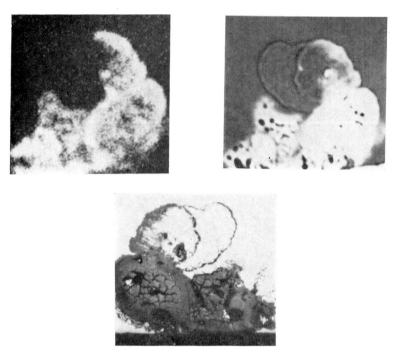

FIG. 102. Corrosion product in pits on the surface of maraging steel, photographed in the electron-probe microanalyser.

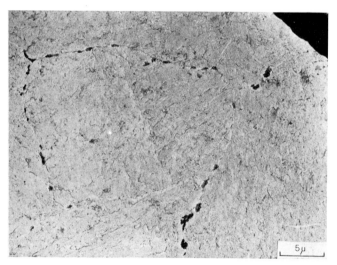

FIG. 103. Extraction replica of grain-boundary precipitates in a maraging steel, photographed in the transmission electron microscope.

by the chloride environment. First, elongated pits were formed containing corrosion product which, having a lower density than the steel from which it formed, acted as a wedge and combined with the external stress to initiate a crack at the root of the pit. Attack then occurred in the crack and produced more corrosion product which, in its turn, stressed the sides of the crack extending it further along the grain boundary. This process continued until the remainder of the structure could no longer support the load and it failed by transgranular shear.

This study provides a good example of the use of a range of techniques in the examination of a failed component and although most failure analyses do not require such a complicated investigation it is unlikely that the use of a single technique will give the complete answer in attempting to determine the causes of failure of an engineering material.

X. PARTICLE AND AEROSOL EXAMINATION

The examination of particles is required in many industrial processes today. Even the term "particle" has a variety of meanings according to its context; for instance, in atmospheric pollution it will be a dust or aerosol, in paints it will be pigments and fillers, it could be sediments from rivers or many types of powders from grinding bulk material. In the majority of these examinations the question will concern size, shape and dispersion and, less frequently, surface topography and composition may be required.

It is remarkably difficult to mix powdered materials to give a uniform composition and many inhomogeneities in a final product can be traced back to poor mixing. The process of mixing can be followed, and recorded, by taking a series of photographs and comparing them to a standard known to be satisfactory. For this purpose some contrasting features within the constituents must be made use of, such as colour, opacity, fluorescence or even secondary electron emission, e.g., in dispersing graphite with uranium dioxide. To illustrate this problem the group of photographs shown in Figs 104 to 108 presents a short study on mixing together colloidal silica and hydrated alumina in the proportions to give a synthetic mullite. The mixed powders were ball-milled wet and spray dried prior to calcining at 1450°C to produce—it was hoped—grains of mullite.

Figure 104 shows a Stereoscan picture at × 500 of a random sample of the powder after calcining. It was immediately evident that some particles were rough, and some were smooth—as shown in Figs 105 and 106 at a magnification × 1500.

To characterize the two types of particle visible, the method of energy dispersive x-ray analysis described in section IV.C was used. In the resulting pictures (Figs 107 and 108) the y-axis represents the x-ray intensity and the x-axis the energies of the x-rays. The energy level

FIG. 104. Synthetic mullite composition. Random field Stereoscan photograph. × 500.

characteristic for aluminium is 1·5 and for silicon 1·75 keV, and with this in mind it is evident that the smooth particles contain an excess of silica and the rough ones an excess of alumina. Segregation has therefore taken place in spite of thorough processing.

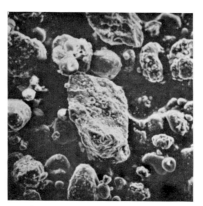

FIG. 105. Scanning electron micrograph of rough particles. × 1500.

Two problems which arise in the examination of particles and which are deceptively difficult to resolve in practice are, first, to decide what state of aggregation exists, and, secondly, to obtain a good dispersion.

These two aspects are linked so that the examination must be relevant to conditions in which the material is to be used. For example, a powder which has been precipitated from an aqueous solution and dried will probably contain small amounts of soluble material which will cement some of the

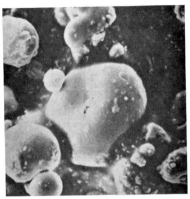

Fig. 106. Scanning electron micrograph of smooth particles. × 1500.

particles together. Such a powder will behave differently on dispersion in an aqueous medium from being dispersed in oil because the water-soluble material would probably redissolve in the aqueous medium, thereby freeing the particles. If this same powder were dispersed in oil, more work

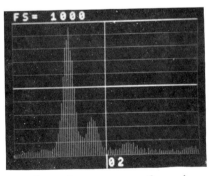

Fig. 107. X-ray energy dispersive response of rough-type mullite particles.

would need to be done on it to produce the same degree of dispersion. Again, some powders may be subjected to very high shear stresses when put to use—such as dispersing paint pigments—or very low stresses as in dry mixing. These facts must be allowed for in preparation, and interpretation of results. It is sometimes instructive to record and compare the dispersions resulting from variations in preparation. Such comparisons would be very cumbersome without photographic recording.

There have been many methods devised for producing adequate dispersions for optical and electron microscopy; the problem is worse the smaller the particles. It is useful to commence with a simple quick method

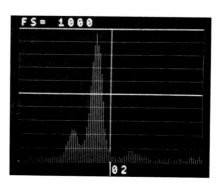

FIG. 108. X-ray energy dispersive response of smooth type mullite particles.

so that the nature of the problem can be assessed. To this end, shearing a small quantity of powder between two glass slides with a viscous liquid is suitable for powders of less than 5 μ. A mixture of:

           10 cc glycerol

           1 drop "Teepol"

           2 cc morpholine (a wetting and dispersing agent)

has been found suitable because both the glycerol and morpholine are volatile *in vacuo* leaving a layer of powder suitable for electron microscopy. The very minimum amount of liquid should be used. Another method which is applicable to optical examinations up to about × 500 is to just melt a small amount of "Lakeside cement"* on a glass slide, and a little of the powder and shear the surface with a second warm slide until the mix is on the point of setting, parting the slides rapidly before this happens. This is very suitable for radioactive or toxic materials since they remain fixed. A smear of liquid paraffin over the rough resin surface improves the imaging of the particles. The method is not so suitable for vertical illumination but very satisfactory for dark ground or transmitted light. The result of these trials will decide if any further preparation is necessary.

* Lakeside Cement: from Cutrock Engineering Ltd, 35 Ballards Lane, London N3.

Many routes are available from this point and the choice will depend on the following considerations:

1. Information required; e.g., size, shape, surface texture, optical properties, etc.
2. Method of examination; transmission electron microscopy, optical or scanning microscopy.
3. Presentation of result: image analysis, exhibition, or for a report, or process control.

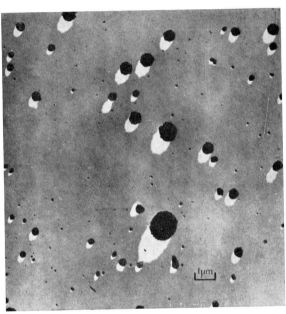

FIG. 109. Transmission electron micrograph showing methylene blue aerosol particles supported on a carbon film. × 6000.

In the examination of dusts, smokes and aerosols the problem of dispersion is largely avoided by the method of collecting the sample. This may be by suction through Millipore* filter pads, thermal or electrostatic preparation, or by cascade impactor where the particles are picked up on an adhesive surface. Reference to these methods of collection and the separate routes required in each case to prepare the specimen for examination by electron microscopy may be found in the literature, and some suggested reading is indicated in the bibliography. However, by way of illustration, Fig. 109 shows methylene blue aerosol particles, which are

* Millipore (UK) Ltd, Millipore House, Abbey Road, Park Royal, London, NW10.

used as a standard for monitoring filters in accordance with BSS 2831—"Methods of Test for Air Filters used in Air Conditioning and General Ventilation". The quantity of material present in the air stream before and after passing through the filter is measured colorimetrically, but the particle sizes which pass through can only be determined by taking actual measurements and counts in a large number of fields such as the one illustrated. The methylene blue, in this case, was collected by thermal

FIG. 110. Transmission electron micrograph showing electrostatically precipitated salt particles. × 6000.

precipitation on to a prepared glass slide. The particles were shadow-cast with gold-palladium alloy in vacuum, stripped from the slide and examined at × 6000 in the electron microscope at 40 kV. The particles were then counted and measured by projecting the negative on to a ruled screen, or, if there are no overlapping or contacting images the negatives, on 35-mm film, can be fed into an image analyser such as the Quantimet 720. Several thousand counts need to be made for the results to be statistically useful.

Electrostatic precipitation, in which the particles receive an electric charge and repeal each other, produces an extremely even dispersion for image analysing. An example of this is given in Fig. 110, where salt particles have been collected by this means and photographed at × 6000.

Figures 111 and 112 are an extension of the work in the previous paragraph. They are both salt particles but the rounded particles have been through a molten stage and solidified as spheres whereas the cubes are produced directly from an aerosol spray. Salt has been suggested as an alternative standard to the methylene blue discussed under Fig. 109. By having the same material in two distinct shapes, it is possible to investigate any "shape factor" without involving further variables as would be the case with two different materials (Dyment, 1970). The total amount of salt present in the air stream before and after can be determined by flame photometer or analytically.

These photographs were taken on an electron microscope at 40 kV thereby giving a higher contrast than that given at the more conventional 100 kV. The method for sample preparation is given in detail in an Atomic Weapons Research Establishment Report No. 0-84/64 (Larner, 1964).

In contrast to transmission viewing which gives essentially a projection picture, the examination of particles by Stereoscan or by replication gives quite different information. Details of very rugged surfaces can be photographed and changes studied. However, the use of these pictures for counting and measuring is much less appropriate, firstly because the shadow effect—which is pictorially valuable—confuses an automatic image analyser, and secondly, in the case of Stereoscan pictures allowance must be made for angle of perspective. These points are demonstrated in Figs 113, 114 and 115 which are best taken as a single study. In Figs 113 and 114 we have Stereoscan photographs of penta erythritol tetra–nitrate (PETN), a conventional high explosive similar to TNT. The powder, a minute amount for obvious reasons, was dispersed on the Stereoscan sample stub (previously treated with a very thin layer of adhesive), by gently teasing it apart with a camel hair brush in the dry state. After coating with gold/palladium alloy in vacuum to render the surface conducting it was examined in a 5 kV beam. It was not possible to use a 20 kV beam—which would have given better resolution—owing to the damage which this was seen to cause to the sample. The object of this examination was to record the appearance before and after certain treatments which were designed to promote recrystallization and rounding of angular edges. The photographs demonstrate a marked change in the material from Fig. 113, before treatment, to Fig. 114, after treatment; a change which renders it less sensitive as an explosive.

Figure 115 was produced by the process of replication. It is an electron micrograph of a sample of PETN which has undergone a similar treatment

FIG. 111. Transmission electron micrograph showing salt aerosol on Millipore. × 9000.

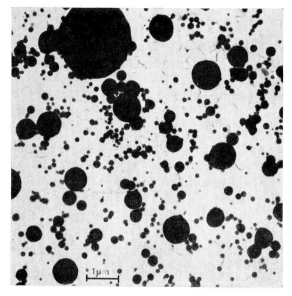

FIG. 112. Transmission electron micrograph showing salt particles after passing through the molten stage. × 9000.

to that shown in Fig. 114. However, this time the surface has been replicated using a gold/palladium contrast coating and a carbon backing film. It should be compared to Fig. 114 as being an alternative route for

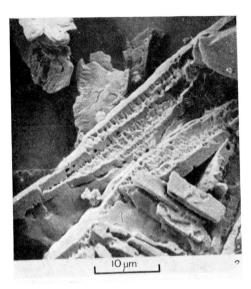

FIG. 113. Scanning electron micrograph showing PETN as initially produced (5 kV beam. × 2000).

demonstrating the same kind of phenomena. The advantages of replication, in addition to not requiring a scanning microscope, are:

1. No instrumental contamination by hazardous or radioactive materials.
2. Resolution of 100 Å are possible—equal to present scanning microscope resolutions at their best.
3. No charging effects or beam damage.

Against this must be set the loss of perspective value in the photograph, and the much easier preparation of the sample for scanning microscopy. In both methods stereo-pair photographs can be produced if needed.

Another example of particle texture photography is shown in Fig. 116. This deals with uranium dioxide, a material much used in nuclear fuel technology, the properties of which are largely determined by the size and surface detail of the particles. At a magnification of × 12,000 the individual crystallites which make up the single particle are clearly visible in the shadowed replica.

Radioactive particles are often detected by their ability to form a latent

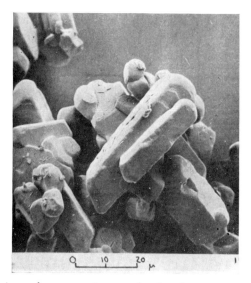

FIG. 114. Scanning electron micrograph showing PETN after treatment (5 kV beam. × 1000).

FIG. 115. Transmission electron micrograph showing replicated surface of PETN after treatment. × 2000.

image on a photographic emulsion. The sample may be collected by the methods listed above and placed in contact with an appropriate photographic emulsion for periods of up to several weeks. The emulsion is processed in the normal way and the result examined as a negative under the optical microscope. High resolution emulsions are necessary for this technique as the negative may be examined at magnifications up to several

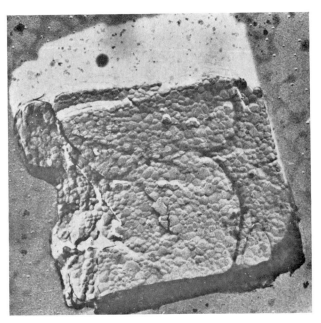

FIG. 116. Transmission electron micrograph showing replicated uranium dioxide particle. × 12,000.

hundred times. Figure 117 shows plutonium particles captured on Millipore filter paper and pressed against a maximum resolution emulsion. The resulting disintegration tracks cause latent image formation in the emulsion which on development show as black streaks emanating from the parent particle. The negative needs to be viewed under the optical microscope at about × 200 and the picture illustrated is representative of the kind of result obtainable. The graininess within the streaks is a function of the emulsion and processing and has no other interpretation.

Figure 118 is another example of autoradiography. In this case "Fall out" particles from a nuclear test have been in contact with the photographic emulsion for about five days, after which it was developed and fixed. This enables the radioactive particles to be distinguished from the non-active ones and by micro-manipulation they can be removed, further examined and analyzed. No optical magnification was needed in this case.

The examination of fine suspensions such as chalk, china clay, etc., in water supplies or trade effluents can be conveniently done by filtering

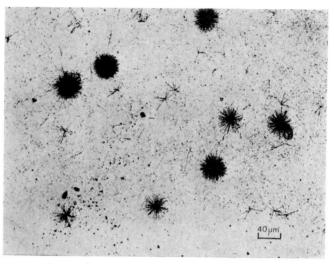

Fig. 117. Autoradiograph of plutonium particles captured on Millipore filter. × 120.

through a Millipore filter, washing with distilled water, drying and treating as an airborne dust. The valuable feature of cellulose acetate membranes such as Millipore is that a carbon film can be vacuum-deposited on them, followed by dissolution of the cellulose acetate in hot acetone (see Appendix C). The fine particles are then left on the film ready for electron microscopy. It is very unwise to evaporate suspensions on a slide in an effort to obtain a deposit for examination as this will cause false aggregation and deposit residues from dissolved materials (e.g., hardness salts in solution).

Sometimes it is necessary to examine the interior of a particle for hollow centres, cracks or layer formation. For this, the particles must be embedded in a setting resin and cross-sectioned by a process of grinding and polishing. However, if the particles are very hard and small (e.g., tungsten carbide particles) the amount of "edge-bevelling" may cause too great a loss of flat field for photomicrography. In such cases the use of a low melting-point glass as a mounting medium often solves the problem.

It is an advantage in the photomicrography of particles by transmitted light, (especially translucent particles), to mount them in a liquid the refractive index of which is close to, but not equal to, that of the particles. By this means many dark shadows are lost and considerable vision into the particles is obtained enabling other phases or pores, etc. to be seen.

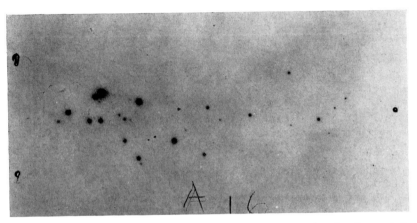

Fig. 118. Autoradiograph of fall-out particles (actual size). (By kind permission of Mrs M. C. Porter, AWRE.)

Unfortunately the method is not applicable to particles of about 3 μ and less owing to Brownian movement. (This is the minute jolting movements seen in small particles mounted in mobile fluids caused by impacts of fluid molecules on the particle.) In these cases a thermal setting resin or "Perspex" cement may be used, a method of special value in viewing radioactive particles as they are then effectively trapped.

A final example relating to particle photography and shown in Figs 119 and 120 is in the use of ultraviolet fluorescence. The material is the dry powder component of a dental cement used in fillings. It consists mostly of glass-like aggregates but contains a few fluorescent particles the purpose of which is to destroy the "off-whiteness" that exists with dental surfaces by superimposing a slight blue fluorescence. We are required to record the distribution of these particles within a batch of material. Figure 119 shows a layer of compacted powder in transmitted light; Fig. 120 is the same field in ultraviolet light showing clearly the presence of fluorescing particles. Some of these are, of course, in depth, presenting a hazed

FIG. 119. Optical micrograph showing dental filling material (dry component before mixing) photographed using ordinary transmitted light. × 60.

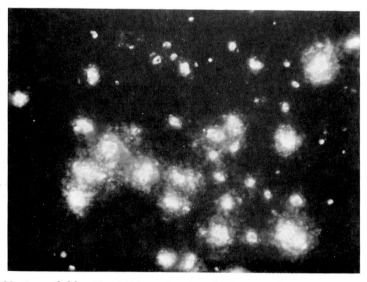

FIG. 120. Same field as Fig. 119 but photographed using ultraviolet illumination. × 60.

appearance, and some are in focus. This material is considered further in the next section.

Most of the electron micrographs presented in this section were taken on a Siemens Elmiskop, or Philips 75 kV electron microscope using Agfa-Gaevert "Scientia" 23 D50 Plates or Ilford EM4 Plates.

XI. EXAMINATION OF NON-METALLIC MATERIALS

A. Introduction

Owing to the great divergence in properties and purpose found with non-metallic materials in use today, any attempt to relate the type of material to a general procedure for its preparation and recording data would be very misleading. For example, although Bakelite and acrylic resin are both plastics, the usual process of replicating a surface of the resin using moistened cellulose acetate (see Appendix B) is applicable only to the Bakelite, because the acetone used to soften the cellulose acetate also softens the acrylic resin. We have, therefore, thought it best to present a selection of non-metallic examinations to illustrate this variety and the problems which usually arise, rather than taking a few materials in greater depth which is more appropriate to metals. However, it is possible to make some useful classification based on the initial preparation rather than the material, and this is given below.

1. Cross-sections. A surface of the material is first exposed by cutting with a diamond or emery wheel cooled with a fluid which is inert with respect to the material. It is then ground to a smoother surface using a series of emery papers and finally polished using fine diamond powders. At this stage some information will already be visible—such as pores, cracks and inclusions. However, not until the amorphous layer which forms over the surface in the final polishing stages has been removed, is the maximum amount of data revealed. This is especially true for plastics which flow and smear readily. The removal of this layer, i.e., etching, may be by controlled chemical attack, solvent etches or ion etching. This method of preparation is particularly suitable for optical work where colour, fluorescence, polarized light and interference techniques can be employed. It is also suitable for autoradiography, e.g., in minerals.

2. Fractured surfaces. A fractured surface may be deliberately induced under closely controlled conditions, such as Izod test pieces, or it may arise as the result of some accident in which the cause of failure is the subject of enquiry. Fractured surfaces are not, as a rule, suitable for obtaining good optical photographs owing to the depth of focus requirements. However, it is with this type of sample that the Stereoscan has been so successful in producing good photographs, and to which must be added the analytical data provided by x-ray energy dispersive methods. The only preparation required is to render the surface conducting by depositing on to it a layer of carbon or gold/palladium alloy. It is also possible to replicate some fractured surfaces (see Appendix B), whereby some increased resolution of fine detail may be obtained.

3. Original surfaces. In this category we have environmental surface attack, abrasion marks, surface textures, deposits, etc. Preparation is confined to rendering the surface conducting, as for fractured surfaces, as these surfaces will be appropriate to scanning microscopy. It is also possible to obtain valuable information using replication, if the sample is too large and must not be cut. Extraction replicas may also be used on corrosion products and paint films.

4. Transmission microscopy. Films or sections of material are prepared which are thin enough for light or electrons to pass through without excessive scattering. The sample is prepared by grinding and polishing until the section is thin enough to give transmission, or it may be microtomed, or thinned by ion bombardment (Clinton, 1972), or in some cases chemical thinning may be used as in the examination of metals. The method is suitable for viewing phases, inclusions, orientation (polarized light or electron beam tilt), pores, etc. For electron transmission work the method is time consuming and carries a rather high failure rate owing to the need to produce sections of 1000 Å or less. A quick, useful but crude variation of this method is to grind the material and examine the particles, some of which will be thin enough to transmit light and/or electrons.

From this brief survey of methods it is evident that metallic materials will also fit into these categories. However, it is convenient to treat metals separately because in practice a different type of problem applies to metals compared to non-metallic materials. This has prompted a somewhat different approach having in mind that metals have been studied in detail longer than non-metals so that more is known about their structure. The chief structural difference lies in the fact that in metals we are considering elements or binary compounds, whereas in plastics, ceramics, etc., we have large complex molecules, sometimes in the form of long chains, sometimes cross-linked, sometimes supercooled giving rise to glassy phases (not found in metals) and in materials like paints we have physically mixed phases which must be considered as an integrated whole.

With such a heterogeneous list we think it is better to take selected specimens which will illustrate the various problems, preparation and recording of data which apply to non-metallic materials.

B. Case studies

1. Fine-grain mullite. Mullite is an aluminium silicate the composition of which can vary from 3 Al_2O_3.2 SiO_2 to 2 Al_2O_3.SiO_2. It is used where

FIG. 121. Transmission electron micrograph of replicated fine grain mullite (etched). × 4000.

good thermal properties are required (e.g., furnaces) and has also been suggested for use in radomes for aircraft because it has the appropriate dialectric properties. Grain size and orientation, and the ratio of Al_2O_3 to SiO_2 are important parameters in meeting the material specification for use in radomes. Since many of the grains are too small to view optically it has been necessary to examine the material by electron microscopy. Figure 121 shows a sample of this material in which the surface was prepared by cutting, grinding and polishing, and the etching agent used was a mixture of equal volumes of hydrochloric and hydrofluoric acids. The surface, after washing and drying, was replicated with cellulose acetate (see Appendices B and C) and given a 45° metal shadow, which helps to give the final picture a 3-dimensional appearance. However, the interpretation of this and many similar pictures needs care since by inverting it the 3D is reversed so that "ridges" can be mistaken for "valleys" and "blisters" for "craters". As the angle moves away from 45°, the chance of confusion decreases, but if the angle is very low a lot of detail is lost in the shadow and if it is very high little differentiation occurs to emphasize the topography.

2. Flame sprayed alumina. It is extremely difficult to mould or cast high melting point materials like alumina, consequently recourse must be made to processes like sintering or flame spraying. In the latter method a rod of alumina is fed into a high-velocity oxy-hydrogen flame which causes

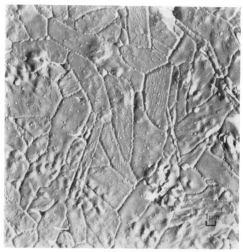

Fig. 122. Transmission electron micrograph of replicated flame-sprayed alumina showing sub-grain features. × 5000.

melting and atomization. The alumina is thereby caused to impinge on the cold surface of a former where it sets, and is built up layer by layer. The sudden chilling which takes place sets up considerable stress in the grains. Figure 122 shows a photograph of alumina which has been prepared in a similar way to the mullite in section XI.B(1) although the etching agent in this case was hot phosphoric acid. Grain boundaries, strain lines and minute pores are clearly visible with a resolution of detail (about 250 Å) equal to or better than that obtainable from the average scanning microscope. These photographs were taken on a Philips 75 kV microscope using Agfa Gaevert Scientia 23 D 50 plates.

3. Ceramic fractures. When certain metallic oxides such as NiO, ZnO, MnO or FeO are heated in intimate contact so that reaction takes place, a series of compounds known as ferrites is produced which have magnetic properties similar to iron. The photograph in Fig. 123 shows that the replication process which was used on the smooth flat surfaces of the previous examples is entirely suitable for rough fractured surfaces. However, greater care is needed when extracting the cellulose triacetate owing to the film weaknesses at the sharp angles. The replica was shadowed at 35° with gold/palladium alloy, and shows a mixed transgranular and intergranular fracture.

FIG. 123. Transmission electron micrograph of a replicated ferrite fracture.
× 5000.

Piezo-electric materials can be polarized by means of an electric charge which a subsequent mechanical impact will depolarize with loss of electrical energy. The photograph shown in Fig. 124, of rounded grains and intergranular fracture, was produced by the same route as the previous example except that while the metal shadow was being cast, the replica was rotated. This process is known as "core shadowing" and produces the same effect that a ring light would in conventional illumination. Its value lies in the fact that no detail is lost in shadows, but on the other hand heights cannot be measured as no distinct shadow is cast.

4. Fluorescent particles in dental filling. The photographs shown in Figs 125 and 126 have been produced from a thin section of dental filling which contains small particles of fluorescent material incorporated to destroy the yellowish colour acquired in use. The first photograph appears to contain a number of bubbles, but on photographing in ultraviolet light it becomes clear that about half of these bubbles are in fact particles of

N

fluorescent material. Excessive trapping of air in a dental filling is undesirable and is dependent on the skill of the operator and the details of the formula. It is also necessary for the fluorescent particles to be evenly dispersed.

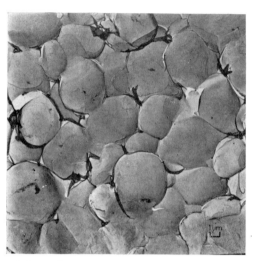

FIG. 124. Transmission electron micrograph of a replicated piezo-electric material fracture. × 5000.

In producing the thin section for this examination it was not necessary to produce a high polish on the surfaces. Surface blemishes are reduced almost to vanishing if the section is immersed in a liquid of similar refractive index.

Exposure time for Fig. 126 was $\frac{1}{4}$ h using an Ilford G 30 plate.

5. *Examination of lithium hydride*. The examination and photography of lithium hydride—used as a concentrated source of hydrogen in nuclear and industrial fields—presents problems which are common to those materials whose surfaces have great sensitivity to moisture or oxygen. There is a choice of two ways. In the first case the viewing microscope, together with preparation equipment is housed in an "Argon box" equipped with sealed-in gloves for manipulation. The microscope tube passes through the box by means of a flexible sleeve so that viewing and photography is executed outside while the stage remains in the inert atmosphere (see Fig. 127). In the second method, after preparing and polishing under an inert liquid, a rehearsal of focusing and other adjustments is carried out in the atmosphere; then a repolish is made and the

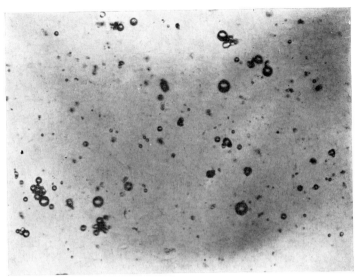

FIG. 125. Optical micrograph showing dental ceramic photographed using transmitted light. × 50.

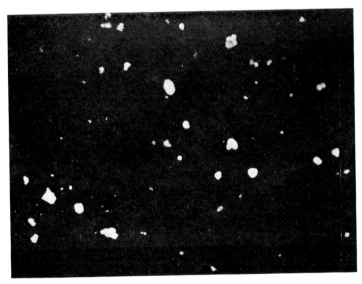

FIG. 126. As Fig. 125 but photographed using ultraviolet illumination. × 50.

surface photographed as quickly as possible. Sometimes dark-ground illumination can be used with a protective oil film on the surface of the sample but this form of illumination does not necessarily show up the

FIG. 127. Photograph showing the installation of a microscope in an argon box. Viewing facilities and camera are outside the box.

features sought after. Figure 128 shows the original broken test piece (oblique light) in a grain deformation study, followed by polished cross-sections in Figs 129 and 130, in which such deformation is clearly visible. Some atmospheric corrosion is already appearing on the surface in Fig. 130 in spite of only about 15 s exposure in air.

FIG. 128. Optical micrograph showing broken lithium hydride test piece. Photographed using oblique illumination. × 4.

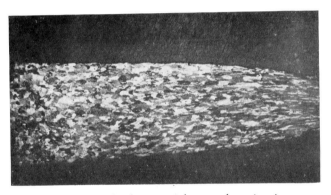

FIG. 129. Optical micrograph showing elongated grains in cross-section of lithium hydride test piece. Photographed using vertical illumination. × 10.

FIG. 130. Optical micrograph showing elongated lithium hydride grains. The photograph obtained using vertical illumination indicates that some moisture attack has occurred. × 50.

Figure 131 is a cross-section through a sintered lithium hydride compact showing grain boundaries within particles. This preparation is less corroded than the previous example because of a much drier atmosphere in the laboratory. However a very thin layer of corrosion product is valuable (and almost unavoidable) since it gives contrast to the differently orientated grains. This is because the thin layer of lithium hydroxide which forms

FIG. 131. Optical micrograph showing a cross-section of a sintered lithium hydride compact. × 50.

on the polished surface gives interference colours which vary with the orientation of the grain. The colours are not of diagnostic value in themselves except to outline the grains. The small black areas in Fig. 131 are pores.

6. Fractured Perspex surface showing secondary shock fronts. When a plastic is abruptly fractured, primary and secondary shock fronts are propagated outwards from the point of initial failure. The point of failure can in fact be deduced from the orientation of the secondary shock fronts since they have their rounded contours directed towards the break point. The features are similar in other plastics where plastic flow has not had time to manifest itself, and no complicating crystallinity or second phases are present. Investigating failures of plastics in service, or obtaining information on new materials, requires that we are able to photograph the topography of fractured surfaces at various magnifications. Three problems arise:

1. The surface is usually severely curved.

2. Most plastics are damaged by high beam energies in the Stereoscan, and they are non-conductors of heat and electricity.
3. Most plastics (including Perspex) are attacked by replicating agent solvents.

The first of these difficulties only affects the optical pictures and there is little one can do except to compromise in "stopping down", varying the convergence of the illumination, and using a lower power objective than normal in conjunction with a higher power eyepiece.

Figures 132 and 133 at magnifications of ×50 and ×500 were both

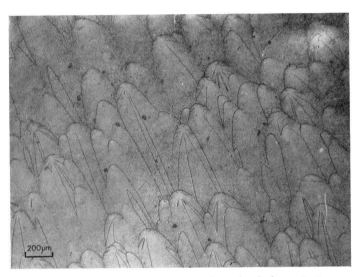

200μm

FIG. 132. Optical micrograph showing secondary shock fronts in Perspex. ×50.

taken in this way; Fig. 134 also at ×500 is an alternative method using Nomarski interference contrast which in spite of vertical illumination, a curved surface, and transparent specimen, has produced a very useful result.

Turning now to examination by Stereoscan, it is necessary first to coat the surface with gold/palladium alloy to render it conducting and give a good secondary electron signal. Also, in the case of Perspex, the instrument could not be used much above 5 kV since the specimen was damaged during focusing. Operation at 5 kV results in poorer resolution, but still greatly superior to optical results particularly as regards depth of focus. Figures 135 and 136 are Stereoscan pictures at ×1500 and ×4500 respectively, and it is noteworthy that Figs 134 and 135 have a great

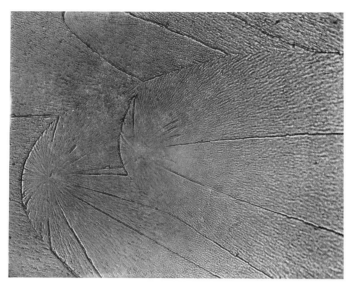

FIG. 133. Optical micrograph showing secondary shock fronts in Perspex.
× 500.

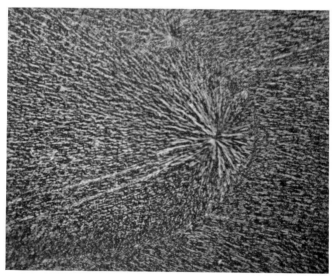

FIG. 134. Optical micrograph showing secondary shock fronts in Perspex
obtained using Nomarski interference contrast. × 500.

similarity in general appearance. However, it is evident from Fig. 136 that the useful limit of resolution at 5 kV has been nearly reached.

The third method of examining and photographing these surfaces is by transmission electron microscopy using a shadowed replica. Figures 137 and 138 are examples taken from the same Perspex surface and it is

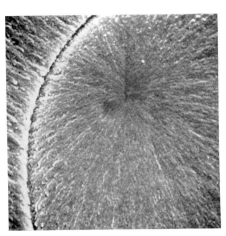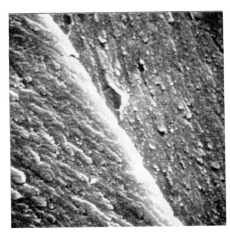

FIG. 135. Scanning electron micrograph showing secondary shock fronts in Perspex. × 1500 (30° tilt).

FIG. 136. Scanning electron micrograph showing secondary shock fronts in Perspex. × 4500 (30° tilt).

immediately evident that we have here a far greater resolution—even the photograph at × 16,000 shows no sign of graininess in the shadowing material which is the limiting factor in replication. Figure 137 may be compared with Fig. 135 by Stereoscan and although there is a certain "flatness" about a replica, the amount of detail is far greater.

The difficulty previously mentioned, of replicating plastic surfaces, was overcome in this case by using a 5% solution of gelatine for replicating. This was applied to the surface, allowed to dry overnight, detached and shadowed in the usual way.* Gelatine is an extremely accurate replicating agent and has no detectable self-structure.

7. *Photography of nuclear fuel granules using atomic number contrast.* When examining materials in the scanning electron microscope we find that a stronger electron signal is produced by materials having a high atomic number, compared to elements like carbon, silicon, boron, etc., of low

* See Appendix B.

N*

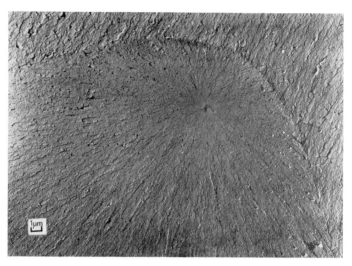

FIG. 137. Transmission electron micrograph showing a replica of secondary shock fronts in Perspex. × 4000 (25° shadow).

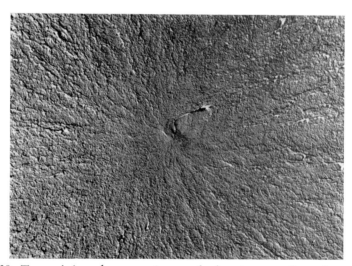

FIG. 138. Transmission electron micrograph showing a replica of secondary shock fronts in Perspex. × 16,000 (25° shadow).

atomic number. This effect can be enhanced by placing a negatively charged grid just before the electron collector so that low energy electrons are rejected and the high energy ones from the heavy elements pass on to produce an image. The process is spoken of as utilizing "back scattered" electrons which are arbitrarily defined as having energies over 50 eV.

Fuel granules sometimes consist of uranium compounds mixed with graphite, compressed and sintered, and a study of the distribution of uranium is essential to their ultimate use. Plutonium may replace part of the uranium but no distinction will be made by this method between these two fuels, as they both have very high atomic numbers.

Figures 139 and 140 are cross-sections of some "green" granules, i.e., the

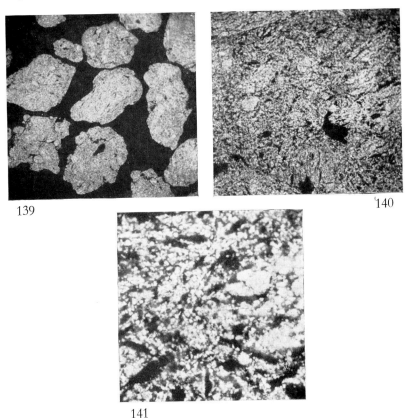

139

'140

141

FIG. 139. Scanning electron micrograph showing the cross-sections of a number of fuel granules. × 200.

FIG. 140. As Fig. 141 at × 1000.

FIG. 141. As Fig. 141 at × 5000.

components, uranium oxide and graphite, have been mixed and pelleted but not yet sintered. They were embedded in Araldite using a vacuum impregnation technique so that they would hold together while being sectioned. After coating with carbon to render the surface conducting they were examined in the scanning microscope. Since the Araldite has the same signal response as the graphite, the pictures show the uranium particle distribution uncomplicated by graphite or porosity, because the pores will be filled with Araldite.

Figure 139 gives a general view of the shapes of the granules at × 200, Fig. 140 at × 1000 shows how the concentration of uranium dioxide particles varies (a few pseudomorphs are visible) and finally in Fig. 141 at × 5000 it is possible to see individual particles and their grouping into small aggregates.

8. *Weathered paint film.* Paint films undergo a continuous breakdown in service so that to illustrate types of failure, or the performance of new materials, a photographic record is essential. Failure may take the form of cracking, chalking, lifting or blistering to name only a few, and to this must be added other disfigurements such as soot retention, mould growth or colour changes. The photographs in Figs 142-148 show optical, Stereoscan and electron transmission pictures of a white paint (based on thermo-setting acrylic resin and Rutile) which has weathered for several years under an oak tree. Cracking, mould growth and chalking are all

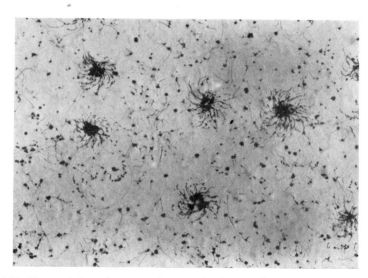

FIG. 142. Transmission electron micrograph of a weathered paint film showing spiral growths and Benard cells. × 20 (Optical).

visible, and the presence of Benard cells—formed by convection of pigment as the paint initially dried—can be seen in the optical photograph. Since we are examining an original surface very little preparation is called for, only a thin layer of vacuum-deposited carbon for making the surface

143

144

145

FIG. 143. Scanning electron micrograph showing mould growth on weathered paint film. × 75.

FIG. 144. Scanning electron micrograph showing mould growth on weathered paint film. × 400.

FIG. 145. Scanning electron micrograph showing mould growth on weathered paint film. × 1800.

conducting in the Stereoscan. These pictures were taken at 5 kV to minimize beam damage, although this is much more likely to occur in fresh paint films than in weathered ones. Figure 142, taken in vertical light at × 20, shows clearly the mould growths which have all grown spirally clockwise. The rounded faint lines are the pigment-deficient boundaries of the Benard cells—difficult to photograph owing to very low contrast, and even less visible in a scanning electron micrograph. It was not possible

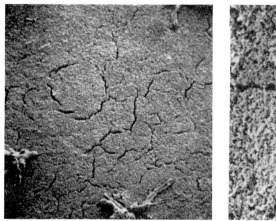 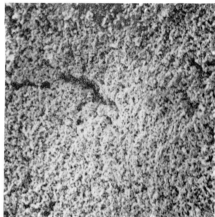

FIG. 146. Scanning electron micrograph of a weathered paint film showing cracking and chalking. × 400.

FIG. 147. Scanning electron micrograph of a weathered paint film showing cracking and chalking. × 1800.

to obtain a satisfying optical micrograph of the moulds at higher magnification as they are up to 50 μ deep. However, as is demonstrated in the scanning electron micrographs, this problem disappears. The first three pictures (Figs 143-145) show the mould growth entirely in focus even at × 1800. The remaining two pictures (Figs 146 and 147) illustrate cracking and chalking in its early stages. The transmission electron micrograph has been produced by applying a piece of cellulose acetate film very slightly softened with acetone to the surface and quickly removing it so that the "chalked" particles remain adhered to the film surface. After coating with a supporting carbon film and extracting the plastic (see Appendix B) the particles can be examined in the transmission microscope. Figure 148 is a picture taken at × 20,000 showing the chalked Rutile (TiO_2) particles. If several pigments are present it is possible to assess differences in "chalking" rate provided the particles are sufficiently distinctive. The fact that some pigment particles appear transparent and others black is dependent on their orientation to the electron beam; it has no bearing on their optical properties.

It has been found that by very careful recording of changes in the first few weeks of an exposed paint film by scanning microscopy much of its long-term performance can be predicted. This may well replace the more artificial "accelerated weathering" tests which are used to evaluate paint performance.

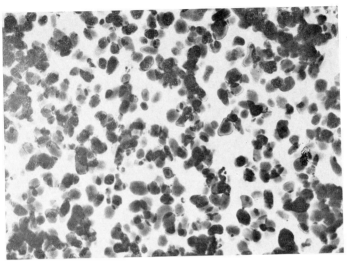

FIG. 148. Transmission electron micrograph showing chalked pigment extracted from the surface of a weathered paint film. × 20,000.

Appendix A

CONTROLLED "DODGING" ENLARGER

Having taken much trouble to obtain the maximum amount of detail in a negative, it is not uncommon to find the printed result disappointing in that detail and contrast vary widely in different areas. Sometimes detail, clearly visible in the negative, is completely lost. A frequent cause of this is varying thickness or density in the transmitting sample—especially in wedge-shape pieces—and it occurs in optical and electron microscopy. Many dark-room operators resort to "dodging" to even up these variations. This is done by making the printing exposure long enough to allow masking of thin areas in the negative by skilled hand movements. The results are at best only a partial solution and not easily repeatable.

To overcome this problem several enlargers have appeared on the market recently, which perform this "dodging" in a very controlled way,

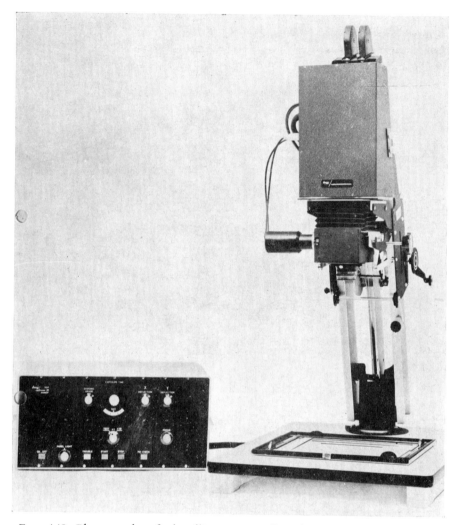

FIG. 149. Photograph of the "Log-E-tronic" enlarger manufactured by Logetronics A.G., Foerrlibuckstrasse 110, Zürich 8005.

and our experience of one of these instruments is to place it almost in the category of a necessity for technical printing. Most prints are improved and some negatives, which may otherwise have been rejected as valueless, have yielded presentable results. The instrument in our possession is shown in Fig. 149 and takes only a little more room than an ordinary enlarger. It may be used as an ordinary enlarger if required. The light source is a cathode ray tube and light from the high intensity scanning spot on the face of the tube passes through the negative and is sampled by a photo-multiplier system above the lens. This system monitors the light intensity and inversely modulates it. In practice this means that when the scanning spot encounters a dense area of the negative its intensity is increased by the electronic control unit, and conversely, when a thin area is encountered its intensity is decreased.

Since the light from the scanning spot also exposes the photographic paper, a print is obtained in which the contrast is lowered. It is therefore possible to use harder grade paper than with a normal enlarger and obtain a print in which the overall contrast is reduced and the detail enhanced.

Three illustrations are given in Figs 150-152 showing a × 2 ordinary

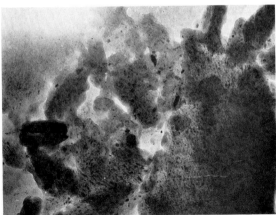

FIG. 150. Transmission electron micrograph of a two-phase system. Undodged. × 50,000 (upper). Dodged. × 50,000 (lower).

FIG. 151. Transmission electron micrograph of a beryllium–iron alloy. Un-dodged (upper). Dodged (lower).

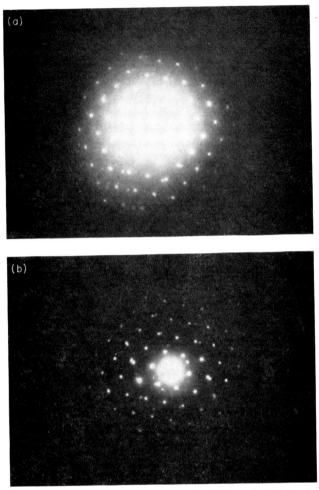

FIG. 152. Electron diffraction pattern. Undodged (upper). Dodged (lower).

enlargement and a × 2 enlargement using the LOG E DS4 enlarger. The amount of beam modulation is of course controllable and will depend on the amount of correction needed.

Appendix B

REPLICATING SURFACES

Replicating surfaces is a very accurate means of displaying small-scale topography and most textbooks which concern themselves with techniques in this field give several methods of producing good replicas. For convenience we give briefly our own processes.

A. Surfaces unaffected by acetone

Several drops of acetone are placed on the area to be replicated and a piece of "Faxfilm" (cellulose triacetate) is immediately placed on top. Very gentle pressure is used to prevent the film from curling up at first, and to keep it in good contact with the surface. After about 20 min the film can be easily detached, and is ready for the next stage of shadowing and backing with carbon. Shadowing (in vacuum with Au/Pd alloy at bright red heat) is the equivalent of arranging the lighting in ordinary photography. It can be done at various angles, or with the sample rotating—resembling a ring source of illumination. If the sample has many linear features a different picture will be formed if the shadow is cast along the furrows compared to casting it across them.

Because the metal shadowing film has no mechanical strength, a film of carbon is deposited on the back of it. This enables the plastic original to be dissolved away (see Appendix C) leaving the carbon/gold-palladium film for viewing.

B. Surfaces affected by acetone (Larner, 1966)

Many plastics are affected by acetone so that the previous method is not suitable for these materials. Some workers use a 5% solution of methyl cellulose to replicate these surfaces but our own preference has been to use 3-5% warm gelatine solution. This is dropped on to the surface and allowed to dry overnight under desiccating conditions. When dry the gelatine layer can be detached either by breathing on it when it may separate spontaneously, or by assisting the separation with a razor. It is then shadowed and filmed as for cellulose triacetate.

Dissolution of the gelatine is brought about by floating small squares of the replica, shadow-side up on the surface of a little 95% v/v concentrated sulphuric acid contained in a small watch-glass. The watch-glass is then heated to about 130°C and tilted backwards and forwards to prevent the replica from adhering to the side. After about 10 min most of the acid may be removed, after cooling, using a pipette. The replica is then allowed to float off on to a large volume of water, collected and viewed.

Appendix C

APPARATUS FOR EXTRACTING CELLULOSE TRIACETATE OR MILLIPORE
FILTER BASE FROM VACUUM DEPOSITED CARBON FILMS

It is necessary, when producing replicas or carbon films on Millipore
carrying particles, to be able to dissolve away the cellulose acetate without
disrupting the film or disturbing the particles. The immediate action of
cold or warm solvents such as acetone, methylethyl keton or esters is to

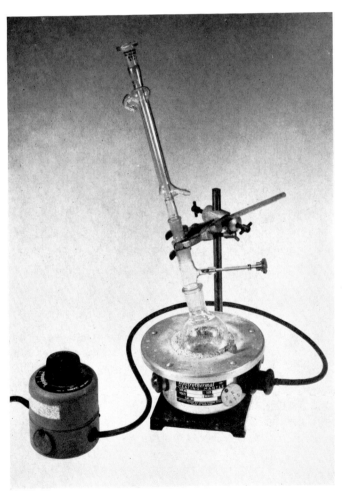

FIG. 153. General view of extraction apparatus.

cause swelling of the plastic before solution takes place, thereby disrupting the carbon film. However, if the coated film is plunged into hot acetone vapour, rapid clean solution takes place and in a few minutes the carbon film is ready for viewing.

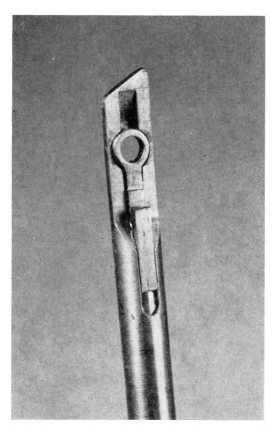

FIG. 154. End of obsolete specimen holder of Philips EM75 which accommodates the grid and specimen, and serves as a cool-finger. (It is often advantageous to have the securing flap up.)

Figures 153 and 154 illustrate the apparatus we have used for this purpose, consisting essentially of a small flask, T-inlet pieces and air reflux condenser with a very loose-fitting stopper on top. The inlet is required to accept loosely a metal rod which acts as a cold-finger and having a recess in the end to carry the grid and film. (Fortuitously, the early specimen holders of the Philips EM75 serve ideally for this if available.) The flask is half-filled with acetone, and a few lumps (not powder) of lithium hydride added to create smooth boiling and also to totally dehydrate the acetone. This latter fact enables the method to be used with moisture-sensitive particles such as sodium chloride which otherwise dissolve or become rounded. The replica or filter is cut into small 2-3 mm squares, one of which is placed, carbon film downwards, on to an electron microscope grid which sits in the recess of the metal holder. When acetone vapour is issuing freely from the side tube the holder is inserted for about 5 min. It is then withdrawn cautiously after first gently absorbing the drop of acetone enveloping the end with filter paper. The film is now ready for viewing.

REFERENCES

AGAR, A. W. (1957). *Br. J. appl. Phys.* **8**, 410.

BAILEY, J. E. and HIRSCH, P. B. (1962). *Proc. R. Soc.* **A267**, 11.

BOLLMANN, W. (1956). *Phys. Rev.* **103**, 1588.

BOWLES, J. S. and MACKENZIE, J. K. (1954). *Acta. Metall.* **2**, 129.

BUSCH, H. (1927). *Arch. Elektrotech.* **18**, 583.

CARRINGTON, W., HALE, K. F. and McLEAN, D. (1960). *Proc. R. Soc.* **A259**, 203.

CASTAING, R. and GUINIER, A. (1949). Proc. Delft Conference on Electron Microscopy, 60.

CASTAING, R. and LABORIE, P. (1953). *C. r. hebd. Séanc. Acad. Sci., Paris* **237**, 1330.

CLARKE, D. R. (1971). *Phil. Mag.* **24**, 973.

CLARKE, D. R. and HOWIE, A. (1971). *Phil. Mag.* **24**, 973.

CLINTON, D. F. (1971). *Micron* **3**, 358.

COCKAYNE, D. J. H. (1973). *J. Microsc.* **98**, 116.

COCKAYNE, D. J. H., JENKINS, M. L., RAY, I. L. F. and WHELAN, M. J. (1972) Proc. Fifth European Congress on Electron Microscopy, 530.

COCKAYNE, D. J. H., PARSONS, J. R. and HOELKE, C. W. (1971). *Phil. Mag.* **24**, 139.

COSSLETT, V. E. and DUNCOMB, P. (1956). *Nature* **177**, 1172.

COTTERILL, R. M. J. and SEGALL, R. L. (1963). *Phil. Mag.* **8**, 1105.

CREWE, A. V. (1970). *Science, N.Y.* **168**, 1338.

DANNOHL, H. D., GRABER, R. and WEGMANN, L. (1971). *Microstructures*, Aug/Sept.

DARKEN, L. S. and FISHER, R. M. (1962). *In* "Decomposition of Austenite by Diffusional Processes", p. 249. Interscience, New York.

DE BROGLIE, L. (1924). *Phil. Mag.* **47**, 446.

DESFORGES, C. D. and FOURDEUX, A. (1972). *Metallography* **5**, 347.

DIGBY, N., FIRTH, K. and HERCOCK, R. J. (1953). *J. photogr. Sci.* **1**, 194.

DOBSON, P. S., GOODHEW, P J. and SMALLMAN, R.E. (1967). *Phil. Mag.* **16**, 9.

DYMENT, J. (1970). *Aerosol Science* **1**, 53.

EDINGTON, J. W. and SMALLMAN, R. E. (1965). *Phil. Mag.* **11**, 1109.

FRANCE, L. K. and LORETTO, M. H. (1965). *Proc. R. Soc.* **A307**, 83.

GIRAUD-HERAUD, F., GUILLAUMIN, J. and SIFFERLEN, R. (1970). *J. nucl. Mater.* **36**, 315.

HAINE, M. E. (1954). "Advances in Electronics and Electron Physics." Vol. VI, pp. 295-369.

HEIDENREICH, R. D. (1949). *J. appl. Phys.* **20**, 993.

HILLERT, M. (1962). *In* "Decomposition of Austenite by Diffusional Processes", p. 197. Interscience, New York.

HIRSCH, P. B., SILCOX, J., SMALLMAN, R. E. and WESTMACOTT, K. H. (1958). *Phil. mag.* **3**, 897.

HU, H. (1962). *Trans. metall. Soc.* A.I.M.E. **224**, 75.

HU, H. (1963). "Electron Microscopy and Strength of Crystals." Interscience, New York.

HUTCHINSON, W. B. and RAY, R. K. (1973). *Phil. Mag.* **27**, 953.

JENKINS, M. L., COCKAYNE, D. J. H. and WHELAN, M. J. (1973). *J. Microsc.* **98**, 155.

KINSMAN, K. R. and AARONSON, H. I. (1971). Proc. Fifth International Materials Symposium, p. 259.

KIRDALDY, W. G. (1891). *In* "Strength and Properties of Materials with Description of the System of Testing." Sampson, Low, Martson and Rivington Ltd, London.

KIRSCH, A. (1889). "Handbook of Testing Materials." Parts I and II. John Wiley, New York.

KNOLL, M. (1935). *Z. tech. Phys.* **16**, 467.

KNOLL, M. and RUSKA, E. (1932). *Z. Phys.* **78**, 318.

KRITZINGER, S., DOBSON, P. S. and SMALLMAN, R. E. (1967). *Phil. Mag.* **16**, 217.

LARNER, E. E. (1964). AWRE Report No. O84/64.

LARNER, E. E. (1966). *Chemy Ind.* **6**, p. 250.

LESLIE, W. C., MICHALAK, J. T. and AUL, F. W. (1963). "Iron and Its Dilute Solid Solutions." Interscience, New York.

LORETTO, M. H. and FRANCE, L. K. (1969). *Phil. Mag.* **19**, 141.

LYTTON, J. L., WESTMACOTT, K. H. and POTTER, L. C. (1965). *Trans. metall. Soc. A.I.M.E.* **233**, 1757.

MAHER, D. M. and EYRE, B. L. (1971). *Phil. Mag.* **23**, 409.

MARTENS, A. (1889). "Handbook of Testing Materials." Parts I and II. John Wiley, New York.

MAY, G. H. (1962). *J. nucl. Mater.* **7**, 72.

MENTOR, J. W. (1966). *Proc. R. Soc.* **A236**, 119.

MOLLENSTÄDT, G. and LENZ, F. (1963). *Adv. Electronics Electron Phys.* **18**, 251.

NICHOLSON, R. B., THOMAS, G. and NUTTING, J. (1958). *Br. J. appl. Phys.* **9**, 25.

OSMOND, F., FREMONT, C. and CARTAUD, G. (1904). *Rev. metal: Lit.* **1**, 10.

PARSONS, J. R., RAINVILLE, M. and HOELKE, C. W. (1970). *Phil. Mag.* **21**, 1105.

PORTEVIN, A. (1931). *Metal Progress* (June), p. 87.

SCHWEIZER, M. and FORM, G. W. (1970). *Metals and Materials* **4**, 369.

SEIDMAN, D. N. (1973). *J. Phys. F.* **3**, 393.

SILCOX, J. and HIRSCH, P. B. (1959). *Phil. Mag.* **4**, 72.

SMITH, C. J. E., RUCKMAN, J. C. and LAWRENCE, G. D. (1973). *Metals and Materials* **7**, 234.

STERN, R. M., ICHINOKAWA, T. TAKASHIMA, S. HASHEMOTOR, H. and KINOTO, S. (1972). *Phil. Mag.* **26**, 1495.

THOMPSON, J. J. (1899). *Phil. Mag.* **48**, 547.

WECHSLER, M. S. LIEBERMAN, D. S. and READ, T. A. (1953). *Trans. metal. Soc. A.I.M.E.* **197**, 1503.

WEGMANN, L. (1972). *J. Microsc.* **96**, 1.

WESTMACOTT, K. H., BARNES, R. S., HULL, D. and SMALLMAN, R.E. (1961). *Phil. Mag.* **6**, 929.

WESTMACOTT, K. H., SMALLMAN, R. E. and DOBSON, P. S. (1968). *Met. Sci. J.* **2**, 177.

ZAPPFE, C. A. (1947). *Metal Progress* **51**, 428.

ZAPPFE, C. A. and CLOGG, M. (1945). *Trans. Am. Soc. Mech. Engrs* **34**, **71**, 108.

ZAPPFE, C. A. and SIMS, C. E. (1941). *Metals Technology* **8**, 1307.

ZAPPFE, C. A. and WARDEN, C. D. (1951). *Trans. Am. Soc. Mech. Engrs* **53**, 958.

SUGGESTIONS FOR FURTHER READING

Optical microscopy

BRADBURY, S. and LE TURNER, G. (eds) (1967). "Historical Aspects of Microscopy." W. Heffer and Sons Ltd, Cambridge.

CHAMOT, E. M. and MASON, C. W. (1958) "Handbook of Chemical Microscopy." Chapman and Hall, London.

LAWSON, D. R. (1960) "Techniques of Photomicrography." George Newnes Ltd, London.

LE TURNER, G. (1972). Queckett Memorial Lecture. *Proc. R. microsc. Soc.* **7**, pt 2.

PAYNE, B. O. (1957) "Microscope Design and Construction." Vickers Instruments Ltd, York.

TOLANSKY, S. (1970). "Multiple Beam Interference Microscopy of Metals." Academic Press Ltd, London and New York.

Transmission electron microscopy

GRIVET, P. (1965). "Electron Optics." Pergamon Press, New York.

HAINE, M. E. and COSSLETT, V. E. (1961). "The Electron Microscope." Interscience, New York.

HALL, C. E. (1966). "Introduction to Electron Microscopy." McGraw-Hill, New York.

HIRSCH, P. B., HOWIE, A. NICHOLSON, R. B., PASHLEY, D. W. and WHELAN, M. J. (1965). "Electron Microscopy of Thin Crystals." Butterworths, London.

KAY, D. (ed.) (1965). "Techniques for Electron Microscopy." 2nd Ed. Blackwell Scientific Publications, Oxford.

MURR, L. E. (1970). "Electron Optical Applications in Materials Science." McGraw-Hill, New York.

VALDRE, U. (ed.) (1971). "Electron Microscopy in Material Science." Academic Press, New York.

ZWORYKIN, V. K. et al. (1957). "Electron Optics and the Electron Microscope." 4th Ed. John Wiley, New York.

Electron probe instruments

ASTM (1971). "Energy Dispersion X-ray Analysis." Proceedings of a Symposium at the 73rd ASTM Meeting, Toronto, Canada, June 21-26, 1970, American Society for Testing Materials.

ANDERSEN, C. A. (ed.) (1973). "Microprobe Analysis." Wiley-Interscience, New York.

BELK, J. A. (1968). "Electron Microscopy and Microanalysis of Metals." Elsevier, Amsterdam.

BIRKS, L. S. (1971). "Electron-probe Microanalysis. 2nd Ed. Wiley-Interscience, New York.

CASTAING, R., DESCAMPS, P. and PHILIBERT, J. (eds) (1966). "X-ray Optics and Microanalysis." Hermann, Paris.

HEARLE, J. W. S. (1972). "Use of the Scanning Electron Microscope." Pergamon Press, Oxford.

MURR, L. E. (1970). "Electron Optical Applications in Materials Science." McGraw-Hill, New York.

OATLEY, C. W. (1972). "Scanning Electron Microscopy." Pt. I. Cambridge University Press, London.

THORNTON, P. R. (1968). "Scanning Electron Microscopy." Chapman and Hall, London.

Electron emission microscopy

L. E. MURR, (1970). "Electron Optical Applications in Materials Science." McGraw-Hill, New York.

X-ray diffraction

BARRETT, C. S. and MASSALSKI, T. B. (1966). "Structure of Metals." 3rd Ed. McGraw-Hill, New York.

CULLITY, B. D. (1959). "Elements of X-ray Diffraction." Addison-Wesley, Reading, Massachusetts.

JAMES, R. W. (1958). "Optical Principles of the Diffraction of X-rays." Bell, London.

JEFFERY, J. W. (1971). "Methods in X-ray Crystallography." Academic Press, New York.

Crystal defect studies
1. *Crystallography*
PHILLIPS, F. C. (1955). "An Introduction to Crystallography." Longmans, London.
2. *Dislocation theory*
COTTRELL, A. H. (1953). "Dislocations and Plastic Flow in Crystals." Oxford University Press, London.
HULL, D. (1965). "Introduction to Dislocations." Pergamon Press, Oxford.
NABARRO, F. R. N. (1967). "Theory of Dislocations". Oxford University Press,
SMALLMAN, R. E. (1962). "Modern Physical Metallurgy." Butterworths, London.
WEERTMAN, J. and WEERTMAN, J. R. (1964). "Elementary Dislocation Theory." Macmillan, New York.
3. *Electron diffraction theory*
HIRSCH, P. B., HOWIE, A., NICHOLSON, R. B., PASHLEY, D. W. and WHELAN, M. J. (1965). "Electron Microscopy of Thin Crystals." Butterworths, London.
MAKIN, M. J. (1968). "The Theory of Image Contrast in Electron Microscopes." *Metallography* **1**, 109.
SMALLMAN, R. E. and ASHBEE, K. H. G. "Modern Metallography", Pergamon Press, Oxford.
THOMAS, G. (1962). "Transmission Electron Microscopy of Metals." John Wiley, New York.
4. *Weak beam techniques*
EMCON 72 (1973). Weak Beam Microscopy Symposium. *J. Microsc.* **98**.
5. *Etch pitting, decoration and x-ray techniques for observing dislocations*
NEWKIRK, J. B. and WERNICK, J. H. (eds). (1962). "Direct Observation of Imperfections in Crystals." Interscience, New York.
6. *Recovery and recrystallisation*
SEMINAR, A. S. M. (1965). "Recrystallisation, Grain Growth and Textures." Detroit.
BYRNE, J. G. (1965). "Recovery, Recrystallisation and Grain Growth." Macmillan, New York and London.
HIMNEL, L. (ed.) (1963). "Recovery and Recrystallisation of Metals." Interscience, New York.
7. *Quenching and irradiation*
COTTERILL, R. M. J., DOYAMA, M., JACKSON, J. J. and MESHII, M. (eds) (1961). "Lattice Defects in Quenched Metals." Academic Press, New York and London.
EYRE, B. L. (1973). Transmission electron microscope studies of point defect clusters in fcc and bcc metals. *J. Phys. F.* **3**, 422.
THOMPSON, M. W. (1969). "Defects and Radiation Damage in Metals." Cambridge University Press, London.

Phase transformations

AMERICAN SOCIETY FOR METALS (1970). "Phase Transformations", presented at seminar, Oct 12-13, 1968, Detroit.

BARRETT, C. S. and MASSALSKI, T. B. (1966). "Structure of Metals." 3rd Ed. McGraw-Hill, New York.

BOWLES, J. S. and DUNNE, D. P. (1973). Critical assessment: the crystallographic theory of martensitic transformations. *J. Met. Sci.* **7**, 118.

CHADWICK, G. A. (1972). "Metallography of Phase Transformations." Butterworths, London.

CHRISTIAN, J. W. (1965). "The Theory of Transformations in Metals and Alloys." Pergamon Press, Oxford.

FINE, M. E. (1964). "Phase Transformations in Condensed Systems." Macmillan, New York.

INSTITUTE OF METALS (1969). "The Mechanism of Phase Transformations in Crystalline solids", Monograph No. 33. Proceedings of Symposium, July 3-5, 1968, Manchester. Institute of Metals.

PETTY, E. R. (ed.) (1970). "Martensite, Fundamentals and Technology." Longmans, London and New York.

WAYMAN, C. M. (1964). "Introduction to the Crystallography of Martensitic Transformations." Macmillan, New York.

Fractography

ASTM (1968). "Electron Fractography." Proceedings of a Symposium, June 25-30, 1967, American Society for Testing Materials. Boston, Massachusetts.

ASTM (1969). "Electron Microfractography." Proceedings of a Symposium, June 23-28, 1968, American Society for Testing Materials, San Francisco, California.

HENRY, G., PLATEAU, J. and ROESCH, L. (1966). "La Microfractographie." 2 Vol. Editions Metaux, IRSIA.

PHILLIPS, A., KERLINS, V. and WHITESON, B. V. (1965). "Electron Fractography Handbook." Tech Rept ML-TDR-64-416 (AD612912), Air Force Materials Lab; Ohio.

Particles

"Particles Atlas." McCrone Research Associates Ltd, London.

International Colloquium (Vol. 2). "Radioactive Pollution of Gaseous Media" (1963). Press Universitaires de France.

GREEN, H. L. and LANE, W. R. (1964). "Particulate Clouds." E. & F. N. Spon Ltd, London.

6
Photographic aspects of archaeology

THOMAS E. WARD

I. INTRODUCTION

The use of photography in archaeological research is indispensable. The archaeologist has at last realized the true importance of the camera as an accurate means of recording an excavation (unlike the subjective drawing of a plan). This realization has led to the employment of photographers by various organizations involved in archaeological research. Whether it be on-site photography or detailed recording of finds the photographer has to produce accurate pictures properly documented. Most organizations have a system of filing that records all relevant details of each photograph taken. One such system relies on the use of 5×3 in index cards and has been formulated specially for use with the $2\frac{1}{4} \times 2\frac{1}{4}$ in or $3\frac{1}{2} \times 2\frac{1}{4}$ in format, but also accommodates 35-mm. This system as set out in Fig. 1 could be adapted for 5×4 in by using 6×4 in cards and recording the details on the back of the card. The card as shown in Fig. 1 is self-explanatory. The contact print is stuck on the right-hand side and the relevant information is recorded on the left and across the top. Reading from left to right, Date is for the date on which the photograph was taken, Area refers to the area of the site, Trench or Box relates to a more specific part of the area, Negative Number is for reference purposes, Facing indicates the compass direction faced whilst taking the photograph and Site refers to the site being excavated. It is essential that transparencies and contact prints be cross-indexed, particularly as the archaeologist relies upon transparencies as a memory aid but inevitably has to publish in monochrome owing to the high cost of reproducing colour.

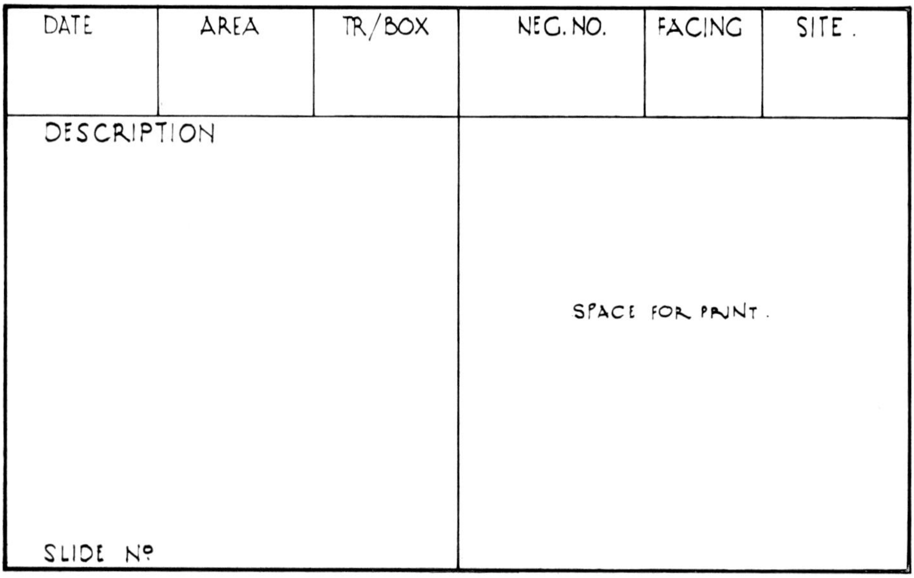

DATE	AREA	TR/BOX	NEG. NO.	FACING	SITE .
DESCRIPTION			SPACE FOR PRINT .		
SLIDE Nº					

FIG. 1. Index card for recording purposes.

Broadly speaking there are two major aspects of archaeological photography, these are, on-site photography and studio/laboratory photograph.

II. SITE PHOTOGRAPHY

The purist would use a 5 × 4 in plate camera although this presents many practical problems such as cost and bulk. Clearly, one has to contrast these with the advantage of movements on the camera and the ability to process negatives immediately after they have been taken. There are very few excavations these days which use such a camera. Far preferred are those cameras that make use of $3\frac{1}{2} \times 2\frac{1}{4}$ in negative size and $2\frac{1}{4}$ in² negative size. Some excavations even use 35-mm cameras for day-to-day record purposes. The ideal is a $2\frac{1}{4}$ in² type camera for monochrome photography and a 35-mm S.L.R. for colour transparency photography. The twin-lens reflex camera providing a $2\frac{1}{4}$ in² negative size is the most popular camera on excavations, providing a good sharp negative which will enlarge to a reasonable size. There is one major drawback—parallax, but one can easily compensate for this. There is one $2\frac{1}{4}$ in² negative format camera which provides interchangeable lenses—the Mamiyaflex. This system is vastly preferable to the use of supplementary lenses on the other variety of camera. In addition, one can focus far closer. With this type of camera, this can be decidedly advantageous in the laboratory and for the more unusual of site photography, e.g., a coin *in situ*. Normally, one has 12 shots on 120 film in a $2\frac{1}{4}$ in² format camera but recently film has been introduced with 24 shots although only certain cameras can take it.

The single-lens reflex camera, known as a 35-mm camera, has many uses on an excavation. One can see through the viewfinder exactly what is required in the picture although most cameras show slightly less than the image produced on the negative. This type of camera is perhaps the most versatile as there are many interchangeable lenses available, from wide angle (of particular importance on site) to the longer focus lenses and other fittings such as extension tubes (for close-ups) and microscope adaptors. Obviously, no camera is perfect and one can level criticism at this variety, especially on grounds of distortion and small negative size. At the present time there are available perspective control lenses for some cameras and these, although expensive, remove the distortion problem.

One should briefly mention the other types of cameras available, namely cine and Polaroid. The cine camera has little use in archaeology except for instructional purposes. The Polaroid type camera provides an instant print and one film provides a negative as well. One can obtain a variety of models and use colour or monochrome film. Of particular use is the Polaroid back for 5×4 in cameras as this avoids expenditure on a new camera.

No matter which, or in what, combination the cameras are used the following remarks about on-site photography apply:

The ideal situation is to record absolutely everything both in colour and monochrome at all stages. One must remember that archaeology is a destructive form of research and one can only rely on memory, drawings and photographs.

The most popular type of photograph is as near to being a plan view as possible and this necessitates a high view-point. This can be achieved by a variety of methods such as an ordinary pair of steps, a ladder tied to scaffolding, a scaffold tower or a mobile tower of some description. The pair of steps is useful for a relatively small area but is totally inadequate for anything other than this. It is also difficult to fix a tripod to it. A long ladder tied to scaffolding (see Fig. 2) can be most useful particularly as it is relatively mobile but it is difficult to fix a tripod to it, although this is not of prime importance in these days of fast film. The most commonly used photographic aid is a scaffolding tower. This can be constructed either from standard frame sections as made by most scaffolding companies or

FIG. 2. Scaffolding tripod for high viewpoint.

from ordinary scaffolding tube. The former can be quite mobile but the latter would have to be fixed in one position. In some cases this is useful but normally a tower that can be moved is of most importance. The mobile platform or tower is advantageous but is normally prohibited by cost. The local Fire Brigade are usually prepared to do an occasional turn-out for purposes other than fire, but do require a fee. One can achieve a height of some 90 ft (see Fig. 3) on a mobile platform as used by the Fire Brigade but if one uses the turntable one can go even higher.

FIG. 3. Fire Brigade mobile platform as used for photography in Chester.

O

In addition to plan type photography there is a need for photographs taken from other angles.

In some cases it is possible to make use of photogrammetry as an alternative to drawing plans. A frame of some sort is required, either a tripod or a more elaborate structure. The camera has to remain at a uniform distance from the trench or area and the film has to be parallel to it. A series of overlapping photographs are taken and then a photo-mosaic is made to produce a composite plan picture. As this is quite complicated to set up it is not used universally but future developments may well produce a simpler system.

The photographer on site should obviously record all details of the photographs he or she takes and this can be done quite simply in any small notebook taking particular care to record details of the excavated feature, i.e., feature number and direction faced.

The ideal weather for most archaeological photography on site is an overcast sky with a reasonable amount of illumination. This provides even overall lighting whereas harsh sunlight usually creates too much contrast and does not provide all the necessary information. There are however, exceptions to this. Strong side lighting can be used to pick out details in relief. This is achieved either by use of the sun or a flash gun. When one is confronted with the situation where there is too much shadow a large sheet of white material can be used as a reflector or else the flash gun may be used as a "fill-in".

The archaeological photographer must know the archaeological aspects of the site to be photographed. Without this knowledge it is not possible to take a photograph which shows all the information required. Similarly, the photographer cannot produce a meaningful picture unless the area has been cleaned to the proper standard. All extraneous clutter such as tools, finds trays and spare clothing must be removed from the picture area. There must be no loose dirt or earth anywhere near the area to be photographed since this can soon be blown over the cleaned surfaces. All trench edges must be immaculate. Grass, if it exists, must be cut and other surfaces must be well brushed. Trench sides must be vertical unless safety reasons disallow, and where a vertical plane meets a horizontal one a right angle is required. Within the trench or area all stone work should be properly cleaned and clearly defined, i.e., pointed with the trowel (see Fig. 4) and surfaces must be clean without showing trowel marks or brush marks. There is no point in taking an archaeological photograph without a scale present whether it be human or a metric pole. In general terms one needs to show both the horizontal and vertical scales. The positioning of these scales is important, whilst one must avoid obscuring the features,

Fig. 4. Record photograph of stone-lined cesspit excavated in Lower Bridge Street, Chester.

one must place them where they have most significance. The vertical scale should be vertical in the picture and this might involve moving it slightly from true vertical, particularly when using wide angle lenses. From time to time excavation reports have had photographs with people as scales. The use of people on an archaeological photograph is most difficult. A stiff upright figure is no better than a scale and possibly worse. People as scales are most effective on large area photographs and then only if they are involved in an activity such as trowelling.

Each archaeological photographic problem should be treated on its own merits. A typical photographic kit should contain a variety of filters to cope with any eventuality, for example, ultraviolet, polarizing filter, infrared and the coloured filters. The ultraviolet filter is normally used at all times when taking coloured transparencies and as an additional usage it acts as a protective covering for the lens. The polarizing filter is most useful in removing unnecessary glare particularly from water and glass as well as increasing the intensity of colour in colour photography. The infrared filter used with infrared film will record items almost or totally invisible to the human eye and is particularly useful in hazy conditions. Care must be taken in focusing and when this is done the lens is readjusted according to the infrared mark on it (if it is a modern lens), otherwise a small aperture should suffice. The coloured filters are normally used with monochrome film and comprise yellow, orange, red, blue and green. The yellow filter can be used to produce greater contrast, particularly in the sky area of a photograph and like the red filter is of assistance in the photography of standing structures. The orange filter is not dissimilar to the previous two filters and like them can be used to increase contrast in the right circumstances. The blue filter has very little use in archaeology as it is rare that blue needs to be emphasized. The green filter can be used as most of the other filters for increased contrast.

The photographer's kit should also include a tripod, a flash system and an exposure meter. The tripod, inevitably, is selected by compromise. The ideal one is made of wood and extremely heavy. This will not waver in the wind or succumb to the accidental blow but is bulky and not particularly mobile. The normal commercial tripod tends to be too light and lacking in rigidity around the central column. A medium-weight metal tripod with telescopic legs and geared central column, preferably including additional struts between the two, is the only real answer to the archaeological photographer who needs mobility. His tripod must also have feet with both spikes and rubber pads for use either in the field or on delicate surfaces and in the studio.

The flash system can either be bulbs or electronic—the latter being the easiest to use in the field. For a reasonable price one can purchase a modest electronic flash gun which will cope with most needs—strong side lighting, illumination in poor conditions and fill-in flash. A sufficient length of cable is required from the camera to the flash gun to enable side-lit photographs to be taken. The flash gun can be mounted separately on a second tripod to achieve the ideal side-lit picture. One must always avoid using the flash gun in close proximity to the camera lens as this provides very dull pictures. On some occasions it is necessary to bounce the flash against a wall or white board to produce a soft lighting effect. A white board is a must on an excavation because it can always be used as a reflector for the sun.

The exposure meter used must be a good reliable one. The archaeological photograph is often one that cannot be retaken and although it is normal practice to bracket exposures, careful reading of the meter is essential. Whereas the monochrome negative allows a reasonable latitude for error, colour reversal film is the exact reverse. The normal care taken over reading off highlights and shadow areas is particularly applicable to archaeology and the photographer has to judge each case on its own merits, not forgetting that he can take readings of reflected light or incident light.

The modern 35-mm type single-lens reflex camera is often equipped with through-the-lens metering. Providing one is aware of the limitations of this feature it is perfectly acceptable to use it. The main advantage of this system is in the studio and laboratory as explained later.

In the event of a film sticking in the camera on site or the urgent need for dark slides to be reloaded a changing bag is a useful addition to the kit.

Finally, the site photographer needs a good range of film. Film is split into two types—colour and monochrome—and is subdivided into negative and reversal.

Monochrome films are available that are either fast or slow (50–1000 A.S.A.). The slow rated films are more suited to archaeology since they possess a very fine grain which produces good quality enlargements. The faster films are quite grainy and, in spite of special developers, are not really suitable. In any case, the use of a tripod obviates the necessity for a fast film. A film perhaps not used as much in photography as it might be is the infrared film mentioned in the paragraph on filters. One should remember to develop the film in a developer suited for such a film as it is somewhat grainy. When used in the field it is best to experiment with a whole film to establish the correct exposure needed. It is used to penetrate hazy conditions and to pick out features not necessarily discernible to the human eye.

If one has a need for monochrome transparencies these can be produced from a normal film by using a processing system that makes negative into positive, or one can use a purpose-made film such as Agfa Dia-Direct which is processed by the manufacturer or can make lantern slides from the negative.

Colour films are available in two forms—negative and reversal—the former producing prints, the latter transparencies. It makes no difference as to what lighting is available when the negative film is used as the colour can be corrected by filtering during the printing stage. Transparency film, on the other hand, is available in two types—daylight and artificial. The artificial type of film is balanced for use with photofloods and is of particular use in the studio and laboratory. Some colour films can be processed by the photographer, but in archaeology one must aim at having as consistent a result as possible. To this end it is sensible to have as much of the same batch of film as possible and to have an absolutely standard system of development. This is normally achieved by using a film such as Kodachrome which is processed by the manufacturers. It is, however, limited by its speed although it has very fine grain. Occasionally one needs transparencies within a day when the use of another type of film, such as Ektachrome with the appropriate chemicals, is recommended. Care must be taken over temperature whilst processing.

Finally in considering the use of photography in the field, there are a few typical problems confronting the photographer.

Pits are the most frequent feature on the majority of excavations and these must be recorded before, during and after excavation. Before excavation the pit will show as a different colour and texture to the surrounding earth, especially if it is a cesspit. If necessary, a filter should be used to emphasize the difference but not with colour film. Also, and this applies to all excavation photography, a water spray could be used to further accentuate any differences. The water spray must be treated as a delicate instrument, otherwise the wrong effect could be created. Normally, the archaeologist will half-section a pit, that is to say he cuts a vertical line through the middle of the pit leaving half the material in (see Fig. 5). This also applies to the treatment of a post-hole. Normally, there will be a considerable fall-off in illumination between the top and bottom of the feature. Either a reflector or a flash gun should be used to light up the bottom to avoid too much contrast on the negative. In any case, colour

FIG. 5. Progress photograph of the excavation of hearths in Lower Bridge Street, Chester. Note the half-sectioned hearth to the right of the 2-m scale.

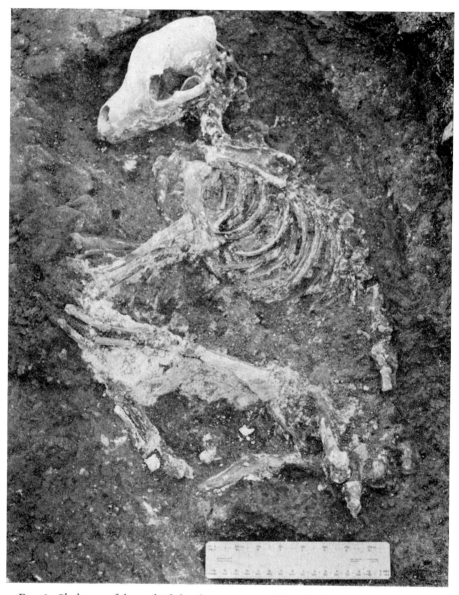

FIG. 6. Skeleton of dog which has been very quickly tidied up for a photograph so as not to hinder progress on the excavation. (Northgate Brewery Excavation, Chester.)

film cannot handle the sort of variations normally encountered in this situation without additional light.

The skeleton is often encountered in archaeology and, in many ways, is one of the most difficult items to record. They are fragile and easily moved, therefore a final photograph of the cleaned article is not sufficient. Some record is better than none. Assuming that nothing untoward happens and the skeletal material is available for complete excavation, it must be cleaned meticulously in such a way that it stands out from the surrounding area. If the situation occurs where the skeleton has, for example, been buried in lime (see Fig. 6) there is little alternative to making the best of a bad job. A scale must be used on the photograph, and if it is a cemetery site with human skeletons, some directors prefer a north pointer.

The versatility of the photographer is often tested in that one day he may be called upon to photograph a Roman hypocaust system and another day it might be a tessellated pavement. In these specialized examples it is important to remember that an overall view is first required to relate the main subject to the surrounding area. Following this, detailed pictures are taken and if the subject is a tessellated pavement, there are a number of points to remember. The pavement must be completely free from dirt and to avoid the usual dull colouration, damping all over with a mixture of water and glycerine serves to bring out the colours. As regards monochrome, a filter is almost always needed and one must study the pavement carefully before selecting the appropriate one. Similarly, when photographing a hypocaust system one has reasonably flat surfaces to record. The upper surface supported by hypocaust Pilae is usually made of Opus Signinum. The nature of Opus Signinum (lime and mortar with tile and brick chips) is such that it inevitably requires wetting to bring up the contrast. When dealing with the hypocaust supports (Pilae) carefully positioned lighting is called for where both floors survive. A flash gun, or series of flash guns, can be hidden behind appropriate Pilae so as to illuminate the lower chamber. Both of these subjects should be recorded vertically after the initial "location" type photograph and then as many angled views taken as is deemed necessary, paying particular attention to doorsills and features in walls.

III. STUDIO AND LABORATORY PHOTOGRAPHY

The archaeological photographer is not always lucky enough to have a studio specially equipped to cater for his needs, and often has to make do with second-best. The work required falls into three categories—first and

o*

most important is publication, secondly, the recording of conservation work (this is particularly important should the object under treatment disintegrate) and, thirdly, the production of display material. Normally, one is handling artifacts from excavations although there are on occasions other subjects to be photographed such as plans, maps and documents.

Clearly, the majority of material found on an excavation is mainly ceramic. Whole vessels are photographed on a background that provides a good contrast and is of a suitable colour since one normally photographs both in colour and monochrome. A scale must be used but ought to be neither garish, nor unnecessarily obtrusive. It must not interfere with the subjects and should be carefully positioned so as to be removable on the print since one does not always require a scale on a display print. The common mistake made in photographing ceramic vessels is insufficient depth of field. Either one uses a longer focus lens which avoids distortion or one uses a small aperture. The plate camera has adjustable movements and so the problem of distortion does not arise. Lighting should be carefully arranged from the side and from above. Quite often it is useful to bounce a photoflood out of an umbrella (the photographic variety) so as to provide soft illumination for overall lighting and a stronger directional light. Once again, circumstances dictate the conditions—one adapts the lighting so that it best displays the objects. The pots must be quite clear, both as shapes and as decorated pieces (if they are decorated externally). Shadows must not conflict in a photograph of a group of pots. Where more contrast is required, for example, an inscription painted on an amphora sherd, an appropriate filter is used. Another complication is the photography of glazed vessels. Too much harsh light produces very bad highlights and so the lighting has to be toned down either by using bounced light or by diffusing the light with ground glass or a similar material. The polarizing filter can be used but tends to produce strange results.

Whilst it gives greater satisfaction to photograph whole pots it is not by any means a significant part of the work of an archaeological photographer. Fragments of pottery are found in abundance and are normally recorded by drawing. The more interesting sherds and representative samples are selected for photography. When dealing with these, there is one rule that must be adhered to, viz, objects being photographed must show lighting from the top left of the picture. This avoids any confusion and applies to small finds as well as sherds of pottery. The objects to be photographed are laid out on a sheet of Perspex or glass raised a suitable distance from a background. The purpose of this is to remove shadows. The main light is positioned as stated before to the top left. Normally, a secondary weaker light source is used to fill in some details on the sides away from the main light. Again, it is necessary to be wary of depth of field.

The same system as that already outlined is used in one form or another to photograph metal objects, flints, textiles and any other items of a small nature from an excavation. A variety of backgrounds is necessary so as to provide a choice or contrasts suited for the photographic subject. If it is an object such as a brooch (see Fig. 7) it is advisable to gently prop it with plasticine to avoid the depth of field problem. Flints are notoriously difficult subjects to photograph as every flake-scar must be perfectly visible in the photograph. This can only be achieved by very careful experimentation with the lighting. Although one does not expect to find

Fig. 7. Brooch excavated in Goss Street, Chester.

much in the way of textiles from excavations in this country there are occasions when they must be photographed. Strong oblique lighting will show them to their best advantage and if mounted on glass or Perspex the shadow problem is removed.

Quite often the photographer is required to photograph larger objects such as carved stone, or lead water-pipes. Particularly when photographing altars the background is very important even if a little difficult to arrange. If the subject is on display in a museum it is unlikely that it can be removed to the studio and so must be photographed *in situ*. For occasions like this the photographer carries a selection of background materials of different colours, paper, card and fabric. If he can afford it, he will even have a proper framed support for rolls of backing paper. Ideally the subject is arranged on the background which is gently curved upwards and held in a vertical position behind it. Where the subject has incised decoration, or writing such as an altar, strong side lighting is essential backed by a certain amount of softer fill-in lighting. Again, a scale must be used but positioned in such a way as to be removable from the print.

Most excavations produce quite a number of coins and all the recognizable ones are photographed (see Fig. 8). The coins are photographed perpendicular to the camera and are lit so as to show as much detail as possible. Once again, glass or Perspex is a most suitable medium for photography. The lighting is set up to accentuate the features on the coin in the best possible way and the rule about lighting can be overlooked in order to achieve the best results.

By far the most difficult subjects are those that are immovably displayed behind glass and the highly polished metal objects such as silver. A polarizing filter used on its own to photograph through glass cuts out some of the reflections but not all. Ideally, all peripheral light should be extinguished and just the interior light left on. The photographer and camera are shrouded in black material except for a hole in front of the camera lens. This method is not perfect, but short of emptying the case, there is no alternative. When confronted with a silver goblet the photographer has to prepare an elaborate set. The two problems are correct lighting and avoidance of reflections. One way of providing even overall lighting is to build a cocoon of tissue paper or similar and shine light on to its outer surface. This creates an evenly lit interior where the subject stands. The camera is set up outside with the lens corresponding to a hole of similar diameter in the cocoon. This method is also used with glass and other highly reflective objects. The alternative to this is to use a normal curved background and plenty of diffused light with the camera and photographer concealed behind a black cloth.

Drawings, plans, prints and sometimes paintings are photographed. In the absence of a copying camera the plate camera is recommended although quite often cameras of a smaller format are used. The subject

FIG. 8. Silver Denarius of Pertinax.

must be absolutely parallel to the camera back otherwise distortion will become apparent. The single-lens reflex camera is often used as well to provide 35-mm transparencies for lecturing. Suitable film (slow panchromatic) is available to produce good crisp negatives. If a coloured subject is being photographed in monochrome, care must be taken to show a tone distinction between colours. The correct filter is selected to cope with this situation. The lighting of these subjects must be absolutely correct. Two matched photofloods are normally used, i.e., reflectors, bulbs, height from ground, distance from subject and angle. The simplest way of checking is to hold a card perpendicular to the centre of the print or drawing and if the shadows are identical the lighting is correct.

Often the camera is used in the conservation laboratory, particularly for close-up photography when bellows or extension tubes are required in conjunction with the standard lens (55- or 50-mm focal length) on the 35-mm single-lens reflex camera. Care has to be taken to obtain an accurate meter reading and in this instance "through-the-lens" metering is most useful. If photographs are required from the microscope an adaptor is used between the camera body and the microscope. Again care has to be taken in working out exposure values. This form of photography is most suited to recording thin sections of pottery, geological specimens and plant remains.

The use of x-rays for archaeological research has increased over recent years. The Egyptian mummy has often been subjected to x-rays with interesting results. X-ray pictures are shadow pictures showing the difference in density of an object when subjected to radiation. If the radiation is sufficient in intensity it will penetrate metal and a seemingly hopelessly rusted piece of sword will reveal traces of inlay (see Fig. 9). It is very difficult to make definite rules about exposure times and amounts of radiation. Careful records of each negative should be kept so that guide lines can be established.

The use of infrared photography has been mentioned previously in reference to site photography. It is probably not realized the use to which this material can be put in the studio. Five-hundred watt photoflood lamps provide radiations of wavelengths longer than 700 nm, i.e., the top end of the visible spectrum. Writing on papyrus invisible to the human eye, or writing on pottery similarly invisible or difficult to decipher, can thereby be rendered readable. Infrared colour film is now available and is opening up new possibilities for the archaeologist both in the field and in the studio. The yellow No. 12 filter is used to absorb blue light, whether in or out of the studio. Illumination in the studio should be by flash. Like x-rays, the only means of establishing guide-lines for exposure, etc., is a notebook with careful documentation of conditions, exposure and lighting.

In the same way that one can subject objects to x-rays so too one can subject them to ultraviolet radiation. This technique could be used in the field but would require some means of removing light from the area to be photographed, e.g., by battery-powered lamps. The lamps, whether used on site or in the studio, are specially screened to produce particular bands of wavelength. The absence of visible light is essential so that reflected ultraviolet is recorded through 18A filter and fluorescence through a 2B or 12 filter. Assuming that one uses a 35-mm camera, a suitable film for this technique is Kodak recording film which has a rating of 1000

FIG. 9. Fragment of sword or dagger excavated in Crook Street, Chester. This picture is a print from an x-ray negative. The inlay is represented by the darker lines and the dark blotches are dense patches of rust. If this object had not been x-rayed it would not have been recognized.

FIG. 10. Pre-excavation photograph of a site in Crook Street, Chester, relating the site to the surrounding structures.

FIG. 11. General view of rescue work on the Westgate centre at Oxford. (Courtesy of Oxford Archaeological Excavation Committee.)

A.S.A. One can use this technique similarly to infrared film, i.e., faded writing or painting on wall plaster. In the field, this technique can be used to show positions of bones, particularly when they are in a fragile state, and there is doubt even about their position. Similarly, pottery with painted decoration can be photographed *in situ*. Fluorescence can be recorded in colour using similar techniques, although previous experimentation is recommended.

Aerial photography does not fall into either main category. Normally, an aircraft takes photographs with an aerial camera, which provides vertical cover. These are taken on parallel runs with an amount of overlap

THOMAS E. WARD

FIG. 12. Photograph of tile matrix—Westgate centre, Oxford. The area has been very quickly cleaned and photographed prior to the removal. The reasonably low light helps to emphasize the tile impressions. (Courtesy of Oxford Archaeological Excavation Committee.)

FIG. 13. Progress photograph of Roman barracks in Crook Street, Chester. Note that all the stones have been clearly defined but that there is not enough definition between the horizontal and the vertical on the far right of the photograph. This was not done, because the side of the trench was unstable.

Fig. 14. Rock cut post-holes excavated in Lower Bridge Street, Chester. Note the clearly defined difference between the sides and bottom of the trench. (All photographs taken by the author. Unless otherwise stated the illustrations are produced by kind permission of the Grosvenor Museum, Chester.)

to allow stereoscopic examination. Normally, monochrome covers all the requirements. Recurrent photography is most important, since changes in the seasons and changes in lighting conditions reveal different features. The oblique photograph in aerial recording has some use, but when compared with verticals taken for stereo pairing it is nowhere near as informative. Aerial photographs do not have to be taken from aeroplanes. Kites, balloons, and even model aircraft, have been tried with varying degrees of success. The archaeologist uses such photographs to identify man-made structures, such as hitherto unrecorded Roman forts. At a time when development is eating up the countryside at such a fast rate this technique is of prime importance.

Over the past few years the archaeologist has come to realize the essential contribution photography can make to his subject. Many new techniques, some outlined above, are in their formative stages and will be developed as time goes by.

BIBLIOGRAPHY

BROTHWELL, D. and HIGGS, E. (eds) (1969). "Science in Archaeology." Thames & Hudson, London

CONLON, V. M. (1973). "Specialised Photographic Techniques." *In* STRONG, D. E. (ed.), "Archaeological Theory and Practice", 283-290. Seminar Press, London and New York.

CONLON, V. M. (1973). "Camera Techniques in Archaeology." John Baker, London.

COOKSON, M. B. (1954) "Photography for Archaeologists." Max Parrish and Co. Ltd, London.

DORREU, P. C. (1973). "The Photography of Flints." *In* STRONG, D. E. (ed.), "Archaeological Theory and Practice", 291-298. Seminar Press, London and New York.

LANGFORD, M. J. (1974). "Basic Photography." Focal Press, London.

STEWART, H. M. (1973). "Photogrammetry in Archaeology." *In* STRONG, D. E. (ed.), "Archaeological Theory and Practice", 275-282. Seminar Press, London and New York.

STRONG, D. E. (ed.) (1973). "Archaeological Theory and Practice." Seminar Press, London and New York.

Author Index

Numbers in italics indicate those pages on which references are given in full.

Subject Index